Asymptotic Methods
in the
Theory of Linear Differential Equations

MODERN ANALYTIC AND COMPUTATIONAL METHODS IN SCIENCE AND MATHEMATICS
A Group of Monographs and Advanced Textbooks

Editor: RICHARD BELLMAN, University of Southern California

Already Published:

1. R. E. Bellman, R. E. Kalaba, and Marcia C. Prestrud
INVARIANT IMBEDDING AND RADIATIVE TRANSFER IN SLABS OF FINITE THICKNESS, 1963

2. R. E. Bellman, Harriet H. Kagiwada, R. E. Kalaba, and Marcia C. Prestrud
INVARIANT IMBEDDING AND TIME-DEPENDENT TRANSPORT PROCESSES, 1964

3. R. E. Bellman and R. E. Kalaba, QUASILINEARIZATION AND NONLINEAR BOUNDARY-VALUE PROBLEMS, 1965

4. R. E. Bellman, R. E. Kalaba, and Jo Ann Lockett, NUMERICAL INVERSION OF THE LAPLACE TRANSFORM: Applications to Biology, Economics, Engineering, and Physics, 1966

5. S. G. Mikhlin and K. L. Smolitskiy, APPROXIMATE METHODS FOR SOLUTION OF DIFFERENTIAL AND INTEGRAL EQUATIONS, 1967

6. R. N. Adams and E. D. Denman, WAVE PROPAGATION AND TURBULENT MEDIA, 1966

8. A. G. Ivakhnenko and V. G. Lapa, CYBERNETICS AND FORECASTING TECHNIQUES, 1967

9. G. A. Chebotarev, ANALYTICAL AND NUMERICAL METHODS OF CELESTIAL MECHANICS, 1967

10. S. F. Feshchenko, N. I. Shkil', and L. D. Nikolenko, ASYMPTOTIC METHODS IN THE THEORY OF LINEAR DIFFERENTIAL EQUATIONS, 1967

In Preparation:

7. R. Stratonovich, CONDITIONAL MARKOV PROCESSES AND THEIR APPLICATION TO THE THEORY OF OPTIMAL CONTROL

A. G. Butkovskii, OPTIMAL CONTROL THEORY FOR DISTRIBUTED PARAMETERS

R. E. Larson, STATE INCREMENT DYNAMIC PROGRAMMING

MODERN ANALYTIC AND COMPUTATIONAL METHODS IN SCIENCE AND MATHEMATICS

MÉTHODES MODERNES D'ANALYSE ET DE COMPUTATION EN SCIENCE ET MATHÉMATIQUE

NEUE ANALYTISCHE UND NUMERISCHE METHODEN IN DER WISSENSCHAFT UND DER MATHEMATIK

НОВЫЕ АНАЛИТИЧЕСКИЕ И ВЫЧИСЛИТЕЛЬНЫЕ МЕТОДЫ В НАУКЕ И МАТЕМАТИКЕ

Editor
RICHARD BELLMAN, UNIVERSITY OF SOUTHERN CALIFORNIA

Asymptotic Methods in the Theory of Linear Differential Equations

by

S. F. FESHCHENKO, N. I. SHKIL', AND L. D. NIKOLENKO
Mathematical Institute
Academy of Sciences of the Ukr. S.S.R.

Translated by *Scripta Technica, Inc.*

Translation Editor: HERBERT EAGLE
University of Wisconsin

AMERICAN ELSEVIER PUBLISHING COMPANY, INC.
NEW YORK 1967

ORIGINALLY PUBLISHED AS
Asimptoticheskiye Metody v Teorii Lineynykh Differentsial'nykh Uravneniy
Naukova Dumka, Kiev, 1966

AMERICAN ELSEVIER PUBLISHING COMPANY, INC.
52 Vanderbilt Avenue
New York, N. Y. 10017

ELSEVIER PUBLISHING CO. LTD.
Barking, Essex, England

ELSEVIER PUBLISHING COMPANY
335 Jan Van Galenstraat
P.O. Box 211, Amsterdam, The Netherlands

Library of Congress Catalog Card Number 67-28448

CONTENTS

INTRODUCTION ix

1. CONSTRUCTION OF ASYMPTOTIC SOLUTIONS FOR SECOND-ORDER LINEAR DIFFERENTIAL EQUATIONS WITH SLOWLY VARYING COEFFICIENTS 1

1. Formulation of the Problem 1
2. A Formal Solution in the Case of Resonance 3
3. A Formal Solution in the "Nonresonance" Case 6
4. The Asymptotic Nature of the Solution 8
5. Finding the Tension in a Visco-Elastic Thread of Variable Length 16

2. CONSTRUCTION OF AN ASYMPTOTIC SOLUTION FOR A SYSTEM OF SECOND-ORDER LINEAR DIFFERENTIAL EQUATIONS WITH SLOWLY VARYING COEFFICIENTS 25

6. Formulation of the Problem 25
7. A Formal Solution in the Resonance Case 26
8. The Nonresonance Case 35
9. The Asymptotic Nature of the Solution 36
10. On the Dynamic Stresses in a Visco-Elastic Thread of Variable Length with a Weight Q at the End 42
11. The Boundary-Value Problem for a System of Second-Order Linear Differential Equations 54

3. ASYMPTOTIC DECOMPOSITION OF A SYSTEM OF LINEAR DIFFERENTIAL EQUATIONS 61

12. Formulation of the Problem 61
13. Formal Decomposition 62
14. Construction of the Transforming Matrix and Differentiability of the Formal Solution 66
15. Proof of Asymptotic Convergence 73
16. Some Special Cases of Decomposition 77

17. Decomposition of a Nonhomogeneous System of Linear Differential Equations 79
18. Asymptotic Decomposition of a System of Ordinary Linear Differential Equations in the Case of Multiple Roots of the Characteristic Equation 85

4. CONSTRUCTION OF AN ASYMPTOTIC SOLUTION IN THE CASE OF MULTIPLE ROOTS OF THE CHARACTERISTIC EQUATION 121

19. General Remarks 121
20. The Case of Simple Elementary Divisors 123
21. A Formal Solution in the Presence of One Multiple Elementary Divisor 125
22. An Example 142
23. The Asymptotic Nature of the Solution 146
24. Asymptotic Solution in the Presence of Several Multiple Elementary Divisors 153
25. Construction of an Asymptotic Solution in the Case of Other Sufficient Conditions 157
26. Differential Equations with a Small Parameter in the Highest Derivatives 170
27. Finding the Characteristic Values of a Boundary-Value Problem for a Fourth-Order Differential Equation Consisting of Two Self-Adjoint Expressions 173

5. ASYMPTOTIC SOLUTIONS OF DIFFERENTIAL EQUATIONS IN BANACH SPACE 187

28. Formulation of the Problem 187
29. Existence and Uniqueness of the Solution 189
30. On the Solvability of Certain Operator Equations in Banach Space 202
31. Construction of a Formal Solution 207
32. Proof of Asymptotic Convergence 213
33. Asymptotic Solutions of the Nonhomogeneous Equation 216
34. Direct Construction of a Particular Solution to the Nonhomogeneous Equation 223
35. Applications 227

6. ASYMPTOTIC METHODS OF SOLVING LINEAR PARTIAL DIFFERENTIAL EQUATIONS 239

36. Formulation of the Problem 239
37. Construction of Formal Solutions 243
38. Proof of Asymptotic Convergence 256

REFERENCES 261

INDEX 269

INTRODUCTION

Solution of many problems in physics and engineering reduces, as is well known, to the study of differential equations with variable coefficients. Since it is possible to obtain an exact solution of such an equation only in exceptional cases, we must resort to various approximate methods of solution. Among the more important approximate methods are asymptotic methods, which are based on the idea of expansion of the desired solution in a series of powers of some small parameter. In spite of the fact that these power series are, as a rule, divergent, the approximate solution obtained by cutting off the formal series at some mth term is quite adequate for a great many practical calculations. The approximate solution obtained in this way has an asymptotic character in the following sense: instead of tending to the corresponding exact solution with increasing m, the approximate solution, for fixed m, tends to the exact solution as the small parameter tends to zero.

Since asymptotic methods offer us the possibility of obtaining an analytical expression for the approximate solution, they are also useful in studying the qualitative behavior of the solution on a rather large, though finite, interval of variation of the independent variable (see, for example, [118]).

In this monograph we will consider asymptotic methods of solution of a certain class of linear differential equations, namely, those equations in which the coefficients are functions of a slow time parameter $\tau = \varepsilon t$, where ε is a small positive parameter; this indicates that the coefficients of the equation vary slowly, i.e., their derivatives with respect to the independent variable t are proportional to the small parameter ε.

Differential equations with slowly varying coefficients are often encountered in practice. This class includes, for example, equations with a small parameter in the highest derivatives; these equations can be reduced to the case of slowly varying coefficients. Work on these equations has been done by

A. N. Tikhonov [78-80], I. S. Gradshteyn [16-17], V. M. Volosov [13-14], A. B. Vasil'yeva [9-11], K. V. Zadiraka [26-28], M. I. Vishik, L. A. Lyusternik [12] and others.

Indeed, let us consider the equation

$$\varepsilon \frac{dy}{dx} + p(x) y = 0. \tag{1}$$

Substituting

$$x = \varepsilon t = \tau, \tag{2}$$

we obtain

$$\frac{dy}{dt} + p(\tau) y = 0, \tag{3}$$

i.e., we obtain an equation in which the coefficient $p(\tau)$ is a slowly varying function of the variable t.

Certain characteristic-value problems can also be transformed to an analogous equation. For example, in the Sturm-Liouville equation

$$\frac{d^2y}{dx^2} + [\lambda g(x) - r(x)] y = 0, \tag{4}$$

where λ is a large parameter, we make the substitution

$$x = \varepsilon t \equiv \tau, \qquad \varepsilon = \frac{1}{\sqrt{\lambda}}, \tag{5}$$

and obtain the equation

$$\frac{d^2y}{dt^2} + [g(\tau) - \varepsilon^2 r(\tau)] y = 0, \tag{6}$$

in which $g(\tau)$, $r(\tau)$ are slowly varying functions.

In addition (and this is especially important for applications), we encounter a whole set of practical problems (see, for example, Secs. 5 and 10 of this book) in which it is possible to separate out a dimensionless combination of known quantities which play the role of a small parameter; this allows us to consider the obtained equation as an equation with slowly varying coefficients (see also [64, 103]).

We now present a short history of the problem.

The idea of an asymptotic representation of solutions to differential equations was already present in the works of Liouville [123, 124]. This was because investigation of the convergence of an expansion of a given "arbitrary" function with respect to the characteristic functions of some boundary-value problem was found to be based on study of the behavior of these characteristic functions themselves. Thus, obtaining asymptotic formulas for the characteristic functions was of considerable interest. Liouville first obtained asymptotic formulas for the solution of second-order equations of type 4, and then for equations of higher order as well.

After Liouville's work, the theory began to develop very rapidly as a result of the importance of questions of asymptotic representation of solutions of differential equations to certain problems in mathematical physics. Subsequently, it became clear that asymptotic representations of solutions were significant not only for analysis of the convergence of expansions with respect to characteristic functions, but for many other problems (especially practical ones) of a completely different nature. Thus, in the works of Fowler and Lock [132] the results of Liouville were applied to solution of the approximate equations of projectile motion. De Sparre [127] applied this method to solution of the problem of rotational motion of a projectile. The asymptotic nature of the solution obtained by De Sparre was proved by Horn [121].

Poincaré made a significant contribution to the development of an asymptotic representation of solutions, in that he systematized and significantly extended the previous ideas.

The asymptotic method was applied with great skill and success in the works of the Russian scientist V. A. Steklov, especially in his paper "The problem of cooling a nonhomogeneous solid body" (Kharkov, 1896). However, all the works listed above revolved around Liouville's idea and concerned the investigation of self-adjoint differential systems. We must therefore realize that, notwithstanding the general results obtained by the investigators in this direction, the area of applicability of the above method remained limited.

We do not encounter these limitations, however, in the works of Birkhoff [119, 120], which are a generalization of the results of Horn and Schlesinger to nth order equations and systems of equations.

We should note that the asymptotic representation of solutions of differential equations containing a parameter is determined, in general, by the behavior of the roots of some algebraic equation, similar to the characteristic equation for linear differential equations with constant coefficients. We will henceforth use the term "characteristic" for this algebraic equation as well.

In the cited works of Schlesinger, Birkhoff considered the case when the roots of the characteristic equation are simple for the whole interval of variation of the argument.

A further generalization of these results appeared in the work of Tamarkin. In [76] he partially considered the case of multiple roots of the characteristic equation by constructing the asymptotic solution for a second-order linear system.

However, the Schlesinger-Birkhoff-Tamarkin theory relates to ordinary homogeneous linear differential equations. It was necessary to generalize the theory of asymptotic representation of a solution to nonhomogeneous differential equations. This gap was filled by Fowler and Lock [132, 133]; they also significantly simplified the proof of Birkhoff's basic results.

In 1936, a paper by Tryizinski [131] appeared which gave a complete exposition of the state of the problem of asymptotic representation of solutions of systems of ordinary linear differential equations. In addition, the Schlesinger-Birkhoff-Tamarkin theory was generalized to the case of linear integral-differential equations containing a parameter.

Generally, for asymptotic representation of solutions of differential equations containing a parameter, we use the expression

$$e^{\alpha^r \sum_{s=0}^{r-1} \Omega_s(x)\alpha^{-s}} \left[\sum_{s=0}^{m} y_s(x)\alpha^{-s} + \eta\alpha^m \right],$$

where α is a large parameter, and η is a quantity which tends to zero as $\alpha \to \infty$ along a path which lies entirely within some region of the α-plane.

In the period 1940-46, a whole series of papers by Pugachev [56-60] were published, in which interesting and substantially new results were presented relating to the theory of asymptotic representations of solutions of nonhomogeneous ordinary differential equations of second and higher order whose coefficients contained a parameter. References [56, 57] contain substantially new results concerning an estimate of the error in approximate representation of solutions by the first terms of their asymptotic expansions.

In addition to theorems generalizing the results of previous investigators, Pugachev presented a new type of asymptotic representation of solutions of systems of ordinary linear homogeneous and nonhomogeneous differential equations.

This new type of representation of a solution has the form:

$$\sum_{h=1}^{n} z_h(x, \alpha)\left\{\sum_{k=0}^{m} y_{hk}(x)\,\alpha^{-k} + \eta_h \alpha^{-m}\right\},$$

where $z_h(x, \alpha)$ $(h = 1, 2, \ldots, n)$ are functions satisfying some system of linear differential equations, and the η_h are quantities which tend to zero as $\alpha \to \infty$.

Pugachev also generalized the theory of asymptotic representation to the case of an arbitrary complex domain of variation of the arguments.

The works of Turrittin [130, 77] and Sibuya [126] should also be noted; basically, the authors have obtained an asymptotic decomposition of the original system of linear differential equations into several subsystems of lower order, the number of subsystems depending on the number of identically multiple roots of the characteristic equation.

Our short historical review would certainly be incomplete if we did not mention the asymptotic methods originated by N. M. Krylov and N. N. Bogolyubov [41, 2-4] for the solution of problems in nonlinear mechanics. These methods have been rigorously substantiated and can be applied for the description of both periodic and quasi-periodic processes, as well as for investigation of the most general nonconservative systems.

We must note that ordinary methods of expansion in powers of a small parameter lead to approximate solutions containing so-called secular terms, in which the independent variable t occurs in trigonometric expressions. As a result of this, the error resulting from substitution of such approximate solutions in differential equations, although it does decrease together with the small parameter in the case of fixed t, does not decrease uniformly with respect to t. We can find a sequence of values $t \to \infty$ for which the error will not tend to zero, but to infinity, regardless of how quickly the small parameter is decreased. Thus, the area of application of the ordinary method of expansion is limited to a rather narrow time interval. On the other hand, in investigation of oscillatory processes, especially high-frequency processes, we require approximate formulas which would be suitable on the longest possible time intervals.

The asymptotic methods originated by Krylov and Bogolyubov lead to approximate formulas which no longer contain secular terms. The asymptotic solutions obtained in this way are applicable to a sufficiently large (though finite) time interval.

Further significant development of the methods of nonlinear mechanics proposed and substantiated by Krylov and Bogolyubov are to be found in the papers of Yu. A. Mitropol'skiy and his school [52-54, 44-46, 55]. The method worked out by Mitropol'skiy permits very effective investigation of nonstationary processes in nonlinear oscillatory systems, which result from variation of the frequency, mass, or other parameters of the linear system. We must note that the area of application of this method is very wide, since its basic condition (the requirement of slow variation of the parameters of the system compared to the "characteristic period" of oscillation) is, in practice, fulfilled in many problems.

We must remember here the works of I. Z. Shtokalo [116-118], who, on the basis of the asymptotic methods of Krylov and Bogolyubov, constructed a method which allows us to determine criteria of stability and instability of solutions of systems of linear differential equations with nearly constant coefficients.

We must also mention the method of investigation of the asymptotic behavior of solutions of linear differential equations developed by I. M. Rapoport [61]. This method is based on the idea of conversion of the given system of differential equations into a special form, which the author calls "L-diagnol." Using this method, Rapoport obtains a number of interesting results relating to the asymptotic properties of solutions of ordinary linear differential equations and to questions of stability of motion.

All the above-mentioned studies in the asymptotic theory of linear differential equations containing a parameter have concerned the case when the roots of the characteristic equation are simple or preserve their multiplicity (in systems of second-order [76]) on the entire domain of variation of the argument. The extremely important and interesting question of asymptotic representation in the case when the multiplicity of the roots of the characteristic equation varies at different points of the domain of variation of the argument had not been investigated at all.

This gap was filled by a number of works by the authors of this book [82-100, 104-115], and also by the fundamental investigations of Yu. L. Daletskiy and S. G. Kreyn [18-22]. We should also note the results obtained by A. G. Ilyukhin [29-31], I. I. Kovtun [34-38], I. I. Markush [50-51], A. A. Stonitskiy [72-75] and others. The present monograph is based on the above works, which were published during the period 1947-1965.

The monograph consists of six chapters.

In the first two chapters we investigate the question of asymptotic representation of solutions of linear differential equations with free terms of the form $p(\tau, \varepsilon)e^{i\theta(t,\varepsilon)}$, where $p(\tau, \varepsilon)$ is a slowly varying function (or vector-function), and $\theta(t, \varepsilon)$ is a scalar function whose derivative is of the form

$$\frac{d\theta}{dt} = k(\tau).$$

Here, we can distinguish two such cases:

1. "resonance"—when for certain values of the argument in the interval $[0, L]$ the function $ik(\tau)$ becomes equal to one (or several) of the roots of the corresponding characteristic equation:

2. "nonresonance"—when the values of $ik(\tau)$ on $[0, L]$ do not coincide with any of the roots of the characteristic equation.

For each of these cases we propose a method of construction of asymptotic solutions of the given differential equations.

The method which we have worked out is very effective in solving a number of practical problems. In this monograph we use these methods to solve differential equations with variable coefficients which reflect the motion of an elevator-shaft cable with a weight at the end.

The third chapter describes an asymptotic method of decomposition of a system of linear differential equations into several independent subsystems of lower order, the number of subsystems depending on the number of isolated groups of roots of the characteristic equation. In the case of simple roots, the separated equations can be integrated by quadrature, i.e. we can obtain asymptotic solutions of the system in question.

The fourth chapter concerns an extremely interesting and at the same time difficult case of constructing asymptotic solutions: the case when among the roots of the characteristic equation there are multiple roots with multiple elementary divisors and the "external frequency"—$ik(\tau)$—becomes equal to one of these (multiple) roots at some points of the considered interval.

The theory presented leads to investigation of differential equations with small parameters for the highest derivatives.

The fifth chapter is devoted to an exposition of the papers of Daletskiy and Kreyn [18-22], which concern asymptotic methods for differential equations in infinite-dimensional spaces.

In Chap. 6, we attempt to apply the asymptotic methods described in the previous chapters to the solution of some problems relating to partial differential equations. Our goal is to obtain computational formulas which are simpler and easier to use.

At the end of the book we present a list of references which concern asymptotic representation of solutions of differential equations containing a parameter. In the short historical review of the problem which we have given, we were unable to elucidate a large number of results which are very interesting both from the point of view of theory [23-25, 47, 48, 5-8] and of engineering applications [63-37].

In conclusion, the authors express sincere thanks to Academician Nikolai Nikolaevich Bogolyubov for his valuable advice, which greatly aided the development of the methods presented here.

The authors also wish to thank Academicians of the Academy of Sciences of the U. S. S. R., Yu. A. Mitropol'skiy and I. Z. Shtokalo for many useful comments which helped improve the book, and Doctor of Physico-Mathematical Sciences, Yu. L. Daletskiy for consenting to be editor-in-chief of this monograph.

We are also grateful to candidates in the physico-mathematical sciences, A. G. Ilyukhin and I. I. Kovtun, who wrote Sec. 18 (A. G. Ilyukhin) and Secs. 11 and 27 (I. I. Kovtun) of this book.

Chapter 1

CONSTRUCTION OF ASYMPTOTIC SOLUTIONS FOR SECOND-ORDER LINEAR DIFFERENTIAL EQUATIONS WITH SLOWLY VARYING COEFFICIENTS

1. Formulation of the Problem

The simplest example of a differential equation to which we can apply the asymptotic method to be presented below is the equation

$$a(\tau, \varepsilon)\frac{d^2x}{dt^2} + \varepsilon c(\tau, \varepsilon)\frac{dx}{dt} + b(\tau, \varepsilon)x = p(\tau, \varepsilon)e^{i\theta(t,\varepsilon)}, \tag{1.1}$$

where $a(\tau, \varepsilon)$, $c(\tau, \varepsilon)$, $b(\tau, \varepsilon)$, $p(\tau, \varepsilon)$ are slowly varying functions, admitting the expansions

$$\begin{aligned} a(\tau, \varepsilon) &= \sum_{s=0}^{\infty} \varepsilon^s a_s(\tau), \qquad & c(\tau, \varepsilon) &= \sum_{s=0}^{\infty} \varepsilon^s c_s(\tau), \\ b(\tau, \varepsilon) &= \sum_{s=0}^{\infty} \varepsilon^s b_s(\tau), \qquad & p(\tau, \varepsilon) &= \sum_{s=0}^{\infty} \varepsilon^s p_s(\tau). \end{aligned} \tag{1.2}$$

Here, τ is so-called "slow" time, defined by the relationship

$$\tau = \varepsilon t, \tag{1.3}$$

where ε is a small real parameter in the interval

$$0 < \varepsilon \leqslant \varepsilon_0. \tag{1.4}$$

We agree to call the equation

$$a_0(\tau)\lambda^2(\tau) + b_0(\tau) = 0 \tag{1.5}$$

the characteristic equation of differential equation (1.1).

In addition, we will assume that for all $\tau \in [0, L]$ the conditions

$$a_0(\tau) \neq 0, \qquad \frac{b_0(\tau)}{a_0(\tau)} > 0, \qquad \frac{d\theta(t, \varepsilon)}{dt} = k(\tau)^* \tag{1.6}$$

are fulfilled. (Actually, the essence of the method below does not require condition (1.6); however, this condition is necessary for division of the class of differential equations describing oscillatory processes.) Thus, from Eq. (1.5) it follows that

$$\lambda_{1,2}(\tau) = \pm i\sqrt{\frac{b_0(\tau)}{a_0(\tau)}}. \tag{1.7}$$

Depending on the values of the function $ik(\tau)$ and the roots (1.7), we can distinguish two cases:

1. "resonance"— when for certain points in the interval $[0, L]$ the function $ik(\tau)$ becomes equal to one of the roots of Eq. (1.5), say, $\lambda_1(\tau)$;
2. "nonresonance"—when

$$ik(\tau) \neq \lambda_{1,2}(\tau) \tag{1.8}$$

for any $\tau \in [0, L]$.

In this chapter we will consider each of these cases separately.

We should note that here we are considering, generally speaking, a Cauchy problem, i.e., we seek a solution of Eq. (1.1) satisfying the initial conditions

$$x(t)\big|_{t=0} = x_0, \qquad \frac{dx}{dt}\bigg|_{t=0} = x_0. \tag{1.9}$$

However, the stated method can also be applied to the solution of boundary-value problems.

2. A Formal Solution in the Case of Resonance

In the "resonance" case we can prove the following theorem:

Theorem I.1. *If the coefficients of Eq. (1.1) and the function $k(\tau)$ are infinitely differentiable with respect to τ on the segment $[0, L]$, then a formal particular solution of the differential equation (1.1) can be written in the form*

$$x(t, \varepsilon) = \xi(t, \varepsilon)\, e^{i\theta(t,\varepsilon)}, \tag{2.1}$$

where the function $\xi(t, \varepsilon)$ satisfies the differential equation

$$\frac{d\xi}{dt} = [D(\tau, \varepsilon) + i(\Omega(\tau, \varepsilon) - k(\tau))]\,\xi + z(t, \varepsilon), \tag{2.2}$$

in which the coefficients admit the formal expansions:

$$D(\tau, \varepsilon) = \sum_{s=1}^{\infty} \varepsilon^s D_s(\tau), \qquad \Omega(\tau, \varepsilon) = \sum_{s=0}^{\infty} \varepsilon^s \Omega_s(\tau),$$
$$z(\tau, \varepsilon) = \sum_{s=0}^{\infty} \varepsilon^s z_s(\tau). \tag{2.3}$$

The proof of this theorem will consist of defining the terms of expansion (2.3) in such a way that expression (2.1), in which $\xi(t, \varepsilon)$ is the solution of Eq. (2.2), formally satisfies Eq. (1.1).

In order to do this, we substitute the function $x(t, \varepsilon)$, as defined by Eqs. (2.1) and (2.2), into Eq. (1.1). We obtain the identity

$$\begin{aligned}&\{a(\tau, \varepsilon)[(D(\tau, \varepsilon) + i\Omega(\tau, \varepsilon))^2 + \varepsilon(D(\tau,\varepsilon) + i\Omega(\tau, \varepsilon))'] +\\ &+ \varepsilon c(\tau, \varepsilon)[D(\tau, \varepsilon) + i\Omega(\tau, \varepsilon)] + b(\tau, \varepsilon)\}\,\xi(t, \varepsilon) + a(\tau, \varepsilon)\{D(\tau, \varepsilon) +\\ &+ i[\Omega(\tau, \varepsilon) + k(\tau)] + z(\tau, \varepsilon) + \varepsilon z'(\tau, \varepsilon)\} + \varepsilon c(\tau, \varepsilon) = p(\tau, \varepsilon)\end{aligned} \tag{2.4}$$

(here and in what follows, the prime (′) indicates differentiation with respect to τ).

We equate separately the coefficients for $\xi(t, \varepsilon)$ and the free terms from both parts of this identity. As a result we obtain two relationships:

$$\begin{aligned}&a(\tau, \varepsilon)\{[D(\tau, \varepsilon) + i\Omega(\tau, \varepsilon)]^2 + \varepsilon[D(\tau, \varepsilon) + i\Omega(\tau, \varepsilon)]'\} +\\ &+ \varepsilon c(\tau, \varepsilon)[D(\tau, \varepsilon) + i\Omega(\tau, \varepsilon)] + b(\tau, \varepsilon) = 0,\end{aligned} \tag{2.5}$$

$$a(\tau, \varepsilon)\{[D(\tau, \varepsilon) + i(\Omega(\tau, \varepsilon) + k(\tau))]z(\tau, \varepsilon) + \varepsilon z'(\tau, \varepsilon)\} + \\ + \varepsilon c(\tau, \varepsilon) z(\tau, \varepsilon) = p(\tau, \varepsilon), \tag{2.6}$$

which allow us to determine the coefficients of the formal series (2.3).

First we use relationship (2.5). Gathering the coefficients of like powers of the parameter ε, we obtain the recurrent formulas:

$$-a_0(\tau)[\Omega_0(\tau)]^2 + b_0(\tau) = 0, \tag{2.7}$$

$$\sum_{j=0}^{s}\sum_{m=0}^{s-j} a_j(\tau)[D_m(\tau) + i\Omega_m(\tau)][D_{s-j-m}(\tau) + i\Omega_{s-j-m}(\tau)] + \\ + \sum_{j=0}^{s-1} a_j(\tau)[D_{s-1-j}(\tau) + i\Omega_{s-1-j}(\tau)]' + \\ + \sum_{j=0}^{s-1} c_j(\tau)[D_{s-1-j}(\tau) + i\Omega_{s-1-j}(\tau)] + b_s(\tau) = 0, \qquad s = 1, 2, \ldots \tag{2.8}$$

[(2.3) implies that $D_0 \equiv 0$].

From Eq. (2.7), we find

$$z(\tau, \varepsilon) = \sum_{s=0}^{\infty} \varepsilon^s z_s(\tau). \tag{2.9}$$

Henceforth, in constructing a particular solution of non-homogeneous equation (1.1) we will choose an arithmetic value for $\Omega_0(\tau)$.

Setting $s = 1$ in Eq. (2.8), we obtain

$$2i\Omega_0(\tau)a_0(\tau)[D_1(\tau) + i\Omega_1(\tau)] - a_1(\tau)\Omega_0^2(\tau) + ia_0(\tau)\Omega_0'(\tau) + \\ + i\Omega_0(\tau)c_0(\tau) + b_1(\tau) = 0, \tag{2.10}$$

from which

$$D_1(\tau) = -\frac{a_0(\tau)\Omega_0'(\tau) + c_0(\tau)\Omega_0(\tau)}{2\Omega_0(\tau)a_0(\tau)}, \\ \Omega_1(\tau) = \frac{b_1(\tau) - a_1(\tau)\Omega_0^2(\tau)}{2\Omega_0(\tau)a_0(\tau)}. \tag{2.11}$$

Analogously, we find recurrent relationships for determination of the functions $D_s(\tau)$ and $\Omega_s(\tau)$ for $s \geqslant 2$, namely:

$$D_s(\tau) + i\Omega_s(\tau) = -\frac{1}{2ia_0(\tau)\Omega_0(\tau)}\Bigg\{-a_0(\tau)\sum_{j=1}^{s-1}[D_j(\tau) + i\Omega_j(\tau)] \times$$

$$\times [D_{s-j}(\tau) + i\Omega_{s-j}(\tau)] + \sum_{j=1}^{s}\sum_{m=0}^{s-j} a_j(\tau)[D_m(\tau) + i\Omega_m(\tau)] \times$$

$$\times [D_{s-j-m}(\tau) + i\Omega_{s-j-m}(\tau)] + \sum_{j=0}^{s-1} a_j(\tau)[D_{s-1-j}(\tau) + i\Omega_{s-1-j}(\tau)]' +$$

$$+ \sum_{j=0}^{s-1} c_j(\tau)[D_{s-1-j}(\tau) + i\Omega_{s-1-j}(\tau)] + b_s(\tau)\Bigg\}. \qquad (2.12)$$

Separating the real and imaginary parts, we find the unknown functions $D_s(\tau)$ and $\Omega_s(\tau)$ $(s = 0, 1, \dots)$ on the segment $[0, L]$.

In order to complete the proof of Theorem I.1, we must determine the function $z(\tau, \varepsilon)$. For this we use relationship (2.6). By equating coefficients of like powers of the parameter ε we have

$$ia_0(\tau)[\Omega_0(\tau) + k(\tau)]z_0(\tau) = p_0(\tau), \qquad (2.13)$$

$$ia_0(\tau)[\Omega_0(\tau) + k(\tau)]z_s(\tau) + \sum_{j=1}^{s}\sum_{j_1=1}^{s-j+1} a_j(\tau)[D_{j_1}(\tau) + i\Omega_{j_1}(\tau)]z_{s-j-j_1}(\tau) +$$

$$+ a_0(\tau)\sum_{j=1}^{s}[D_j(\tau) + i\Omega_j(\tau)]z_{s-j}(\tau) + \sum_{j=0}^{s-1} a_j(\tau)z'_{s-1-j}(\tau) +$$

$$+ \sum_{j=0}^{s-j} c_j(\tau)z_{s-j}(\tau) = p_s(\tau), \qquad s = 1, 2, \dots, \qquad (2.14)$$

from which

$$z_0(\tau) = \frac{p_0(\tau)}{ia_0(\tau)[\Omega_0(\tau) + k(\tau)]}, \qquad (2.15)$$

$$z_s(\tau) = \frac{1}{ia_0(\tau)[\Omega_0(\tau) + k(\tau)]}\Bigg\{p_s(\tau) - a_0(\tau)\sum_{j=1}^{s}[D_j(\tau) + i\Omega_j(\tau)]z_{s-j}(\tau) -$$

$$-\sum_{j=1}^{s}\sum_{j_1=0}^{s-j} a_j(\tau)[D_{j_1}(\tau) + i\Omega_{j_1}(\tau)]z_{s-j-j_1}(\tau) -$$

$$-\sum_{j=0}^{s-1} a_j(\tau) z'_{s-1-j}(\tau) + \sum_{j=0}^{s-1} c_j(\tau) z_{s-j}(\tau) \Bigg\}, \qquad s=1,\ 2, \ldots . \tag{2.16}$$

Thus, by exhibiting a way of determining the coefficients of series (2.3), we have proved Theorem I.1.

Note. Theorem I.1 gives the possibility of constructing a particular solution of nonhomogeneous equation (1.1).

To construct the general solution, we must, of course, add to the obtained particular solution, the general solution of the corresponding homogeneous equation

$$a(\tau, \varepsilon)\frac{d^2x}{dt^2} + \varepsilon c(\tau, \varepsilon)\frac{dx}{dt} + b(\tau, \varepsilon)\, x(t, \varepsilon) = 0. \tag{2.17}$$

A formal particular solution of this equation can be sought in the form

$$x(t, \varepsilon) = \xi(t, \varepsilon),$$

where

$$\frac{d\xi}{dt} = [D(\tau, \varepsilon) + i\Omega(\tau, \varepsilon)]\, \xi.$$

Here $D(\tau, \varepsilon)$ and $\Omega(\tau, \varepsilon)$ are constructed as in Theorem I.1.

For $\Omega_s(\tau)$ $(s = 0, 1, \ldots)$, in accordance with (2.9), we obtain two different values, which allows us to construct two linearly independent particular solutions of Eq. (2.17), and, thus, a general solution for it as well.

3. A Formal Solution in the "Nonresonance" Case

Theorem I.2. *If the coefficients of Eq. (1.1) and the function $k(\tau)$ possess, on the closed interval $[0, L]$, derivatives with respect to τ of all orders, then the formal general solution of the differential equation (1.1) in the nonresonance case can be written in the form*

$$x(t, \varepsilon) = X(t, \varepsilon) + F(\tau, \varepsilon)\, e^{i\theta(t,\varepsilon)} \tag{3.1}$$

where $X(t, \varepsilon)$ is a general solution of the homogeneous equation (2.17), and $F(\tau, \varepsilon)$ is a function which admits a formal expansion of the form

$$F(\tau, \varepsilon) = \sum_{s=0}^{\infty} \varepsilon^s F_s(\tau). \tag{3.2}$$

Proof. Since the method of determination of the general solution $X(t, \varepsilon)$ is described in Sec. 2, to prove the given theorem we must show only a method of construction of the coefficients of the series (3.2). To this end, we substitute

$$x(t, \varepsilon) = F(\tau, \varepsilon) e^{i\theta(t,\varepsilon)} \tag{3.3}$$

into Eq. (1.1). As a result of this we obtain

$$a(\tau, \varepsilon)[\varepsilon^2 F''(\tau, \varepsilon) + 2\varepsilon F'(\tau, \varepsilon) + \varepsilon i k'(\tau) F(\tau, \varepsilon) - k^2(\tau) F(\tau, \varepsilon)] + \\ + \varepsilon c(\tau, \varepsilon)[\varepsilon F'(\tau, \varepsilon) + ik(\tau) F(\tau, \varepsilon)] + b(\tau, \varepsilon) F(\tau, \varepsilon) = p(\tau, \varepsilon). \tag{3.4}$$

In relationship (3.4) we equate the coefficients of like powers of the parameter ε; we obtain

$$a_0(\tau)\left[\frac{b_0(\tau)}{a_0(\tau)} - k^2(\tau)\right] F_0(\tau) = p_0(\tau), \tag{3.5}$$

$$a_0(\tau)\left[\frac{b_0(\tau)}{a_0(\tau)} - k^2(\tau)\right] F_s(\tau) = H_s(\tau), \qquad s = 1, 2, \ldots, \tag{3.6}$$

where

$$H_s(\tau) = p_s(\tau) - \sum_{j=0}^{s-2} a_j(\tau) F_{s-2-j}(\tau) - 2\sum_{j=0}^{s-1} a_j(\tau) F'_{s-1-j}(\tau) - \\ - ik'(\tau)\sum_{j=0}^{s-1} a_j(\tau) F_{s-1-j}(\tau) - k^2(\tau)\sum_{j=1}^{s} a_j(\tau) F_{s-j}(\tau) - \\ - \sum_{j=0}^{s-2} c_j(\tau) F'_{s-2-j}(\tau) - ik(\tau)\sum_{j=0}^{s-1} c_j(\tau) F_{s-1-j}(\tau) - \\ - \sum_{j=1} b_j(\tau) F_{s-j}(\tau), \qquad s = 1, 2, \ldots. \tag{3.7}$$

From this, taking account of conditions (1.5) and (1.6), we find

$$F_0(\tau) = \frac{p_0(\tau)}{b_0(\tau) - a_0(\tau) k^2(\tau)}, \\ F_s(\tau) = \frac{H_s(\tau)}{b_0(\tau) - a_0(\tau) k^2(\tau)}, \qquad s = 1, 2, \ldots. \tag{3.8}$$

Theorem I.2 is proved.

4. The Asymptotic Nature of the Solution

In the preceding sections, we have presented a method of constructing a solution, formally satisfying Eq. (1.1) in the resonance and nonresonance cases. In this section we will show that the solution constructed in this way is of an asymptotic nature.

Let us investigate the resonance case in detail.

We introduce the function

$$x^{(m)}(t, \varepsilon) = \xi^{(m)}(t, \varepsilon)\, e^{i\theta(t,\varepsilon)}, \tag{4.1}$$

where $\xi^{(m)}(t, \varepsilon)$ is defined by the differential equation

$$\frac{d\xi^{(m)}}{dt} = [D^{(m)}(\tau, \varepsilon) + i\,(\Omega^{(m)}(\tau, \varepsilon) - k(\tau))]\,\xi^{(m)} + z^{(m)}(t, \varepsilon), \tag{4.2}$$

in which

$$D^{(m)}(\tau, \varepsilon) = \sum_{s=1}^{m} \varepsilon^s D_s(\tau), \qquad \Omega^{(m)}(\tau, \varepsilon) = \sum_{s=0}^{m} \varepsilon^s \Omega_s(\tau),$$
$$z^{(m)}(\tau, \varepsilon) = \sum_{s=0}^{m} \varepsilon^s z_s(\tau). \tag{4.3}$$

The function $x^{(m)}(t, \varepsilon)$ [m is a natural number] will henceforth be called the mth approximate solution of Eq. (1.1).

Substituting the value $x^{(m)}(t, \varepsilon)$, with allowance for Eq. (4.2), into the expression

$$a(\tau, \varepsilon)\frac{d^2x^{(m)}}{dt^2} + \varepsilon c(\tau, \varepsilon)\frac{dx^{(m)}}{dt} + b(\tau, \varepsilon)\, x^{(m)} - p(\tau, \varepsilon)\, e^{i\theta(t,\varepsilon)},$$

we obtain

$$a(\tau, \varepsilon)\frac{d^2x^{(m)}}{dt^2} + \varepsilon c(\tau, \varepsilon)\frac{dx^{(m)}}{dt} + b(\tau, \varepsilon)\, x^{(m)}(t, \varepsilon) - p(\tau, \varepsilon)\, e^{i\theta(t,\varepsilon)} =$$
$$= \{a(\tau, \varepsilon)\,[(D^{(m)}(\tau, \varepsilon) + i\Omega^{(m)}(\tau, \varepsilon))^2 + \varepsilon\,(D^{(m)}(\tau, \varepsilon) + i\Omega^{(m)}(\tau, \varepsilon))'] +$$
$$+ \varepsilon c(\tau, \varepsilon)\,[D^{(m)}(\tau, \varepsilon) + i\Omega^{(m)}(\tau, \varepsilon)] + b^{(m)}(\tau, \varepsilon)\}\, \xi^{(m)}(t, \varepsilon) e^{i\theta(t,\varepsilon)} +$$

$$+\{a(\tau,\varepsilon)[(D^{(m)}(\tau,\varepsilon)+i\Omega^{(m)}(\tau,\varepsilon)+ik(\tau))z^{(m)}(\tau,\varepsilon)+ \\ +\varepsilon z^{(m)\prime}(\tau,\varepsilon)]+\varepsilon c(\tau,\varepsilon)z^{(m)}(\tau,\varepsilon)-p(\tau,\varepsilon)\}e^{i\theta(t,\varepsilon)}. \tag{4.4}$$

In accordance with the way in which we have constructed the quantities entering into the mth approximation, the functions in front of $\xi^{(m)}(t,\varepsilon)e^{i\theta(t,\varepsilon)}$ and $e^{i\theta(t,\varepsilon)}$ on the right-hand side of Eq. (4.4) are of the order of ε^{m+1}. Therefore, we can write

$$a(\tau,\varepsilon)\frac{d^2x^{(m)}}{dt^2}+\varepsilon c(\tau,\varepsilon)\frac{dx^{(m)}}{dt}+b(\tau,\varepsilon)x^{(m)}(t,\varepsilon)= \\ =p(\tau,\varepsilon)e^{i\theta(t,\varepsilon)}+\varepsilon^{m+1}[r_m(\tau,\varepsilon)\xi^{(m)}(t,\varepsilon)+f_m(\tau,\varepsilon)], \tag{4.5}$$

where $r_m(\tau,\varepsilon)$, $f_m(\tau,\varepsilon)$ are functions which are holomorphic (regular analytic) with respect to ε in a neighborhood of the point $\varepsilon=0$.

Integrating Eq. (4.2), we find

$$\xi^{(m)}(t,\varepsilon)=Ae^{\int_0^t[D^{(m)}(\tau,\varepsilon)+i(\Omega^{(m)}(\tau,\varepsilon)-k(\tau))]dt}+ \\ +\int_0^t z^{(m)}(\sigma,\varepsilon)e^{\int_s^t[D^{(m)}(\tau,\varepsilon)+i(\Omega^{(m)}(\tau,\varepsilon)-k(\tau))]dt}ds, \tag{4.6}$$

where A is a constant of integration, and $\sigma=\varepsilon s$.

Since the functions $D^{(m)}(\tau,\varepsilon)$ and $z^{(m)}(\tau,\varepsilon)$ are differentiable with respect to τ on the closed interval $[0,L]$, then they are bounded for all ε in (1.4).

Consequently, we can find constants M_1 and M_2, independent of ε, such that

$$\left|\sum_{j=1}^{m}\varepsilon^{j-1}D_j(\tau)\right|\leqslant M_1, \qquad |z^{(m)}(\tau,\varepsilon)|\leqslant M_2. \tag{4.7}$$

Using these inequalities we obtain, in accordance with (4.6), an estimate for $\xi^{(m)}(t,\varepsilon)$:

$$|\xi^{(m)}(t,\varepsilon)|\leqslant Ae^{M_1L}+M_2e^{M_1L}t\leqslant\left(A+\frac{M_2L}{\varepsilon}\right)e^{M_1L}. \tag{4.8}$$

Now Eq. (4.5) can be written in the form

$$a(\tau,\varepsilon)\frac{d^2x^{(m)}}{dt^2}+\varepsilon c(\tau,\varepsilon)\frac{dx^{(m)}}{dt}+b(\tau,\varepsilon)x^{(m)}(t,\varepsilon)= \tag{4.9}$$
$$=p(\tau,\varepsilon)e^{i\theta(t,\varepsilon)}+\varepsilon^m g_m(\tau,\varepsilon),$$

where $g_m(\tau,\varepsilon)$ is a function which is bounded for all $\tau\in[0,L]$ and $0<\varepsilon\leqslant\varepsilon_0$.

Thus, the mth approximation satisfies the original equation with an accuracy up to quantities of the order of ε^m uniformly with respect to t on the closed interval $0\leqslant t\leqslant\frac{L}{\varepsilon}$.

Theorem I.3. *If the conditions of Theorem I.1. are satisfied and, in addition,*

$$x(t,\varepsilon)|_{t=0}=x^{(m)}(t,\varepsilon)|_{t=0}=x_0,\ \frac{dx}{dt}\bigg|_{t=0}=\frac{dx^{(m)}}{dt}\bigg|_{t=0}=\dot{x}_0, \tag{4.10}$$

then for any $L>0$ and $0<\varepsilon\leqslant\varepsilon_0$ we can find a constant C, independent of ε, such that the following inequalities hold:

$$|x(t,\varepsilon)-x^{(m)}(t,\varepsilon)|\leqslant\varepsilon^{m-1}C,\qquad \left|\frac{dx}{dt}-\frac{dx^{(m)}}{dt}\right|\leqslant\varepsilon^{m-1}C. \tag{4.11}$$

Rather than going directly to the proof of this theorem, we will first prove two lemmas.

Lemma I.1. *If for all $t\in[0,L/\varepsilon]$, the inequality*

$$r(t)\leqslant c\int_0^t r(s)\,ds+f(t), \tag{4.12}$$

is satisfied, where c is a positive constant and the function f(t) is differentiable on the given closed interval, then

$$r(t)\leqslant f(0)e^{ct}+\int_0^t e^{c(t-s)}f'(s)\,ds. \tag{4.13}$$

The proof of this lemma has been borrowed from [39]. We set

$$R(t)=\int_0^t r(s)\,ds. \tag{4.14}$$

Then inequality (4.12) can be rewritten in the form

$$R'(t)\leqslant cR(t)+f(t). \tag{4.15}$$

Multiplying both sides of inequality (4.15) by e^{-ct} and integrating the obtained result from 0 to t, we find

$$R(t) \leqslant \int_0^t e^{c(t-s)} f(s)\, ds. \tag{4.16}$$

Integrating by parts, we can represent inequality (4.16) in the form

$$R(t) \leqslant \frac{1}{c}\left[\int_0^t e^{c(t-s)} f'(s)\, ds + e^{ct} f(0) - f(t)\right]. \tag{4.17}$$

Now, in accordance with inequalities (4.14) and (4.17), we can write the original inequality (4.12) in the form (4.13), which was to be proved.

Lemma I.2. *If $y(t, \varepsilon)$ is a solution of the differential equation*

$$\frac{d^2y}{dt^2} + \omega^2(\tau, \varepsilon) y = q(\tau, \varepsilon) \tag{4.18}$$

with the initial conditions

$$y(0) = \left.\frac{dy}{dt}\right|_{t=0} = 0, \tag{4.19}$$

where

$$\omega(\tau, \varepsilon) = \sum_{s=0}^{\infty} \varepsilon^s \omega_s(\tau), \qquad \omega_0(\tau) \neq 0, \qquad \tau \in [0, L], \tag{4.20}$$

then for any $L > 0$ we can find a constant S_1, independent of ε, such that, on the closed interval $0 \leqslant t \leqslant L/\varepsilon$, the following inequalities will hold:

$$|y(t, \varepsilon)| \leqslant 2e^{2S_1 L} \int_0^t \left|\frac{q(\tau, \varepsilon)}{\omega(\tau, \varepsilon)}\right| dt,$$

$$\left|\frac{dy}{dt}\right| \leqslant 2\omega^* e^{2S_1 L} \int_0^t \left|\frac{q(\tau, \varepsilon)}{\omega(\tau, \varepsilon)}\right| dt, \tag{4.21}$$

$$\omega^* = \max_{\substack{0 \leqslant \tau \leqslant L \\ 0 < \varepsilon \leqslant \varepsilon_0}} \omega(\tau, \varepsilon).$$

Proof. We introduce the new variables u and v by using the formulas

$$y = u \cos \theta_1 + v \sin \theta_1,$$
$$\frac{dy}{dt} = -\omega(\tau, \varepsilon) u \sin \theta_1 + \omega(\tau, \varepsilon) v \cos \theta_1, \tag{4.22}$$

where

$$\theta_1 = \int_0^t \omega(\tau, \varepsilon)\, dt. \tag{4.23}$$

Then Eq. (4.18) can be transformed to an equivalent system of equations of the first order of the form

$$\frac{du}{dt} = q_1(\tau, \varepsilon) + \varepsilon [a(\tau, \varepsilon) u + b(\tau, \varepsilon) v],$$
$$\frac{dv}{dt} = q_2(\tau, \varepsilon) + \varepsilon [a_1(\tau, \varepsilon) u + b_1(\tau, \varepsilon) v], \tag{4.24}$$

where

$$a(\tau, \varepsilon) = -\frac{\omega'(\tau, \varepsilon)\sin^2\theta_1}{\omega(\tau, \varepsilon)}, \qquad b_1(\tau, \varepsilon) = -\frac{\omega'(\tau, \varepsilon)\cos^2\theta_1}{\omega(\tau, \varepsilon)},$$
$$a_1(\tau, \varepsilon) = b(\tau, \varepsilon) = \frac{\omega'(\tau, \varepsilon)\sin 2\theta_1}{2\omega(\tau, \varepsilon)}, \qquad q_1(\tau, \varepsilon) = \frac{q(\tau, \varepsilon)\sin\theta_1}{\omega(\tau, \varepsilon)},$$
$$q_2(\tau, \varepsilon) = \frac{q(\tau, \varepsilon)\cos\theta_1}{\omega(\tau, \varepsilon)}. \tag{4.25}$$

Since, in accordance with condition (4.19),

$$u|_{t=0} = v|_{t=0} = 0, \tag{4.26}$$

system (4.24) can be converted to an equivalent integral system

$$u = \int_0^t [q_1(\tau, \varepsilon) + \varepsilon (a(\tau, \varepsilon) u + b(\tau, \varepsilon) v)]\, dt,$$
$$v = \int_0^t [q_2(\tau, \varepsilon) + \varepsilon (a_1(\tau, \varepsilon) u + b_1(\tau, \varepsilon) v)]\, dt, \tag{4.27}$$

from which it follows that

$$|u| \leqslant \int_0^t \left| \frac{q(\tau, \varepsilon)}{\omega(\tau, \varepsilon)} \right| dt + \varepsilon S_1 \int_0^t [|u| + |v|]\, dt,$$
$$|v| \leqslant \int_0^t \left| \frac{q(\tau, \varepsilon)}{\omega(\tau, \varepsilon)} \right| dt + \varepsilon S_1 \int_0^t [|u| + |v|]\, dt, \tag{4.28}$$

where

$$S_1 = \max \{|a(\tau, \varepsilon)|, \ |a_1(\tau, \varepsilon)|, \ |b_1(\tau, \varepsilon)|\},$$
$$\tau \in [0, L], \qquad \varepsilon \in (0, \varepsilon_0]. \tag{4.29}$$

As a result of summation of the inequalities (4.28), we obtain

$$r \leqslant 2 \int_0^t \left| \frac{q(\tau, \varepsilon)}{\omega(\tau, \varepsilon)} \right| dt + 2\varepsilon S_1 \int_0^t r\, dt, \tag{4.30}$$

where

$$r = |u(t, \varepsilon)| + |v(t, \varepsilon)|. \tag{4.31}$$

Inequality (4.30) is analogous to inequality (4.12), therefore, according to Lemma I.1:

$$r \equiv |u| + |v| \leqslant 2 \int_0^t \left| \frac{q(\tau_1, \varepsilon)}{\omega(\tau_1, \varepsilon)} \right| e^{2\varepsilon S_1 (t - t_1)} dt_1, \qquad \tau_1 = \varepsilon t_1,$$

or

$$|u| + |v| \leqslant 2e^{2S_1 L} \int_0^t \left| \frac{q(\tau_1, \varepsilon)}{\omega(\tau_1, \varepsilon)} \right| dt_1. \tag{4.32}$$

The proof of Lemma I.2 follows from inequality (4.32) and formula (4.22). Now we turn to the proof of Theorem I.3.

We set

$$y(t, \varepsilon) = x(t, \varepsilon) - x^{(m)}(t, \varepsilon), \tag{4.33}$$

where $x(t, \varepsilon)$ is the exact solution of Eq. (1.1) and $x^{(m)}(t, \varepsilon)$ is its mth approximation. Then, by (1.1) and (4.9), the function $y(t, \varepsilon)$ satisfies the equation

$$a(\tau, \varepsilon)\frac{d^2y}{dt^2} + \varepsilon c(\tau, \varepsilon)\frac{dy}{dt} + b(\tau, \varepsilon)y = -\varepsilon^m g(\tau, \varepsilon), \tag{4.34}$$

which can be represented in the form (4.18), where

$$q(\tau, \varepsilon) = -\frac{1}{a(\tau, \varepsilon)}\left[\varepsilon^m g(\tau, \varepsilon) + \varepsilon c(\tau, \varepsilon)\frac{dy}{dt} + \varepsilon b_1(\tau, \varepsilon)y\right],$$

$$b_1(\tau, \varepsilon) = \sum_{s=0}^{\infty}\varepsilon^s b_{s+1}(\tau), \tag{4.35}$$

$$\omega^2(\tau, \varepsilon) = \frac{b_0(\tau)}{a(\tau, \varepsilon)},$$

for which

$$y(0) = \left.\frac{dy}{dt}\right|_{t=0} = 0.$$

Using Lemma I.2, which we just proved, we obtain

$$|y(t, \varepsilon)| \leqslant S_2\int_0^t\left|\frac{q(\tau, \varepsilon)}{\omega(\tau, \varepsilon)}\right|dt,$$

$$\left|\frac{dy}{dt}\right| \leqslant S_3\int_0^t\left|\frac{q(\tau, \varepsilon)}{\omega(\tau, \varepsilon)}\right|dt, \tag{4.36}$$

where

$$S_2 = 2e^{2S_1L}, \qquad S_3 = \omega^* S_2. \tag{4.37}$$

Inequality (4.36), in accordance with (4.35), acquires the form

$$|y| \leqslant S_2\int_0^t\left|\frac{1}{\sqrt{b_0(\tau)a(\tau, \varepsilon)}}\left[\varepsilon^m g_m(\tau, \varepsilon) + \varepsilon c(\tau, \varepsilon)\frac{dy}{dt} + b_1(\tau, \varepsilon)y\right]\right|dt,$$

$$\left|\frac{dy}{dt}\right| \leqslant S_3\int_0^t\left|\frac{1}{\sqrt{b_0(\tau)a(\tau, \varepsilon)}}\left[\varepsilon^m g_m(\tau, \varepsilon) + \varepsilon c(\tau, \varepsilon)\frac{dy}{dt} + b_1(\tau, \varepsilon)y\right]\right|dt. \tag{4.38}$$

Since the functions $b_0(\tau)$, $a(\tau, \varepsilon)$, $g_m(\tau, \varepsilon)$, $c(\tau, \varepsilon)$ and $b_1(\tau, \varepsilon)$ are differentiable with respect to τ, we can, for all $t \in [0, L/\varepsilon]$ and $\varepsilon\ (0 < \varepsilon \leqslant \varepsilon_0)$, find two constants C_1 and C_2, independent of ε, such that the following inequalities hold:

$$\left|\frac{g_m(\tau, \varepsilon)}{\sqrt{b_0(\tau)\, a(\tau, \varepsilon)}}\right| \leqslant C_1, \qquad \left|\frac{c(\tau, \varepsilon)}{\sqrt{b_0(\tau)\, a(\tau, \varepsilon)}}\right| \leqslant C_2,$$

$$\left|\frac{b_1(\tau, \varepsilon)}{\sqrt{b_0(\tau)\, a(\tau, \varepsilon)}}\right| \leqslant C_2. \tag{4.39}$$

Consequently, the inequalities (4.38) can be rewritten in the form

$$|y(t, \varepsilon)| \leqslant \varepsilon S_2 C_2 \int_0^t \left(|y| + \left|\frac{dy}{dt}\right|\right) dt_1 + \varepsilon^m S_3 C_1 t,$$

$$\left|\frac{dy}{dt}\right| \leqslant \varepsilon S_3 C_2 \int_0^t \left(|y| + \left|\frac{dy}{dt}\right|\right) dt_1 + \varepsilon^m S_3 C_1 t. \tag{4.40}$$

Adding the obtained inequalities and introducing the notation

$$W = |y| + \left|\frac{dy}{dt}\right|, \tag{4.41}$$

we obtain the inequality

$$W \leqslant \varepsilon K_1 \int_0^t W dt + \varepsilon^{m-1} K_2, \tag{4.42}$$

in which

$$K_1 = C_2(S_2 + S_3), \qquad K_2 = C_1 L(S_1 + S_2). \tag{4.43}$$

According to Lemma I.1, from inequality (4.42) we find

$$W \leqslant \varepsilon^{m-1} C, \quad \text{where} \quad C = K_2 e^{KL}, \tag{4.44}$$

which also means that

$$|y| \leqslant \varepsilon^{m-1} C, \left|\frac{dy}{dt}\right| \leqslant \varepsilon^{m-1} C. \tag{4.45}$$

The theorem is proved.

From the obtained inequalities (4.45) it follows that the mth approximation $x^{(m)}(t, \varepsilon)$ and its derivative $dx^{(m)}/dt$ tend to the exact solution $x(t, \varepsilon)$ and its derivative dx/dt, respectively, as $\varepsilon \to 0$, beginning with $m \geqslant 2$. In this way we have proved the asymptotic nature of the solution which we constructed for the resonance case.

For the nonresonance case, repeating analogous considerations, we obtain, given the conditions of the theorem, the estimates

$$|x(t, \varepsilon) - x^{(m)}(t, \varepsilon)| \leqslant \varepsilon^m C, \qquad \left| \frac{dx}{dt} - \frac{dx^{(m)}}{dt} \right| \leqslant \varepsilon^m C, \tag{4.46}$$

where C is a constant which is independent of ε.

For the case of a small free term ($p_0(\tau) \equiv 0$) the asymptotic estimate is of the form (4.46) in the resonance case as well.

Note. Here we have exhibited an algorithm for construction of an asymptotic solution for the differential equation (1.1) with the right-hand side $p(\tau, \varepsilon)e^{i\theta(t,\varepsilon)}$. The obtained results can easily be applied to the case when the right-hand side of differential equation (1.1) is of the form

$$\sum_{j=1}^{N} p_j(\tau, \varepsilon)\, e^{i\theta_j(t,\varepsilon)}.$$

5. Finding the Tension in a Visco-Elastic Thread of Variable Length

As an example of the theory presented above, we consider the problem of finding the tension in a visco-elastic thread of variable length $l = l(t)$ with a weight Q at the end. This problem, as is shown in [32, 63], can be reduced to solving the equation

$$\begin{gathered} \frac{l}{g}\left(Q + \frac{1}{3}ql\right)\frac{d^2\varphi}{dt^2} + \left[\alpha + \frac{1}{g}\left(Q + \frac{ql}{2}\right)\frac{dl}{dt}\right]\frac{d\varphi}{dt} + K\varphi = \\ = \frac{1}{g}\left(Q + \frac{ql}{2}\right)\left(g - \frac{dV_c}{dt}\right), \end{gathered} \tag{5.1}$$

where φ is the relative elongation of the thread; q is the weight per unit length of the thread; α is a coefficient which characterizes the damping of dynamical stresses in the thread; g is the acceleration of gravity; v_c is the linear velocity of a point on the contour of the drum on which the thread is wound; $K = E\sigma$, E is the modulus of elasticity of the thread; σ is the cross-sectional area of the thread.

In practice, the lifting of the weight Q is most often accomplished by using a trapezoidal tachogram (Fig. 1, see also [67], pp. 48-50).

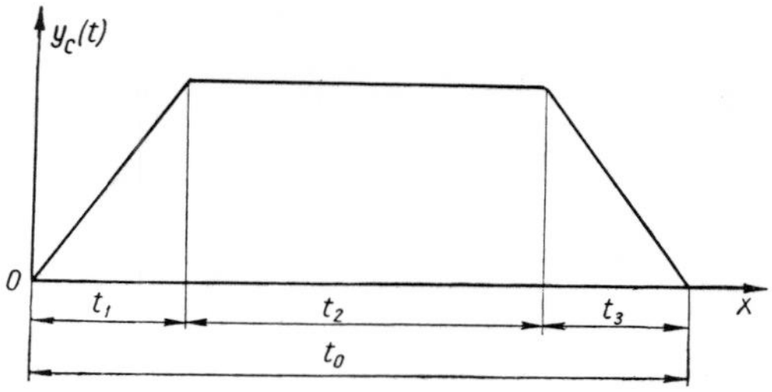

FIG. 1.

Consequently, Eq. (5.1) should be integrated on each of these three segments:

1) the segment of uniformly accelerated motion

$$l = l_0 - \frac{at^2}{2}, \qquad v_c = \frac{dl}{dt} = -at, \qquad \frac{dv_c}{dt} = -a: \tag{5.2}$$

2) the segment of uniform motion

$$l = l_1 - v_0 t, \qquad v_c = \frac{dl}{dt} = -v_0, \qquad \frac{dv}{dt} = 0.$$

$$l_1 = l_0 - \frac{at_1^2}{2}, \qquad v_0 = at_1; \tag{5.3}$$

3) the segment of uniformly decelerated motion

$$l = l_2 - v_0 t + \frac{at^2}{2}, \qquad v_c = \frac{dl}{dt} = -v_0 + at,$$

$$\frac{dv}{dt} = a, \qquad l_2 = l_1 - v_0 (t_2 - t_1), \tag{5.4}$$

where l_0 is the initial length of the thread.

In order to apply the asymptotic method which we have developed to solution of differential equation (5.1), we must represent the latter in the form (1.1) on each of the three segments. In order to do this, using the approach in [103], we introduce, on the first segment, the quantities

$$T = \omega_0 t, \qquad \omega_0 = \frac{Q^2}{aql_0}, \qquad \varepsilon = \sqrt[3]{\frac{a}{\omega_0^2 l_0}}. \tag{5.5}$$

Then Eq. (5.1) is converted to the form

$$\left[\left(\frac{Q}{l_0}+\frac{q}{3}\right)-\varepsilon\left(\frac{1}{2}\cdot\frac{Q}{l_0}+\frac{1}{3}q\right)\tau^2+\varepsilon^2\frac{q\tau^4}{12}\right]\frac{d^2\varphi}{dT^2}+$$
$$+\varepsilon\left\{\frac{\alpha g}{l_0^2}\sqrt[3]{\frac{\alpha q l_0^2}{aQ^2}}-\varepsilon\left[\left(\frac{Q}{l_0}+\frac{1}{2}q\right)\tau-\frac{q}{4}\sqrt[3]{\frac{\alpha^2q^2al_0}{Q^4}}\tau^3\right]\right\}\frac{d\varphi}{dT}+$$
$$+\frac{Kg\alpha^2q^2}{Q^4}\varphi=\varepsilon\left[\left(\frac{Q}{l_0}+\frac{q}{2}\right)-\varepsilon\frac{q\tau^2}{4}\right]\left(1+\frac{g}{a}\right)\sqrt[3]{\frac{\alpha^4q^4l_0^2a^2}{Q^8}}, \tag{5.6}$$

where

$$\tau=\varepsilon T. \tag{5.7}$$

On the second segment of motion of the weight Q, Eq. (5.1), after elementary transformations, can be written in the form

$$\left[\frac{Q}{l_1}+\frac{1}{3}q-\varepsilon\left(\frac{Q}{l_1}+\frac{2}{3}q\right)\tau+\varepsilon^2\frac{q\tau^2}{3}\right]\frac{d^2\varphi}{dT^2}+$$
$$+\varepsilon\left\{\left[\frac{\alpha g}{l_1v_0}-\left(\frac{Q}{l_1}+\frac{1}{2}q\right)\right]\sqrt{\frac{v_0}{l_1\omega_1}}+\varepsilon\frac{q}{2}\sqrt{\frac{v_0}{l_1\omega_1}}\tau\right\}\frac{d\varphi}{dT}+$$
$$+\frac{Kg}{l_1^2\omega_1^2}\varphi=\varepsilon\left[\frac{Q}{l_1}+\frac{q}{2}-\varepsilon\frac{q\tau}{2}\right]\frac{g}{v_0\omega_1}\sqrt{\frac{v_0}{l_1\omega_1}}, \tag{5.8}$$

where

$$T=\omega_1t,\qquad \omega_1=\frac{Q^2}{\alpha g l_1},\qquad \tau=\varepsilon T,\qquad \varepsilon=\sqrt{\frac{v_0}{l_1\omega_1}}, \tag{5.9}$$

and, finally, on the third segment;

$$\left\{\frac{Q}{l_2}+\frac{q}{3}-\varepsilon\left[\left(\frac{Q}{l_2}+\frac{2}{3}q\right)\tau-\sqrt{\frac{v_0}{l_1\omega_2}}\left(\frac{Q}{2v_0^2}+\frac{q}{3}+\frac{qal_2}{3v_0^2}\right)\tau^2\right]-\right.$$
$$\left.-\varepsilon^2\left[\sqrt{\frac{v_0}{l_2\omega_2}}\frac{qal_2}{3v_0^2}\tau^3-\frac{qa^2l_2}{12v_0^3\omega_2}\tau^4\right]\right\}\frac{d^2\varphi}{dT^2}+$$
$$+\varepsilon\left\{\sqrt{\frac{v_0}{l_2\omega_2}}\left[\frac{\alpha g}{v_0l_2}-\left(\frac{Q}{l_2}+\frac{q}{2}\right)+\left(\frac{Qa}{v_0^2}+\frac{q}{2}+\frac{qal_2}{2v_0^2}\right)\sqrt{\frac{v_0}{l^2\omega^2}}\tau\right]-\right.$$
$$\left.-\varepsilon\left[\frac{3aq}{4v_0\omega_2}\tau^2-\frac{qa^2l_2}{4v_0^2\omega_2}\sqrt{\frac{v_0}{l_2\omega_2}}\tau^3\right]\right\}\frac{d\varphi}{dT}+\frac{Kg}{l_2^2\omega_2^2}\varphi=$$

$$= \varepsilon\left[\frac{Q}{l_2} + \frac{q}{2} - \varepsilon\left(\frac{q\tau}{2} - \frac{qal_2}{4v_0}\sqrt{\frac{v_0}{l_2\omega_2}}\,\tau^2\right]\frac{g-a}{v_0\omega_2}\sqrt{\frac{v_0}{l_2\omega_2}}, \qquad (5.10)$$

where

$$T = \omega_2 t, \qquad \omega_2 = \frac{Q^2}{aql_2}, \qquad \tau = \varepsilon T, \qquad \varepsilon = \sqrt{\frac{v_0}{l_2\omega_2}}. \qquad (5.11)$$

The obtained equations (5.6), (5.8), (5.10) are equations of the form (1.1) in which

$$\theta(t, \varepsilon) \equiv 0. \qquad (5.12)$$

Hence, in this case, we will apply Theorem I.2, which relates to the nonresonance case.

Using the formulas of Sec. 3, we can construct an asymptotic solution $\varphi^{(m)}$ for the above equations for any natural number m. In particular, for the second approximation ($m = 2$), the solution of Eq. (5.6) takes the form

$$\varphi^{(2)} = Be^{-(\beta_1 t + \beta_2 t^2 + \beta_3 t^3 + \beta_4 t^4)}\cos(\delta_0 + \delta_1 t + \delta_2 t^2 + \delta_3 t^3 + \delta_4 t^4) + \\ + \frac{a+g}{Kg}\left(Q + \frac{ql_0}{2} - \frac{qat^2}{4}\right), \qquad (5.13)$$

where

$$\beta_1 = \frac{ag}{2l_0\left(Q + \frac{ql_0}{3}\right)}, \qquad \beta_2 = -\frac{a}{8l_0}, \qquad \beta_3 = \frac{aag\left(\frac{Q}{2} + \frac{ql_0}{3}\right)}{6l_0^2\left(Q + \frac{ql_0}{3}\right)},$$

$$\beta_4 = \frac{a^2 g}{32l_0\left(Q + \frac{ql_0}{3}\right)}, \qquad \delta_1 = \nu_0 - \frac{\alpha^2\nu_0^3}{8K^2},$$

$$\delta_2 = \frac{a\nu_0^3}{6Kg}\left(\frac{KQ}{l_0\nu_0^2} - \frac{1}{2}Q\right), \qquad \nu_0 = \sqrt{\frac{Kg}{l_0\left(Q + \frac{1}{3}ql_0\right)}},$$

$$\delta_3 = \frac{a\nu_0^5}{40K^2g^2}\left[3\left(\frac{Kg}{l_0\nu_0^2} - \frac{1}{2}Q\right)^2 - \frac{qKg}{3\nu_0^2}\right], \qquad (5.14)$$

B, δ_0 are constants of integration, determined from the initial conditions.

We write the solution of Eq. (5.8) in the form

$$\varphi^{(2)} = B_1 e^{-(\beta_{11}t+\beta_{21}t^2)} \cos(\delta_{01} + \delta_{11}t + \delta_{21}t^2 + \delta_{31}t^3) + \\ + \frac{1}{K}\left[Q + \frac{q}{2}(l_1 - v_0 t)\right], \tag{5.15}$$

where

$$\beta_{11} = \frac{2\alpha g - v_0\left(Q + \frac{1}{3}ql_1\right)}{4l_1\left(Q + \frac{1}{3}ql_1\right)},$$

$$\beta_{21} = \frac{v_0^2 g}{8l_1\left(Q + \frac{1}{3}ql_1\right)} + \frac{v_0\left(Q + \frac{2}{3}ql_1\right)\left[\alpha g - v_0\left(Q + \frac{1}{2}ql_1\right)\right]}{4l_1^2\left(Q + \frac{1}{3}ql_1\right)^2},$$

$$\delta_{11} = \nu_{11} - \frac{\left[\alpha g - v_0\left(Q + \frac{1}{2}ql_1\right)\right]^2 \nu_{11}^3}{8K^2g^2},$$

$$\delta_{21} = \frac{v_0\left(Q + \frac{2}{3}ql_1\right)\nu_{11}^3}{4Kg},$$

$$\delta_{31} = \frac{v_0\left(Q + \frac{2}{3}ql_1\right)^2 \nu_{11}^5}{8K^2g^2} - \frac{v_0^2 g \nu_{11}^3}{18Kg},$$

$$\nu_{11} = \sqrt{\frac{Kg}{l_1\left(Q + \frac{1}{3}gl_1\right)}}, \tag{5.16}$$

B_1, δ_{01} are constants of integration. And, finally, solving Eq. (5.10), we obtain

$$\varphi^{(2)} = B_2 e^{-(\beta_{12}t+\beta_{22}t^2+\beta_{32}t^3+\beta_{42}t^4)} \cos(\delta_{02} + \delta_{12}t + \delta_{22}t^2 + \delta_{32}t^3 + \delta_{42}t^4 + \\ + \delta_{52}t^5) + \frac{g-a}{Kg}\left[Q + \frac{1}{2}q\left(l_2 - v_0 t + \frac{1}{2}at^2\right)\right], \tag{5.17}$$

where

$$\beta_{12} = \frac{2\alpha g - v_0\left(Q + \frac{1}{3}ql_2\right)}{4l_2\left(Q + \frac{1}{3}ql_2\right)},$$

$$\beta_{22} = \frac{Qa + \frac{1}{3}qv_0^2 + \frac{qal_2}{3}}{8l_2\left(Q + \frac{1}{3}ql_2\right)} + \frac{v_0\left(Q + \frac{2}{3}ql_2\right)\left[\alpha g - v_0\left(Q + \frac{ql_2}{2}\right)\right]}{4l_2^2\left(Q + \frac{1}{3}ql_2\right)^2},$$

$$\beta_{32} = \frac{v_0\left(Q + \frac{2}{3}ql_2\right)\left(Qa + \frac{qv_0^2}{2} + \frac{qal_2}{2}\right)}{6l_2^2\left(Q + \frac{ql_2}{3}\right)^2} - \frac{aqv_0}{8l_2\left(Q + \frac{ql_2}{3}\right)^2} -$$

$$- \frac{\left(\frac{1}{2}Qa + \frac{qv_0^2}{3} + \frac{qal_2}{3}\right)\left[\alpha g - v_0\left(Q + \frac{ql_2}{2}\right)\right]}{6l_2^2\left(Q + \frac{1}{3}ql_2\right)^2},$$

$$\beta_{42} = \frac{qa^2}{32l_2\left(Q + \frac{1}{3}ql_2\right)} -$$

$$- \frac{\left(\frac{1}{2}Qa + \frac{1}{3}qv_0^2 + \frac{1}{3}qal_2\right)\left(Qa + \frac{1}{2}ql_2^2 + \frac{1}{2}qal_2\right)}{8l_2^2\left(Q + \frac{1}{3}ql_2\right)^2},$$

$$\delta_{12} = \nu_2 - \frac{\left[\alpha g - v_0\left(Q + \frac{1}{2}ql_2\right)^2\right]\nu_2^3}{8K^2g^2} - \frac{\left(Qa + \frac{1}{2}qv_0^2 + \frac{1}{2}qal_2\right)\nu_2}{4Kg},$$

$$\delta_{22} = \frac{v_0\left(Q + \frac{2}{3}ql_2\right)\nu_2^3}{4Kg} -$$

$$- \frac{\left[\alpha g - v_0\left(Q + \frac{1}{2}ql_2\right)\right]\left[Qa + \frac{1}{2}(qv_0^2 + qal_2)\right]\nu_2^3}{8K^2g^2},$$

$$\delta_{23} = \frac{v_0^2\left(Q + \frac{2}{3}ql_2\right)^2\nu_2^5}{8K^2g^2} - \frac{\left[\frac{1}{2}Qa + \frac{1}{3}q(v_0^2 + al_2)\right]\nu_2^3}{6Kg} -$$

$$
-\frac{\left[Qa + \frac{1}{2} q\,(v_0^2 + al_2)\right] \nu_2^3}{24K^2g^2},
$$

$$
\delta_{24} = \frac{v_0 q a \nu_2^3}{24Kg} - \frac{3v_0\left(Q + \frac{2}{3} q l_2\right)\left[\frac{1}{2} Qa + \frac{1}{3} q\,(v_0^2 + al_2)\right] \nu_2^5}{16K^2g^2},
$$

$$
\delta_{25} = \frac{3\left[\frac{1}{2} Qa + \frac{1}{3} q\,(v_0^2 + al_2)\right]^2 \nu_2^5}{40K^2g^2} - \frac{qa^2\nu_2^3}{120\,Kg},
$$

$$
\nu_2 = \sqrt{\frac{Kg}{l_2\left(Q + \frac{1}{3} q l_2\right)}}, \tag{5.18}
$$

B_2, δ_{02} are constants of integration.

Using the obtained solutions, on each of the segments of raising or lowering the weight Q, we can calculate the tension $T_1 = K\varphi$, arising in the thread during raising (lowering) of the weight Q. Such calculations, for raising the weight, were carried out in [64] for the following initial data:

$v_0 = 3724$ *meters/sec;* $a = 0.98$ *meters/sec*^{2}; $l_0 = 105$ *meters;*

$Q = 5200$ *kG (kilogram-force);* $q = 2.48$ *kG/meter;*

$\alpha = 4.45 \cdot 10^6$ *kg,* $a = 0$ (Fig. 2).

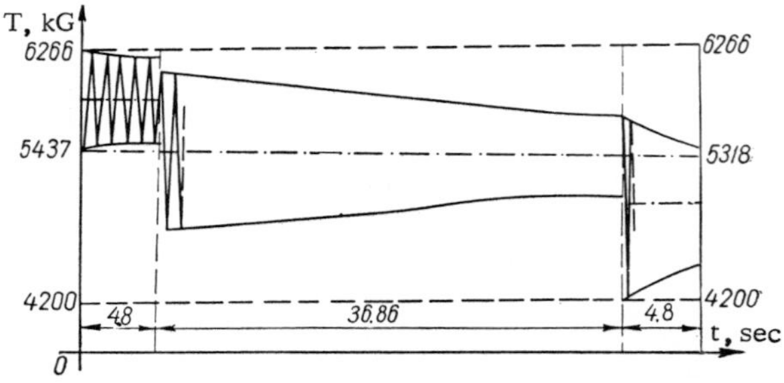

FIG. 2.

Figure 3 shows a graph of the tension in a visco-elastic thread in the case of the following initial data:

v_0 = 3.6 *meters/sec*; a = 0.75 *meters/sec* ; l_0 = 182 *meters*;

Q = 5200 *kG*; q = 2.6 *kG/meter*; α = 3000 *kG·sec*;

$K = 4.64 \cdot 10^6$ *kG*.

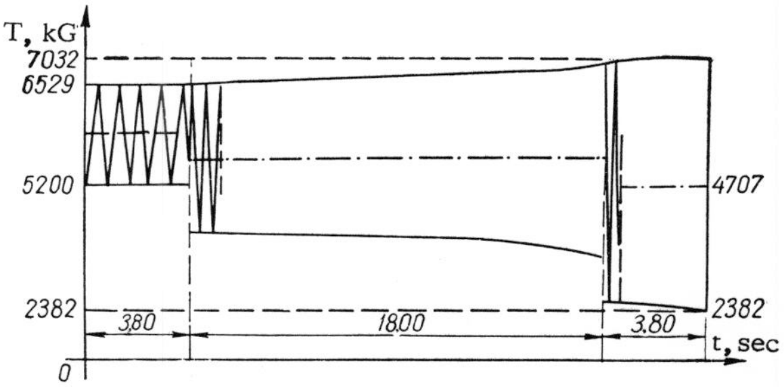

FIG. 3.

This last example was also calculated by using Sturm's method. It is clear that the deviation in the results obtained by these two methods does not exceed 7%.

Chapter 2

CONSTRUCTION OF AN ASYMPTOTIC SOLUTION FOR A SYSTEM OF SECOND-ORDER LINEAR DIFFERENTIAL EQUATIONS WITH SLOWLY VARYING COEFFICIENTS

6. Formulation of the Problem

We consider, in finite-dimensional space, a system of linear differential equations of the form

$$A(\tau, \varepsilon)\frac{d^2x}{dt^2} + \varepsilon C(\tau, \varepsilon)\frac{dx}{dt} + B(\tau, \varepsilon)x = P(\tau, \varepsilon)e^{i\theta(t,\varepsilon)}, \tag{6.1}$$

where $A(\tau, \varepsilon)$, $C(\tau, \varepsilon)$, $B(\tau, \varepsilon)$ are real square matrices of order n, and $x(t, \varepsilon)$ and $P(\tau, \varepsilon)$ are n-dimensional vectors. We assume that the following formal expansions hold:

$$A(\tau, \varepsilon) = \sum_{s=0}^{\infty} \varepsilon^s A_s(\tau), \quad C(\tau, \varepsilon) = \sum_{s=0}^{\infty} \varepsilon^s C_s(\tau),$$

$$B(\tau, \varepsilon) = \sum_{s=0}^{\infty} \varepsilon^s B_s(\tau), \quad P(\tau, \varepsilon) = \sum_{s=0}^{\infty} \varepsilon^s P_s(\tau), \tag{6.2}$$

in which $A_0(\tau)$, $B_0(\tau)$ are symmetric positive-definite matrices[1], and the matrix $A_0(\tau)$ is nonsingular for all $\tau \in [0, L]$.

In particular, the sums (6.2) may even be finite.

---

[1] With reference to this assumption, see the remark following Eq. (1.6).

In this chapter (Secs. 7–9), we will present a method of constructing an asymptotic solution of the Cauchy problem for Eq. (6.1) with initial conditions

$$x(t, \varepsilon)|_{t=0} = x_0, \quad \left.\frac{dx}{dt}\right|_{t=0} = \dot{x}_0 \tag{6.3}$$

and we will show (Sec. 11) a way of finding the asymptotic form of the characteristic values of some boundary-value problems.

First we will make some preliminary remarks.

In the course of the proofs of the theorems in Chap. II, we will have to turn to solution of a system of n linear algebraic equations

$$[B_0(\tau) - \omega(\tau) A_0(\tau)]\mu(\tau) = 0, \tag{6.4}$$

where $\omega(\tau) = \omega_\nu(\tau)$ $(\nu = 1, 2, \ldots, n)$ are the roots of the characteristic equation

$$\det[B_0(\tau) - \omega(\tau) A_0(\tau)] = 0. \tag{6.5}$$

We will assume that for any $\tau \in [0, L]$ all the roots of Eq. (6.5) are simple and not equal to zero.

In addition, we will number the mutually orthogonal solutions of system (6.4) $\mu_\nu(\tau)$ $(\nu = 1, 2, \ldots, n)$ in such a way that the condition

$$(A_0(\tau)\mu_i(\tau), \mu_k(\tau)) = \delta_{ik}, \tag{6.6}$$

will be fulfilled, where δ_{ik} is the Kronecker delta.

Furthermore, we let $d\theta(t, \varepsilon)/dt = k(\tau)$. Then, depending on the values of the functions $k^2(\tau)$ and $\omega_\nu(\tau)$ we can distinguish two cases:

1. "resonance"—when for certain points in the interval $[0, L]$ the function $k^2(\tau)$ becomes equal to one or several of the functions $\omega_\nu(\tau)$:
2. "nonresonance"—when

$$k^2(\tau) \neq \omega_\nu(\tau), \quad \nu = 1, 2, \ldots, n \tag{6.7}$$

for all $\tau \in [0, L]$.

Below we will consider each case separately.

7. A Formal Solution in the Resonance Case

Let

$$k^2(\tau) = \omega_1(\tau) \tag{7.1'}$$

for some values of $\tau \in [0, L]$. However, $k^2(\tau)$ is not equal to $\omega_p(\tau)$ ($p = 2, 3, \ldots, n$) for any τ in the closed interval $[0, L]$. Then the following theorem holds.

Theorem II.1. If the matrices $A_s(\tau)$, $C_s(\tau)$, $B_s(\tau)$, *the vectors* $P_s(\tau)$ ($s = 0, 1, 2, \ldots$) *and the function* $k(\tau)$ *have derivatives of all orders with respect to* τ *on the closed interval* $[0, L]$[1], *then a formal particular solution of system (6.1) in the resonance case can be represented in the form*

$$x(t, \varepsilon) = [\Pi(\tau, \varepsilon)\xi + H(\tau, \varepsilon)]\, e^{i\theta(t,\varepsilon)}, \tag{7.1}$$

where the scalar function $\xi(t, \varepsilon)$ *is determined by a differential equation of the first order*

$$\frac{d\xi}{dt} = [D(\tau, \varepsilon) + i(\Omega(\tau, \varepsilon) - k(\tau))]\,\xi + Z(\tau, \varepsilon), \tag{7.2}$$

and the vectors $\Pi(\tau, \varepsilon)$, $H(\tau, \varepsilon)$ *and the functions* $D(\tau, \varepsilon)$, $\Omega(\tau, \varepsilon)$, $Z(\tau, \varepsilon)$ *admit formal expansions of the form*

$$\Pi(\tau, \varepsilon) = \mu_1(\tau) + \sum_{s=1}^{\infty} \varepsilon^s \Pi_s(\tau)^*,$$

$$H(\tau, \varepsilon) = \sum_{s=0}^{\infty} \varepsilon^s H_s(\tau), \quad D(\tau, \varepsilon) = \sum_{s=1}^{\infty} \varepsilon^s D_s(\tau), \tag{7.3}$$

$$\Omega(\tau, \varepsilon) = \sum_{s=0}^{\infty} \varepsilon^s \Omega_s(\tau), \quad Z(\tau, \varepsilon) = \sum_{s=0}^{\infty} \varepsilon^s Z_s(\tau).$$

Proof. First of all, we note that the characteristic roots $\omega_\nu(\tau)$ and the characteristic vectors $\mu_\nu(\tau)$ ($\nu = 1, 2, \ldots$) have as many derivatives with respect to τ on the interval $[0, L]$ as do the matrices $A_0(\tau)$, $B_0(\tau)$ (cf. [87]).

To determine the terms of the formal series (7.3), we substitute the vector $x(t, \varepsilon)$ from (7.1) into Eq. (6.1), also taking into account Eq. (7.2). In the obtained identity, we equate separately the coefficients of the function $\xi(t, \varepsilon)$ and the free terms; thus we obtain the two equations:

[1] By differentiability of a matrix, we mean differentiability of all of its elements.

$$\begin{gathered} A(\tau,\ \varepsilon)\{\varepsilon^2\Pi''(\tau,\ \varepsilon)+2\varepsilon\Pi'(\tau,\ \varepsilon)[D(\tau,\ \varepsilon)+i\Omega(\tau,\ \varepsilon)]+ \\ +\varepsilon\Pi(\tau,\ \varepsilon)[D(\tau,\ \varepsilon)+i\Omega(\tau,\ \varepsilon)]'+\Pi(\tau,\ \varepsilon)[D(\tau,\ \varepsilon)+i\Omega(\tau,\ \varepsilon)]^2\}+ \\ +\varepsilon C(\tau,\ \varepsilon)\{\varepsilon\Pi'(\tau,\ \varepsilon)+\Pi(\tau,\ \varepsilon)[D(\tau,\ \varepsilon)+i\Omega(\tau,\ \varepsilon)]\}+ \\ +B(\tau,\ \varepsilon)\Pi(\tau,\ \varepsilon)=0, \end{gathered} \tag{7.4}$$

$$\begin{gathered} A(\tau,\varepsilon)\{[D(\tau,\ \varepsilon)+i(\Omega(\tau,\ \varepsilon)+k(\tau))]\Pi(\tau,\ \varepsilon)Z(\tau,\ \varepsilon)+ \\ +\varepsilon Z'(\tau,\ \varepsilon)\Pi(\tau,\ \varepsilon)+2\varepsilon Z(\tau,\ \varepsilon)\Pi'(\tau,\ \varepsilon)+i\varepsilon k'(\tau)H(\tau,\ \varepsilon)- \\ -k^2(\tau)H(\tau,\ \varepsilon)+2i\varepsilon k(\tau)H'(\tau,\ \varepsilon)+\varepsilon^2H''(\tau,\ \varepsilon)\}+ \\ +\varepsilon C(\tau,\ \varepsilon)[\Pi(\tau,\ \varepsilon)Z(\tau,\ \varepsilon)+ik(\tau)H(\tau,\ \varepsilon)+\varepsilon H'(\tau,\ \varepsilon)]+ \\ +B(\tau,\ \varepsilon)H(\tau,\ \varepsilon)=P(\tau,\ \varepsilon). \end{gathered} \tag{7.5}$$

1. To determine the vectors $\Pi_s(\tau)$, and the functions $D_{s+1}(\tau)$ and $\Omega_s(\tau)$ $(s=0,\ 1,\ \ldots)$, we use Eq. (7.4). Collecting the coefficients of like powers of the parameter ε, we obtain

$$[B_0(\tau)-\Omega_0^2(\tau)\ A_0(\tau)]\mu_1(\tau)=0, \tag{7.6}$$

$$[B_0(\tau)-\Omega_0^2(\tau)A_0(\tau)]\Pi_s(\tau)=E_s(\tau), \tag{7.7}$$

where

$$s=1,\ 2,\ \ldots,$$

$$\begin{gathered} E_s(\tau)=-A_{s-2}(\tau)\mu_1''(\tau)-\sum_{j=0}^{s-3}A_j(\tau)\Pi_{s-2-j}''(\tau)- \\ -2\sum_{j=0}^{s-1}A_j(\tau)[D_{s-1-j}(\tau)+i\Omega_{s-1-j}(\tau)]\mu_1'(\tau)- \\ -2\sum_{j_1=0}^{s-2}\sum_{j=1}^{s-j_1-1}A_{j_1}(\tau)\Pi_j'(\tau)[D_{s-j_1-j-1}(\tau)+i\Omega_{s-j_1-j-1}(\tau)]- \\ -\sum_{j=0}^{s-1}A_j(\tau)[D_{s-j-1}(\tau)+i\Omega_{s-j-1}(\tau)]'\mu_1(\tau)- \\ -\sum_{j_1=0}^{s-2}\sum_{j=1}^{s-j_1-1}A_{j_1}(\tau)\Pi_j(\tau)[D_{s-j_1-j-1}(\tau)+i\Omega_{s-j_1-j-1}(\tau)]- \\ -\sum_{j_2=1}^{s-1}\sum_{j_1=1}^{s-1-j_2}\sum_{j=1}^{s-1-j_1-j_2}A_{j_2}(\tau)\Pi_{j_1}(\tau)[D_j(\tau)+i\Omega_j(\tau)][D_{s-j_2-j_1-j}(\tau)+ \\ +i\Omega_{s-j_2-j_1-j}(\tau)]-\sum_{j_1=0}^{s}\sum_{j=0}^{s-j_1}A_{j_1}(\tau)\mu_1(\tau)[D_j(\tau)+i\Omega_j(\tau)][D_{s-j_1-j}(\tau)+ \end{gathered}$$

$$+ i\Omega_{s-j_1-j}(\tau)] - C_{s-2}(\tau)\mu_1'(\tau) - \sum_{j=0}^{s-3} C_j(\tau)\Pi_{s-2-j}'(\tau) -$$

$$- \sum_{j=0}^{s-1} C_j(\tau)[D_{s-1-j}(\tau) + i\Omega_{s-1-j}(\tau)] -$$

$$- \sum_{j_1=0}^{s-2} \sum_{j=1}^{s-1-j_1} C_{j_1}(\tau)\Pi_j(\tau)[D_{s-j_1-j-1}(\tau) + i\Omega_{s-j_1-j-1}(\tau)] -$$

$$- B_s(\tau)\mu_1(\tau) - \sum_{j=1}^{s-1} B_j(\tau)\Pi_{s-j}(\tau),$$

$$s = 1, 2, \ldots . \tag{7.8}$$

Applying scalar multiplication by the vector $\mu_1(\tau)$ to (7.6) and (6.4) [setting $\mu(\tau) = \mu_1(\tau)$ in the latter], and taking account of condition (6.6), it is easy to find the function $\Omega_0(\tau)$:

$$\Omega_0(\tau) = \pm\sqrt{\omega_1(\tau)}.$$

Henceforth, we shall set

$$\Omega_0(\tau) = +\sqrt{\omega_1(\tau)}. \tag{7.9}$$

We now turn to construction of the functions $D_1(\tau)$, $\Omega_1(\tau)$, and the vector $\Pi_1(\tau)$, for which we use the relationship (7.7) for $s = 1$, namely:

$$[B_0(\tau) - A_0(\tau)\omega_1(\tau)]\Pi_1(\tau) = E_1(\tau), \tag{7.10}$$

where

$$E_1(\tau) = [A_1(\tau)\omega_1(\tau) - B_1(\tau)]\mu_1(\tau) - iA_0(\tau)[2\mu_1'(\tau)\Omega_0(\tau) -$$

$$- \mu_1(\tau)\Omega_0'(\tau) + 2\Omega_0(\tau)(D_1(\tau) + i\Omega_1(\tau))\mu_1(\tau)] -$$

$$- i\Omega_0(\tau)C_0(\tau)\mu_1(\tau). \tag{7.11}$$

Thus, the desired vector $\Pi_1(\tau)$ is the solution of the nonhomogeneous system of linear algebraic equations (7.10); the right-hand side of which—the vector $E_1(\tau)$—is, in turn, dependent on the unknown function $D_1(\tau) + i\Omega_1(\tau)$, We take note of the fact that the determinant $\det |B_0(\tau) - \omega_1(\tau)A_0(\tau)|$ of the system (7.10), according to a previous assumption [see (6.5)], is equal to zero on some points of the interval $[0, L]$, Therefore, we can find the vector $\Pi_1(\tau)$ and the function $D_1(\tau) + i\Omega_1(\tau)$ by using a well-known theorem in linear algebra [68]: the nonhomogeneous system of linear algebraic equations

$$TX = f,$$

whose determinant is equal to zero, is solvable if and only if the vector f is orthogonal to all vectors which are solutions of the homogeneous system $T^*y = 0$ (T^* is the adjoint matrix of T).

In the case we are considering, the matrices $B_0(\tau)$ and $A_0(\tau)$ are symmetric and all the roots of Eq. (6.5) are simple; therefore, at points for which the determinant of system (7.10) becomes zero, the condition

$$(E_s(\tau),\ \mu_1(\tau)) = 0, \qquad s = 1,\ 2,\ \ldots \tag{7.12}$$

is necessary and sufficient for solvability of the system. We make use of this condition to determine the function $D_1(\tau) + i\Omega_1(\tau)$ on the whole interval $[0, L]$. Then, in accordance with (7.11), we find

$$D_1(\tau) + i\Omega_1(\tau) = \frac{1}{2i\Omega_0(\tau)}[(A_1(\tau)\mu_1(\tau),\ \mu_1(\tau))\,\omega_1(\tau) -$$
$$-(B_1(\tau)\mu_1(\tau),\ \mu_1(\tau)) - 2i\Omega_0(\tau)(A_0(\tau)\mu_1'(\tau),\ \mu_1(\tau)) -$$
$$-i\Omega_0'(\tau) - i(C_0(\tau)\mu_1(\tau),\ \mu_1(\tau))\,\Omega_0(\tau)],$$

or

$$D_1(\tau) = -(A_0(\tau)\mu_1'(\tau),\ \mu_1(\tau)) - \frac{\Omega_0'(\tau)}{2\Omega_0(\tau)} -$$
$$-\frac{1}{2}(C_0(\tau)\mu_1(\tau),\ \mu_1(\tau)),$$

$$\Omega_1(\tau) = \frac{(A_1(\tau)\mu_1(\tau),\ \mu_1(\tau))\,\omega_1(\tau) - (B_1(\tau)\mu_1(\tau),\ \mu_1(\tau))}{2\Omega_0} \tag{7.13}$$

Having determined the function $D_1(\tau) + i\Omega_1(\tau)$, and, consequently, the vector $E_1(\tau)$, we can find the desired vector $\Pi_1(\tau)$.

We will seek $\Pi_1(\tau)$ in the form

$$\Pi_1(\tau) = \sum_{j=1}^{n} V_{j_1}(\tau)\,\mu_j(\tau), \tag{7.14}$$

where the $V_{j_1}(\tau)$ are scalar functions which are to be determined.

Substituting (7.14) into Eq. (7.10) and taking the scalar product of the obtained result with the vector $\mu_r(\tau)$, we find

$$[\omega_r(\tau)-\omega_1(\tau)]\, V_{r_1}(\tau)=(E_1(\tau),\ \mu_r(\tau)). \tag{7.15}$$

From this it follows that

$$V_{p_1}(\tau)=\frac{(E_1(\tau),\ \mu_p(\tau))}{\omega_p(\tau)-\omega_1(\tau)},\qquad p=2,\ 3,\ \ldots.\ n. \tag{7.16}$$

On the basis of Eqs. (7.12) and (7.15), the function $V_{11}(\tau)$ remains arbitrary. Let us set it equal to zero.

In this way we can determine all the subsequent functions $D_s(\tau)$, $\Omega_s(\tau)$ and vectors $\Pi_s(\tau)$ $(s=2,\ 3,\ \ldots)$. In fact, let us assume that we have, in the indicated way, already found all the vectors $\Pi_s(\tau)$ and functions $D_s(\tau)$, $\Omega_s(\tau)$ for all values of s less than some number m. Then, using Eq. (7.7) for $s=m$, we can determine the functions $D_m(\tau)$, $\Omega_m(\tau)$ and the vector $\Pi_m(\tau)$ from the system of equations

$$[B_0(\tau)-\omega_1(\tau)\, A_0(\tau)]\, \Pi_m(\tau)=E_m(\tau). \tag{7.17}$$

As in the case of $s=1$, we begin by finding the function $D_m(\tau)+i\Omega_m(\tau)$ from the condition

$$(E_m(\tau),\ \mu_1(\tau))=0, \tag{7.18}$$

and then we construct the vector $\Pi_m(\tau)$ in the form of the sum

$$\Pi_m(\tau)=\sum_{j=1}^{n} V_{jm}(\tau)\, \mu_j(\tau), \tag{7.19}$$

where the scalar functions $V_{jm}(\tau)$ are defined by the relationships

$$V_{jm}=\frac{(E_m(\tau),\ \mu_j(\tau))}{\omega_j(\tau)-\omega_1(\tau)},\qquad j=2,\ 3,\ \ldots,\ n. \tag{7.20}$$

The arbitrary function V_{1m}, as previously, is set equal to zero.

Thus, our algorithm allows us to find the functions $D_m(\tau)$, $\Omega_m(\tau)$ and the vector $\Pi_m(\tau)$ for any natural number m.

We note that from the form of the obtained formulas it follows (on the basis of the conditions of the theorem) that the functions $D_s(\tau)$, $\Omega_s(\tau)$ and the vectors $\Pi_s(\tau)$ $(s=0,\ 1,\ \ldots, m)$ have any number of derivatives with respect to τ on the closed interval $[0,\ L]$.

2. We turn to finding the vector $H(\tau, \varepsilon)$ and the function $Z(\tau, \varepsilon)$ in Eqs. (7.1) and (7.2). To do this, we equate the coefficients of like powers of the parameter ε in the identity (7.5); as a result, we obtain

$$[B_0(\tau) - k^2(\tau) A_0(\tau)] H_s(\tau) = F_s(\tau), \quad s = 0, 1, \dots, \tag{7.21}$$

where

$$\begin{aligned}
F_s(\tau) = {} & P_s(\tau) - ik(\tau) \sum_{j=0}^{s} A_j(\tau) \mu_1(\tau) Z_{s-j}(\tau) - \\
& - \sum_{j=0}^{s} \sum_{j_1=0}^{s-j} A_j(\tau) \mu_1(\tau) (D_{j_1}(\tau) + i\Omega_{j_1}(\tau)) Z_{s-j-j_1}(\tau) - \\
& - \sum_{j=0}^{s} \sum_{j_1=0}^{s-j} \sum_{j_2=0}^{s-j-j_1} A_j(\tau) \Pi_{j_1}(\tau) (D_{j_2}(\tau) + i\Omega_{j_2}(\tau)) Z_{s-j_1-j_2-j}(\tau) - \\
& - \sum_{j=0}^{s-1} A_j(\tau) \mu_1(\tau) Z'_{s-1-j}(\tau) - \sum_{j=0}^{s-1} \sum_{j_1=1}^{s-1-j} A_j(\tau) \Pi_{j_1}(\tau) Z'_{s-1-j-j_1}(\tau) - \\
& - \sum_{j=0}^{s-1} A_j(\tau) \mu_1(\tau) Z'_{s-1-j}(\tau) - \sum_{j=0}^{s-1} \sum_{j_1=1}^{s-1-j} A_j(\tau) \Pi_{j_1}(\tau) Z'_{s-1-j_1-j}(\tau) - \\
& - 2 \sum_{j=0}^{s-1} A_j(\tau) \mu'_1(\tau) Z_{s-1-j}(\tau) - \sum_{j=0}^{s-1} \sum_{j_1=1}^{s-1-j} A_j(\tau) \Pi'_{j_1}(\tau) Z_{s-1-j_1-j}(\tau) - \\
& - ik'(\tau) \sum_{j=0}^{s-1} A_j(\tau) H_{s-1-j}(\tau) + k^2(\tau) \sum_{j=1}^{s} A_j(\tau) H_{s-j}(\tau) - \\
& - 2ik(\tau) \sum_{j=0}^{s-1} A_j(\tau) H'_{s-1-j}(\tau) - \sum_{j=0}^{s-2} A_j(\tau) H''_{s-2-j}(\tau) - \\
& - \sum_{j=0}^{s-1} C_j(\tau) \mu_1(\tau) Z_{s-1-j}(\tau) - \sum_{j=0}^{s-2} \sum_{j_1=1}^{s-1-j} C_j(\tau) \Pi_{j_1}(\tau) Z_{s-j_1-j-1}(\tau) - \\
& - ik(\tau) \sum_{j=0}^{s-1} C_j(\tau) H_{s-1-j}(\tau) - \sum_{j=0}^{s-2} C_j(\tau) H_{s-2-j}(\tau) - \\
& - \sum_{j=1}^{s} B_j(\tau) H_{s-j}(\tau), \quad s = 0, 1, 2, \dots .
\end{aligned} \tag{7.22}$$

Thus, the determination of the vectors $H_s(\tau)$ and the functions $Z_s(\tau)$ $(s = 0, 1, 2, \dots)$ reduces to the solution of a system of algebraic equations (7.21), which is analogous to the system (7.7) which we have just considered. We recall that the determinant of system (7.21) becomes equal to zero for some values of τ in $[0, L]$, since we are considering the construction of a formal solution in the case of resonance, i.e., for some values of τ, $k^2(\tau)$ and $\omega_1(\tau)$ are equal [see (7.1′)].

In accordance with what was said above, we will find the unknown function $z_s(\tau)$ $(s = 0, 1, 2, \ldots)$ from the condition

$$(F_s(\tau),\ \mu_1(\tau)) = 0, \qquad s = 0,\ 1,\ \ldots . \tag{7.23}$$

After that the construction of the vector $H_s(\tau)$ will not present any difficulty, if we seek it, as a solution of system (7.21), in the form

$$H_s(\tau) = \sum_{j=1}^{n} C_{js}(\tau)\mu_j(\tau), \qquad s = 0,\ 1,\ 2,\ \ldots, \tag{7.24}$$

where the $C_{js}(\tau)$ are coefficients which are to be determined.

In fact, substituting (7.24) into (7.21) and taking the scalar product of the result with $\mu_r(\tau)$, we determine the unknown coefficients $C_{js}(\tau)$:

$$C_{rs}(\tau) = \frac{(F_s(\tau),\ \mu_r(\tau))}{\omega_r(\tau) - k^2(\tau)}, \qquad r = 2,\ 3,\ \ldots,\ n. \tag{7.25}$$

According to Eqs. (7.23) and (7.1′), the function $C_{1s}(\tau)$ $[s = 0, 1, \ldots]$ remains arbitrary. We will set it equal to zero. Thus, in the indicated way, we can sequentially determine the value of $Z_s(\tau)$ and $H_s(\tau)$ for any natural number s.

For example, for $s = 0$ we have

$$Z_0(\tau) = -i\frac{(P_0(\tau),\ \mu_1(\tau))}{k(\tau) + \Omega_0(\tau)},$$

and for $s = 1$

$$\begin{aligned} Z_1(\tau) = -\frac{i}{\Omega_0(\tau) + k(\tau)}\{&(P_1(\tau),\ \mu_1(\tau)) - ik(\tau)(A_1(\tau)\mu_1(\tau),\ \mu_1(\tau)) - \\ &- [D_1(\tau) + i\Omega_1(\tau)]Z_0(\tau) - i(A_1(\tau)\mu_1(\tau),\ \mu_1(\tau))\Omega_0(\tau)Z_0(\tau) - \\ &- i(A_0(\tau)\Pi_1(\tau),\ \mu_1(\tau))\Omega_0(\tau)Z_0(\tau) - Z_0'(\tau) - \\ &- 2(A_0(\tau)\mu_1'(\tau),\ \mu_1(\tau)) + k^2(\tau)(A_1(\tau)H_0(\tau),\ \mu_1(\tau)) - \\ &- ik'(\tau)(A_0(\tau)H_1(\tau),\ \mu_1(\tau)) - 2ik(\tau)(A_0(\tau)H_0(\tau),\ \mu_1(\tau)) - \end{aligned}$$

$$-(C_0(\tau)\mu_1(\tau),\ \mu_1(\tau))Z_0(\tau)-ik(\tau)(C_0(\tau)H_0(\tau),\ \mu_1(\tau))-$$
$$-(B_0(\tau)H_0(\tau),\ \mu_1(\tau))\}. \qquad (7.26)$$

It is not difficult to write out the corresponding formulas for determination of the coefficients $C_{rs}(\tau)$ $(r=2,\ 3,\ \ldots,\ n;\ s=0,\ 1,\ 2,\ \ldots)$.

Thus, Theorem II.1 is proved.

Note 1. Theorem II.1 can be carried over to a more general case of resonance, namely: 1) when the value of the function $k^2(\tau)$ can coincide, for separate $\tau\in[0,\ L]$, with several roots $\omega_r(\tau)$ $(1\leqslant r\leqslant n)$ of Eq. (6.5); 2) when the right-hand side of Eq. (6.1) is of the form $\sum_{n=1}^{N}P_n(\tau,\ \varepsilon)e^{i\theta_n}$ and the values of different functions $k_n^2(\tau)$ coincide with various roots of Eq. (6.5).

Note 2. To construct a formal general solution of system (6.1) we must add to the obtained particular solution (7.1) the formal general solution of the corresponding homogeneous system

$$A(\tau,\ \varepsilon)\frac{d^2x}{dt^2}+\varepsilon C(\tau,\ \varepsilon)\frac{dx}{dt}+B(\tau,\ \varepsilon)x=0. \qquad (7.27)$$

A certain ν th $(\nu=1,\ 2,\ \ldots,\ n)$ particular solution of system (7.27) is sought, by using the above-described algorithm, in the form

$$x_\nu(t,\ \varepsilon)=\Pi_\nu(\tau,\ \varepsilon)\xi_\nu(t,\ \varepsilon), \qquad (7.28)$$

where $\Pi_\nu(\tau,\ \varepsilon)$ is an n-dimensional vector of the form (7.3), and $\xi_\nu(\tau,\ \varepsilon)$ is a scalar function satisfying the first-order differential equation

$$\frac{d\xi_\nu}{dt}=[D_\nu(\tau,\ \varepsilon)+i\Omega_\nu(\tau,\ \varepsilon)]\,\xi_\nu,\qquad \nu=1,\ 2,\ \ldots,\ n, \qquad (7.29)$$

in which

$$D_\nu(\tau,\ \varepsilon)=\sum_{s=1}^{\infty}\varepsilon^s D_{\nu s}(\tau),\qquad \Omega_\nu(\tau,\ \varepsilon)=\sum_{s=0}^{\infty}\varepsilon^s\Omega_{\nu s}(\tau),\qquad \nu=1,\ 2,\ \ldots,\ n. \qquad (7.30)$$

In this case, the functions $D_{\nu s}(\tau)$, $\Omega_{\nu s}(\tau)$ and the vectors $\Pi_{\nu s}(\tau)$ $(s=0,\ 1,\ \ldots;\ \nu=1,\ 2,\ \ldots,\ n)$ are determined by the corresponding formulas given earlier in this section, providing we change $\omega_1(\tau)$, $\mu_1(\tau)$ to $\omega_\nu(\tau)$, $\mu_\nu(\tau)$. Since all the $\omega_\nu(\tau)$ $[\nu = 1, 2, \ldots, n]$ are different, then by using both values of the function $\Omega_{\nu s}(\tau)$, we obtain the $2n$ linearly independent particular solutions necessary for constructing a formal general solution of Eq. (7.27).

8. The Nonresonance Case

For the nonresonance case, we can prove the following theorem.

Theorem II.2. If the coefficients in Eq. (6.1) and the function $k(\tau)$ *have derivatives of all orders with respect to* τ, *on the closed interval* $[0, L]$, *then the formal general solution of system (6.1) in the nonresonance case can be represented in the form*

$$x(t, \varepsilon) = \sum_{\nu=1}^{n} \Pi_\nu(\tau, \varepsilon)\xi_\nu(t, \varepsilon) + R(\tau, \varepsilon)e^{i\theta(t,\varepsilon)}, \tag{8.1}$$

where $\sum_{\nu=1}^{n} \Pi_\nu(\tau, \varepsilon)\xi_\nu(t, \varepsilon)$ *is the general solution of Eq. (7.27), and* $R(\tau, \varepsilon)$ *is an n-dimensional vector, admitting the expansion*

$$R(\tau, \varepsilon) = \sum_{s=0}^{n} \varepsilon^s R_s(\tau). \tag{8.2}$$

Proof. In view of Note 2 on Sec. 7, the proof of this theorem reduces to determining the elements of the formal series (8.2). For this we substitute

$$\tilde{x}(t, \varepsilon) = R(\tau, \varepsilon)e^{i\theta(t,\varepsilon)} \tag{8.3}$$

into system (6.1). In the obtained identity

$$\begin{gathered} A(\tau, \varepsilon)\{\varepsilon^2 R''(\tau, \varepsilon) + \varepsilon i[2k(\tau)R'(\tau, \varepsilon) + k'(\tau)R(\tau, \varepsilon)] - \\ - k^2(\tau)R(\tau, \varepsilon)\} + \varepsilon^2 C(\tau, \varepsilon)[R'(\tau, \varepsilon) + ik'(\tau)R(\tau, \varepsilon)] + \\ + B(\tau, \varepsilon)R(\tau, \varepsilon) = P(\tau, \varepsilon) \end{gathered} \tag{8.4}$$

we equate the coefficients of ε^s $(s = 0, 1, \ldots)$. As a result we obtain the following recurrent relationships:

$$[B_0(\tau) - k^2(\tau)A_0(\tau)]R_s(\tau) = G_s(\tau), \qquad s = 0, 1, \ldots; \tag{8.5}$$

where

$$G_s(\tau) = P_s(\tau) - \sum_{j=0}^{s-2} A_j(\tau) R_{s-2-j}(\tau) - 2ik(\tau) \sum_{j=0}^{s-1} A_j(\tau) R'_{s-1-j}(\tau) -$$
$$- ik'(\tau) \sum_{j=0}^{s-1} A_j(\tau) R_{s-1-j}(\tau) - \sum_{j=0}^{s-2} C_j(\tau) R'_{s-2-j}(\tau) -$$
$$- ik(\tau) \sum_{j=0}^{s-1} C_j(\tau) R_{s-1-j}(\tau) - \sum_{j=1}^{s} B_j(\tau) R_{s-j}(\tau). \tag{8.6}$$

Since, in accordance with (6.7),

$$\det [B_0(\tau) - k^2(\tau) A_0(\tau)] \neq 0 \tag{8.7}$$

for any $\tau \in [0, L]$, then from Eqs. (8.5), we find

$$R_s(\tau) = [B_0(\tau) - k^2(\tau) A_0(\tau)]^{-1} G_s(\tau), \qquad s = 0, 1, \ldots . \tag{8.8}$$

We note that here the vector $G_s(\tau)$, during sequential solution of system (8.5), is determined by using previously known quantities.

The theorem is proved.

9. The Asymptotic Nature of the Solution

As we have already noted in the introduction, the practical applicability of the method presented here is determined not by the convergence of the series (7.3) or (8.2) [in many cases these series are divergent], but by the asymptotic behavior of the vector $x^{(m)}(t, \varepsilon)$, defined in the following way:

$$x^{(m)}(t, \varepsilon) = [\Pi^{(m)}(\tau, \varepsilon) \xi^{(m)}(t, \varepsilon) + H^{(m)}(\tau, \varepsilon)] e^{i\theta(t,\varepsilon)}, \tag{9.1}$$

$$\frac{d\xi^{(m)}}{dt} = [D^{(m)}(\tau, \varepsilon) + i(\Omega^{(m)}(\tau, \varepsilon) - k(\tau))] \xi^{(m)} + Z^{(m)}(\tau, \varepsilon), \tag{9.2}$$

where

$$\Pi^{(m)}(\tau, \varepsilon) = \mu_1(\tau) + \sum_{s=1}^{m} \varepsilon^s \Pi_s(\tau), \quad H^{(m)}(\tau, \varepsilon) = \sum_{s=0}^{m} \varepsilon^s H_s(\tau),$$
$$D^{(m)}(\tau, \varepsilon) = \sum_{s=1}^{m} \varepsilon^s D_s(\tau), \quad \Omega^{(m)}(\tau, \varepsilon) = \sum_{s=0}^{m} \varepsilon^s \Omega_s(\tau),$$

$$Z^{(m)}(\tau, \varepsilon) = \sum_{s=0}^{m} \varepsilon^s Z_s(\tau) \tag{9.3}$$

(m is any natural number).

Below we will show that the absolute value of the difference between the exact particular solution $x(t, \varepsilon)$ of system (6.1) and the corresponding vector $x^{(m)}(t, \varepsilon)$ of the mth approximation can be made as small as we like, for sufficiently small ε.

Here we will take, as an example, the resonance case (analogous results can be obtained for the nonresonance case as well).

First we will prove the following Lemma.

Lemma II.1. If the conditions of Theorem II.1 are satisfied, then the mth approximation satisfies the original system of differential equations (6.1) with accuracy up to quantities of the order of ε^m uniformly with respect to t on the closed interval $0 \leqslant t \leqslant L / \varepsilon$ for any ε in the interval $0 < \varepsilon \leqslant \varepsilon_0$.

Proof. In fact, substituting the vector $x^{(m)}(t, \varepsilon)$, defined by formula (9.1), into the expression

$$A(\tau, \varepsilon) \frac{d^2 x^{(m)}}{dt^2} + \varepsilon C(\tau, \varepsilon) \frac{dx^{(m)}}{dt} + B(\tau, \varepsilon) x^{(m)} - P(\tau, \varepsilon) e^{i\theta(t,\varepsilon)},$$

we obtain

$$\begin{aligned}
A(\tau, \varepsilon) \frac{d^2 x^{(m)}}{dt^2} &+ \varepsilon C(\tau, \varepsilon) \frac{dx^{(m)}}{dt} + B(\tau, \varepsilon) x^{(m)} - P(\tau, \varepsilon) e^{i\theta(t,\varepsilon)} = \\
&= \{A(\tau, \varepsilon) [\varepsilon^2 \Pi^{(m)''}(\tau, \varepsilon) + 2\varepsilon \Pi^{(m)'}(\tau, \varepsilon)(D^{(m)}(\tau, \varepsilon) + i\Omega^{(m)}(\tau, \varepsilon)) + \\
&+ \varepsilon \Pi^{(m)}(\tau, \varepsilon)(D^{(m)}(\tau, \varepsilon) + i\Omega^{(m)}(\tau, \varepsilon))' + \Pi^{(m)}(\tau, \varepsilon)(D^{(m)}(\tau, \varepsilon) + \\
&+ i\Omega(\tau, \varepsilon))^2] + \varepsilon C(\tau, \varepsilon) [\varepsilon \Pi^{(m)'}(\tau, \varepsilon) + \Pi^{(m)}(\tau, \varepsilon)(D^{(m)}(\tau, \varepsilon) + \\
&+ i\Omega^{(m)}(\tau, \varepsilon))] + B(\tau, \varepsilon) \Pi^{(m)}(\tau, \varepsilon)\} \xi^{(m)}(t, \varepsilon) e^{i\theta(t,\varepsilon)} + \\
&+ \{A(\tau, \varepsilon) [(D^{(m)}(\tau, \varepsilon) + i\Omega^{(m)}(\tau, \varepsilon) - ik(\tau)) \Pi^{(m)}(\tau, \varepsilon) Z^{(m)}(\tau, \varepsilon) + \\
&+ \varepsilon Z^{(m)'}(\tau, \varepsilon) \Pi^{(m)}(\tau, \varepsilon) + 2\varepsilon Z^{(m)}(\tau, \varepsilon) \Pi^{(m)'}(\tau, \varepsilon) + \\
&+ \varepsilon i k'(\tau) H^{(m)}(\tau, \varepsilon) - k^2(\tau) H^{(m)}(\tau, \varepsilon) + 2\varepsilon i k(\tau) H^{(m)'}(\tau, \varepsilon) + \\
&+ \varepsilon^2 H^{(m)''}(\tau, \varepsilon)] + \varepsilon C(\tau, \varepsilon) [\Pi^{(m)}(\tau, \varepsilon) Z^{(m)}(\tau, \varepsilon) + \\
&+ ik(\tau) H^{(m)}(\tau, \varepsilon) + \varepsilon H^{(m)'}(\tau, \varepsilon)] + B(\tau, \varepsilon) H^{(m)}(\tau, \varepsilon) - \\
&- P(\tau, \varepsilon)\} e^{i\theta(t,\varepsilon)}.
\end{aligned} \tag{9.4}$$

In accordance with the definition of the elements of the series (7.3), the expression on the right-hand side of Eq. (9.4) is of the order of ε^{m+1}. Therefore expression (9.4) can be represented in the form

$$A(\tau,\ \varepsilon)\frac{d^2x^{(m)}}{dt^2}+\varepsilon C(\tau,\ \varepsilon)\frac{dx^{(m)}}{dt}+B(\tau,\ \varepsilon)\,x^{(m)}=$$
$$=P(\tau,\ \varepsilon)\,e^{i\theta(t,\varepsilon)}+\varepsilon^{m+1}\left[F_m(\tau,\ \varepsilon)\,\xi^{(m)}(t,\ \varepsilon)+R_m(\tau,\ \varepsilon)\right]e^{i\theta(t,\varepsilon)}, \quad (9.5)$$

where $F_m(\tau,\ \varepsilon)$, $R_m(\tau,\ \varepsilon)$ are vectors which are holomorphic with respect to ε in a neighborhood of the point $\varepsilon = 0$.

Integrating Eq. (9.2), we find

$$\xi^{(m)}(t,\ \varepsilon) = ae^{\int_0^t D^{(m)}(\tau,\varepsilon)dt}\left\{\cos\int_0^t\left[\Omega^{(m)}(\tau,\ \varepsilon)-k(\tau)\right]dt+\right.$$
$$\left.+\,i\sin\int_0^t\left[\Omega^{(m)}(\tau,\ \varepsilon)-k(\tau)\right]dt\right\}+$$
$$+\int_0^t Z^{(m)}(\tau_1,\ \varepsilon)\,e^{\int_{t_1}^t D^{(m)}(\tau,\varepsilon)dt}\left[\cos\int_{t_1}^t\left(\Omega^{(m)}(\tau,\ \varepsilon)-k(\tau)\right)dt+\right. \quad (9.6)$$
$$\left.+\,i\sin\int_{t_1}^t\left(\Omega^{(m)}(\tau,\ \varepsilon)-k(\tau)\right)dt\right]dt_1,$$

where a is a constant of integration.

Since the functions $D^{(m)}(\tau,\ \varepsilon)$, $Z^{(m)}(\tau,\ \varepsilon)$, $\Omega^{(m)}(\tau,\ \varepsilon)$, $k(\tau)$ are differentiable with respect to τ, which means that they are bounded on the closed interval $[0,\ L]$, then from Eq. (9.6) we obtain

$$|\xi^{(m)}(t,\ \varepsilon)| \leqslant \frac{C_1}{\varepsilon}, \quad (9.7)$$

where C_1 is a constant which is independent of ε.

Taking account of estimate (9.7), Eq. (9.5) can be rewritten in the form

$$A(\tau,\ \varepsilon)\frac{d^2x^{(m)}}{dt^2}+\varepsilon C(\tau,\ \varepsilon)\frac{dx^{(m)}}{dt}+B(\tau,\ \varepsilon)\,x^{(m)}=$$
$$=P(\tau,\ \varepsilon)\,e^{i\theta(t,\varepsilon)}+\varepsilon^m\Phi_m(\tau,\ \varepsilon), \quad (9.8)$$

where $\Phi_m(\tau, \varepsilon)$ is a vector which is uniformly bounded in absolute value for all $t \in [0, L/\varepsilon]$ and $0 < \varepsilon \leqslant \varepsilon_0$.

The lemma is proved.

Now we can prove a theorem which establishes the asymptotic nature of the solution $x^{(m)}(t, \varepsilon)$.

Theorem II.3. Let the exact solution $x(t, \varepsilon)$ *of the system (6.1) and the mth approximation* $x^{(m)}(t, \varepsilon)$ *be taken for the same initial conditions*

$$x(0) = x^{(m)}(0) = x_0, \quad \left.\frac{dx}{dt}\right|_{t=0} = \left.\frac{dx^{(m)}}{dt}\right|_{t=0} = \dot{x}_0. \tag{9.9}$$

Then, provided that the conditions of Theorem II.1 are satisfied, given any $L > 0$ *we can find a constant C, independent of* ε, *such that for all* $t \in [0, L/\varepsilon]$ and $0 < \varepsilon \leqslant \varepsilon_0$, *the following inequalities will hold:*

$$\begin{gathered} \| x(t, \varepsilon) - x^{(m)}(t, \varepsilon) \| \leqslant \varepsilon^{m-1} C, \\ \left\| \frac{dx}{dt} - \frac{dx^{(m)}}{dt} \right\| \leqslant \varepsilon^{m-1} C. \end{gathered} \tag{9.10}$$

Proof. To prove the given theorem, we introduce into consideration the vector

$$y(t, \varepsilon) = x(t, \varepsilon) - x^{(m)}(t, \varepsilon). \tag{9.11}$$

It is easy to see that the vector $y(t, \varepsilon)$ satisfies the zero initial conditions

$$y(0) = 0, \qquad \left.\frac{dy}{dt}\right|_{t=0} = 0$$

and the system

$$A(\tau, \varepsilon)\frac{d^2y}{dt^2} + \varepsilon C(\tau, \varepsilon)\frac{dy}{dt} + B(\tau, \varepsilon)y = -\varepsilon^m \Phi_m(\tau, \varepsilon). \tag{9.12}$$

We rewrite the obtained system (9.12) in the following form:

$$\begin{gathered} A_0(\tau)\frac{d^2y}{dt^2} + B_0(\tau)y = -\varepsilon A_1(\tau, \varepsilon)\frac{d^2y}{dt^2} - \varepsilon C(\tau, \varepsilon)\frac{dy}{dt} - \\ - \varepsilon B_1(\tau, \varepsilon)y - \varepsilon^m \Phi_m(\tau, \varepsilon), \end{gathered} \tag{9.13}$$

where

$$A_1(\tau, \varepsilon) = \sum_{s=0}^{\infty} \varepsilon^s A_{s+1}(\tau), \quad B_1(\tau, \varepsilon) = \sum_{s=0}^{\infty} \varepsilon^s B_{s+1}(\tau). \tag{9.14}$$

We represent the desired vector $y(t, \varepsilon)$ in the form

$$y(t, \varepsilon) = \sum_{j=1}^{n} \mu_j(\tau) b_j(t, \varepsilon), \tag{9.15}$$

where $b_j(t, \varepsilon)$ are scalar functions.

Substituting (9.15) into system (9.13) and taking the scalar product of the result with the vector μ_k $(k = 1, 2, \ldots, n)$, we obtain

$$\begin{aligned} \frac{d^2 b_k}{dt^2} + \varrho_k^2(\tau) b_k = -\varepsilon \sum_{j=1}^{n} \{\varepsilon^2 (A_1(\tau, \varepsilon) \mu_j''(\tau), \mu_k(\tau)) + \\ + \varepsilon (C(\tau, \varepsilon) \mu_j'(\tau), \mu_k(\tau)) + (B_1(\tau, \varepsilon) \mu_j(\tau), \mu_k(\tau)) b_j + \\ + (A_1(\tau, \varepsilon) \mu_j(\tau), \mu_k(\tau)) \frac{d^2 b_j}{dt^2} + (C(\tau, \varepsilon) \mu_j(\tau), \mu_k(\tau)) \frac{db_j}{dt} - \\ - \varepsilon^m (\Phi_m(\tau, \varepsilon), \mu_k(\tau)), \qquad k = 1, 2, \ldots, n, \end{aligned} \tag{9.16}$$

where

$$\varrho_k^2(\tau) = \omega_k(\tau), \qquad k = 1, 2, \ldots, n. \tag{9.17}$$

We solve the obtained system (9.16) with respect to the second derivatives, taking into account that for sufficiently small values of ε, the determinant of the system does not differ greatly from one. We write the result in the form

$$\begin{aligned} \frac{d^2 b_k}{dt^2} + \varrho_k^2(\tau, \varepsilon) b_k = \varepsilon \sum_{j=1}^{n} \left[\alpha_{kj}(\tau, \varepsilon) b_j + \beta_{kj}(\tau, \varepsilon) \frac{db_j}{dt} \right] + \\ + \varepsilon^m f_k(\tau, \varepsilon), \qquad k = 1, 2, \ldots, n, \end{aligned} \tag{9.18}$$

where the functions $\varrho_k^2(\tau, \varepsilon)$, $\alpha_{kj}(\tau, \varepsilon)$, $\beta_{kj}(\tau, \varepsilon)$ and $f_k(\tau, \varepsilon)$ are bounded on the closed interval $[0, L]$; here, according to (9.17),

$$\varrho_k^2(\tau, \varepsilon) \neq 0 \tag{9.19}$$

for any $\tau \in [0, L]$, $0 < \varepsilon \leqslant \varepsilon_0$.

Applying Lemma I.2 to system (9.18) we obtain

$$|b_k(t, \varepsilon)| \leqslant S_k \int_0^t \left| \frac{P_k(\tau, \varepsilon)}{\varrho_k(\tau, \varepsilon)} \right| dt,$$
$$\left| \frac{db_k}{dt} \right| \leqslant S_{1k} \int_0^t \left| \frac{P_k(\tau, \varepsilon)}{\varrho_k(\tau, \varepsilon)} \right| dt, \tag{9.20}$$

where

$$P_k(\tau, \varepsilon) = \varepsilon \sum_{j=1}^{n} \left[\alpha_{kj}(\tau, \varepsilon) b_j(t, \varepsilon) + \beta_{kj}(\tau, \varepsilon) \frac{db_j}{dt} \right] + \varepsilon^m f_k(\tau, \varepsilon). \tag{9.21}$$

Let

$$W = \sum_{j=1}^{n} \left(|b_j(t, \varepsilon)| + \left| \frac{db_j}{dt} \right| \right). \tag{9.22}$$

Adding the inequalities (9.20) termwise, and taking account of the fact that the functions $\alpha_{kj}(\tau, \varepsilon)$, $\beta_{kj}(\tau, \varepsilon)$, $\varrho_k(\tau, \varepsilon)$ and $f_k(\tau, \varepsilon)$ are bounded for any $\tau \in [0, L]$, and $0 < \varepsilon \leqslant \varepsilon_0$, we find

$$W \leqslant \varepsilon K \int_0^t W dt + \varepsilon^{m-1} K_1, \tag{9.23}$$

where K, K_1 are constants which are independent of ε.

Applying Lemma I.1 to inequality (9.23), we obtain the inequality

$$W \leqslant \varepsilon^{m-1} C, \quad C = K_1 e^{KL}. \tag{9.24}$$

This implies the following estimates:

$$|b_j(t, \varepsilon)| \leqslant \varepsilon^{m-1} C, \quad \left| \frac{db_j}{dt} \right| \leqslant \varepsilon^{m-1} C, \quad j = 1, 2, \ldots, n. \tag{9.25}$$

The proof of Theorem II.3 follows from inequality (9.25) and Eqs. (9.11) and (9.15).

We note that in the nonresonance case we obtain an even better estimate, namely,

$$\| x(t, \varepsilon) - x^{(m)}(t, \varepsilon) \| \leqslant \varepsilon^m C, \qquad \left\| \frac{dx}{dt} - \frac{dx^{(m)}}{dt} \right\| \leqslant \varepsilon^m C. \tag{9.26}$$

In addition, in the case of resonance, for a small free term ($P_0(\tau) \equiv 0$), the estimate will also take the form (9.26).

10. On the Dynamic Stresses in a Visco-Elastic Thread of Variable Length with a Weight Q at the End

In Sec. 5 we considered the question of finding the tension in a visco-elastic thread (cable) of variable length with a weight Q at the end. This problem reduced to that of solving an ordinary linear differential equation (5.1).

In [69], Sokolov showed that the problem of finding the tension in a visco-elastic thread of variable length $l = l(t)$ with a weight Q at the end, for fixed conditions, reduced to a system of two ordinary linear differential equations

$$\begin{aligned} l^2(t) \frac{d^2\varphi}{dt^2} &= -6\,[2\gamma + \gamma_1 l(t)] \frac{d\varphi}{dt} - 3(\gamma_1 - v) \frac{d\psi}{dt} - \\ &- 3\beta_1 \psi - 6\,[2\beta + \beta_1 l(t) - v^2]\,\varphi - 3\left(g - \frac{dv}{dt}\right), \\ l(t) \frac{d^2\psi}{dt^2} &= 4\,[3\gamma + \gamma_1 l(t) - v l(t)] \frac{d\varphi}{dt} + \\ &+ 2(\gamma_1 - 2v) \frac{d\psi}{dt} + 4\,[3\beta + \beta_1 l(t) - 2v^2]\,\varphi + 2\beta_1 \psi + 4\left(g - \frac{dv}{dt}\right), \end{aligned} \tag{10.1}$$

where

$$\begin{gathered} \gamma = \frac{g\alpha}{q}, \quad \gamma_1 = \frac{g\alpha}{Q}, \quad \beta = \frac{gK}{q}, \quad \beta_1 = \frac{gK}{Q}, \\ K = E\sigma, \qquad v = \frac{dl}{dt}, \end{gathered} \tag{10.2}$$

The symbols g, q, E, σ, α have the same meaning as in Eq. (5.1).

In system (10.1) the function $\varphi(t)$ determines the relative elongation of the thread, and $\psi(t)$ characterizes the tension

T_1 arising at the upper end of the thread, since, according to [69], we can approximately take

$$T_1 \approx K\psi(t). \tag{10.3}$$

In this section we will show that the system (10.1) can be solved by the asymptotic method described in Secs. 7 and 8 of this chapter.

We will assume, as in the solution of Eq. (5.1), that the lifting of the weight is accomplished by a trapezoidal tachogram (Fig. 1), i.e., the law of motion of the weight is given by formulas (5.2), (5.3) and (5.4). Then, on each segment of the ascent of the weight, system (10.1) must be reduced to the form (6.1).

1. We begin by considering the first segment of the ascent of the weight. Introducing the quantities

$$\varphi = \frac{x_1 - x_2}{l_0}, \quad \psi = \frac{4x_2 - 3x_1}{3}, \quad T = \omega_0 t, \quad \tau = \varepsilon T, \tag{10.4}$$

where

$$\omega_0 = \frac{c}{l_0}, \quad c = \sqrt{\frac{Kg}{q}}, \quad \varepsilon = \sqrt[3]{\frac{al_0}{2c^2}}, \tag{10.5}$$

we reduce system (10.1) to the form (6.1), where

$$\begin{gathered} A(\tau, \varepsilon) = \sum_{s=0}^{2} \varepsilon^s A_s(\tau), \quad C(\tau, \varepsilon) = \sum_{s=0}^{2} \varepsilon^s C_s(\tau), \\ B(\tau, \varepsilon) = \sum_{s=0}^{4} \varepsilon^s B_s(\tau), \quad P(\tau, \varepsilon) = P_0, \end{gathered} \tag{10.6}$$

$$A_0(\tau) = \begin{bmatrix} 1 & -1 \\ -1 & \frac{4}{3} \end{bmatrix}, \quad A_1(\tau) = \begin{bmatrix} -2 & 2 \\ 1 & -\frac{4}{3} \end{bmatrix} \tau^2, \quad A_2 = \begin{bmatrix} 1 & -1 \\ 0 & 0 \end{bmatrix} \tau^4,$$

$$B_0(\tau) = \begin{bmatrix} 3(4+\eta_0) & -2(6+\eta_0) \\ -2(6+\eta_0) & 4\left(3 + \frac{1}{3}\eta_0\right) \end{bmatrix},$$

$$B_1(\tau) = \begin{bmatrix} -6 & 6 \\ 4 & -4 \end{bmatrix} \eta_0 \tau^2, \quad B_2(\tau) \equiv B_3(\tau) \equiv 0,$$

$$B_4(\tau) = \begin{bmatrix} -24 & 24 \\ 32 & -32 \end{bmatrix} \tau^2, \tag{10.7}$$

$$C_0(\tau) = \begin{bmatrix} 3\left(\dfrac{4\gamma}{l_0} + \gamma_1\right) & -2\left(\dfrac{6\gamma}{l_0} + \gamma_1\right) \\ -2\left(\dfrac{6\gamma}{l_0} + \gamma_1\right) & 4\left(\dfrac{3\gamma}{l_0} + \dfrac{1}{3}\gamma_1\right) \end{bmatrix} \delta_1^0,$$

$$C_1(\tau) = \begin{bmatrix} -6(\gamma_1\delta_1\tau + 1) & 6\left(\gamma_1\delta_1\tau + \dfrac{4}{3}\right) \\ 4\gamma_1\delta_1\tau & -4\left(\gamma_1\delta_1\tau + \dfrac{2}{3}\right) \end{bmatrix} \tau,$$

$$C_2(\tau) = \begin{bmatrix} 0 & 0 \\ 1 & -1 \end{bmatrix} 8\tau^2,$$

$$P_0 = \frac{p_0}{K}\left(1 + \frac{a}{g}\right)\begin{bmatrix} -3 \\ 4 \end{bmatrix},$$

$$p_0 = l_0 q, \quad \delta_1^0 = \sqrt[3]{\frac{2}{a l_0 C}}, \quad \eta_0 = \frac{p_0}{Q}.$$

To construct the desired solution, we find, first of all, the characteristic values and the characteristic vectors of the matrix $B_0(\tau)$ with respect to the matrix $A_0(\tau)$. From Eqs. (6.4) and (6.5), we find

$$\begin{gathered} \omega_1 = 6 + 2\eta_0 + 2\sqrt{9 + 3\eta_0 + \eta_0^2}, \\ \omega_2 = 6 + 2\eta_0 - 2\sqrt{9 + 3\eta_0 + \eta_0^2}, \\ \mu_1 = \frac{1}{R_1}\begin{bmatrix} 2(6 + \eta_0) - \omega_1 \\ 3(4 + \eta_0) - \omega_1 \end{bmatrix}, \quad \mu_2 = \frac{1}{R_2}\begin{bmatrix} 2(6 + \eta_0) - \omega_2 \\ 3(4 + \eta_0) - \omega_2 \end{bmatrix}, \end{gathered} \tag{10.8}$$

where

$$\begin{gathered} R_1 = \sqrt{\frac{\omega_1^2}{3} - 2(4 + \eta_0)\omega_1 + 4(12 + 6\eta_0 + \eta_0^2)}, \\ R_2 = \sqrt{\frac{\omega_2^2}{3} - 2(4 + \eta_0)\omega_2 + 4(12 + 6\eta_0 + \eta_0^2)}. \end{gathered} \tag{10.9}$$

Then, according to the formulas of Secs. 7 and 8, the asymptotic solution of the system of differential equations (10.1) on the first segment of the ascent of the weight Q, in the second approximation, has the form

$$l_0\varphi = N_1 e^{-(\beta_1 t+\beta_2 t^2+\beta_3 t^3)}\{[\mu_{11}-\mu_{21}+(\mu_{12}-\mu_{22})\times$$
$$\times(\Delta_0 t^2+\Delta_1 t^4)]\sin(\delta_1 t+\delta_2 t^3+\delta_3 t^5+\theta_1)+$$
$$+(\mu_{22}-\mu_{12})(\Delta_2 t+\Delta_3 t^2)\cos(\delta_1 t+\delta_2 t^3+\delta_3 t^5+\theta_1)\}+$$
$$+N_2 e^{-(\bar\beta_1 t+\bar\beta_2 t^2+\bar\beta_3 t^3)}\{[\mu_{12}-\mu_{22}+(\mu_{11}-\mu_{21})(\bar\Delta_0 t^2+\bar\Delta_1 t^4)]\times$$
$$\times\sin(\bar\delta_1 t+\bar\delta_2 t^3+\bar\delta_3 t^5+\theta_2)+$$
$$+(\mu_{21}-\mu_{11})(\bar\Delta_2 t+\bar\Delta_3 t^2)\cos(\bar\delta_1 t+\bar\delta_2 t^3+\bar\delta_3 t^5+\theta_2)\}-\frac{p_0}{2K}\left(1+\frac{a}{g}\right);$$
$$\psi = N_1 e^{-(\beta_1 t+\beta_2 t^2+\beta_3 t^3)}\left\{\left[\frac{4}{3}\mu_{21}-\mu_{11}+\right.\right.$$
$$+\left(\frac{4}{3}\mu_{22}-\mu_{12}\right)(\Delta_0 t^2+\Delta_1 t^4)]\sin(\delta_1 t+\delta_2 t^3+\delta_3 t^5+\theta_1)+$$
$$+\left(\mu_{12}-\frac{4}{3}\mu_{22}\right)(\Delta_2 t+\Delta_3 t^3)\cos(\delta_1 t+\delta_2 t^3+\delta_3 t^5+\theta_1)\Big\}+$$
$$+N_2 e^{-(\bar\beta_1 t+\bar\beta_2 t^2+\bar\beta_3 t^3)}\left\{\left[\frac{4}{3}\mu_{22}-\mu_{12}+\left(\frac{4}{3}\mu_{21}-\mu_{11}\right)\times\right.\right.$$
$$\times(\bar\Delta_0 t^2+\bar\Delta_1 t^4)]\sin\overline{(\delta_1 t}+\bar\delta_2 t^3+\bar\delta_3 t^5+\theta_2)+$$
$$+\left(\mu_{11}-\frac{4}{3}\mu_{21}\right)(\bar\Delta_2 t+\bar\Delta_3 t^2)\cos(\bar\delta_1 t+\bar\delta_2 t^3+\bar\delta_3 t^5+\theta_2)\Big\}+$$
$$+\frac{Q}{K}\left(1+\frac{a}{g}\right)\left[1+\eta_0\left(1-\frac{at^2}{2l_0}\right)\right], \tag{10.10}$$

where

$$\beta_1 = \frac{ga\left(\frac{1}{3}\omega_1^2-8\omega_1+48+12\eta_0\right)}{2Ql_0R_1^2},$$

$$\beta_2 = \frac{a\left[24\eta_0^2-12(4+\eta_0)\omega_1+(8-\eta_0)\omega_1^2-\frac{1}{3}\omega_1^3\right]}{8\omega_1 l_0 R_1^2},$$

$$\beta_3 = \frac{gaa}{12l_0^2QR_1^4}\left[\frac{1}{9}\omega_1^4-\frac{1}{3}(16+3\eta_0)\omega_1^3+\right.$$
$$+\left(96+40\eta_0+\frac{14}{3}\eta_0^2\right)\omega_1^2-(768+528\eta_0+124\eta_0^2+8\eta_0^3)\omega_1+$$
$$\left.+2304(1+\eta_0)+816\eta_0^2+120\eta_0^3\right],$$

$$\Delta_0 = \frac{a\eta_0[\omega_1^2-2\eta_0(\omega_1-\omega_2)-24\eta_0]}{2l_0R_1R_2(\omega_2-\omega_1)},$$

$$\Delta_1 = -\frac{a^2\eta_0}{2l_0^2R_1^3R_2^3(\omega_2-\omega_1)^2}\left\{12\eta_0\left[\frac{\omega_1^3}{3}-(8+\eta_0)\omega_1^2+12(4+\eta_0)\omega_1+\right.\right.$$

$$\left.+24\eta_0^2\right]R_2^2+4\,|\omega_1^2-2\eta_0(\omega_1-\omega_2)-24\eta_0|\,[\eta_0\omega_2-24\eta_0+$$

$$\left.+3\eta_0^2+3(4+\eta_0)\omega_1]\,R_1^2+\omega_1(\omega_2-\omega_1)(12+2\eta_0-\omega_2)R_1^2R_2^2\right\},$$

$$\delta_1 = \nu_0 - \frac{g^2a^2\left(\frac{1}{3}\omega_1^2-8\omega_1+48+12\eta_0\right)^2}{8Q^2l_0^2\nu_0R_1^4},$$

$$\delta_2 = \frac{a\nu_0\left[\frac{1}{3}\omega_1^3-(8+\eta_0)\omega_1+12(4+\eta_0)\omega_1+24\eta_0^2\right]}{12l_0\omega_1R_1^2}, \qquad (10.11)$$

$$\delta_3 = \frac{a^2\nu_0}{160\omega_1^2l_0^2R_1^4}\left\{4\omega_1\left[\frac{\omega_1^3}{3}-(8+\eta_0)\omega_1^2+12(4+\eta_0)\omega_1+\right.\right.$$

$$\left.+24\eta_0^2\right]\left[\frac{1}{3}\omega_1^2-(8+\eta_0)\omega_1+48-12\eta_0+2\eta_0^2\right]-$$

$$-\left[\frac{\omega_1^3}{3}-(8+\eta_0)\omega_1^2+12(4+\eta_0)\omega_1+24\eta_0^2\right]^2-$$

$$-4\omega_1^2\eta_0R_1^2(\omega_1-12-2\eta_0)+\frac{4\omega_1R_1^2\eta_0(12+3\eta_0-\omega_1)}{R_2^2(\omega_2-\omega_1)}\times$$

$$\left.\times[16\eta_0+4\eta_0^2-\eta_0(\omega_2+2\omega_1)-4\omega_1]\,|\omega_1^2-2\eta_0(\omega_1-\omega_2)-24\eta_0|\right\},$$

$$\nu_0 = \sqrt{\frac{Kga}{l_0p_0}}, \quad \Delta_2 = -\frac{2a\omega_1\eta_0\,|\omega_2^2+2(\omega_1-\omega_2)(\eta_0+3)|}{l_0\nu_0R_1R_2(\omega_2-\omega_1)^2},$$

$$\Delta_3 = \frac{ga\omega_1a}{2l_0^2(\omega_2-\omega_1)^2R_1^3R_2^3Q\nu_0}\left\{12\eta_0^2R_2^2\left(\frac{\omega_1^2}{3}-8\omega_1+48+12\eta_0\right)+\right.$$

$$+\eta_0R_1^2\,|\omega_1^2-2\eta_0(\omega_1-\omega_2)-24\eta_0|\left[\frac{\omega_2^2}{3}-8\omega_2+48+12\eta_0\right]-$$

$$\left.-2R_1^2R_2^2(\omega_2-\omega_1)(12+3\eta_0-\omega_2)(\omega_1-12-4\eta_0)\right\},$$

N_1, N_2, θ_1, θ_2 are constants of integration which are determined from the initial conditions, and the coefficients $\bar{\beta}_1$, $\bar{\beta}_2$, $\bar{\beta}_3$, $\bar{\Delta}_0$, $\bar{\Delta}_1$, $\bar{\delta}_1$, $\bar{\delta}_2$, $\bar{\delta}_3$, $\bar{\Delta}_2$, $\bar{\Delta}_3$ coincide with the coefficients β_1, β_2, β_3, Δ_0, Δ_1, δ_1, δ_2, δ_3, Δ_2, Δ_3, respectively, provided in the latter we change ω_1 and R_1 to ω_2 and R_2 and vice versa.

2. We now turn to finding the solution of the system of differential equations (10.1) on the second segment of motion

of the weight Q. For this we introduce new variables, according to the formulas

$$\varphi = \frac{x_1 - x_2}{l_1}, \quad \psi = \frac{4x_2 - 3x_1}{3},$$

$$T = \omega_{01} t, \quad \tau = \varepsilon T, \tag{10.12}$$

where

$$\omega_{01} = \frac{c}{l_1}, \quad \varepsilon = \sqrt{\frac{v_0}{c}}. \tag{10.13}$$

System (10.1) reduces to the form (6.1), where

$$A(\tau, \varepsilon) = \sum_{s=0}^{2} \varepsilon^s A_s(\tau), \quad C(\tau, \varepsilon) = \sum_{s=0}^{2} \varepsilon^s C_s(\tau),$$

$$B(\tau, \varepsilon) = \sum_{s=0}^{4} \varepsilon^s B_s(\tau), \quad P(\tau, \varepsilon) = P_0, \tag{10.14}$$

here

$$A_0(\tau) = \begin{bmatrix} 1 & -1 \\ -1 & \frac{4}{3} \end{bmatrix}, \quad A_1(\tau) = \begin{bmatrix} -2 & 2 \\ 1 & -\frac{4}{3} \end{bmatrix} \tau,$$

$$A_2(\tau) = \begin{bmatrix} 1 & -1 \\ 0 & 0 \end{bmatrix} \tau^2 \qquad C_0(\tau) =$$

$$= \begin{bmatrix} 3\left(\frac{4\gamma}{l_1} + \gamma_1\right) & -2\left(6\frac{\gamma}{l_1} + \gamma_1\right) \\ -2\left(6\frac{\gamma}{l_1} + \gamma_1\right) & 2\left(6\frac{\gamma}{l_1} + \frac{2}{3}\gamma_1\right) \end{bmatrix} f^{(1)},$$

$$C_1(\tau) = \begin{bmatrix} -3(2\gamma_1 f^{(1)}\tau + 1) & 3\left(2\gamma_1 f^{(1)}\tau + \frac{4}{3}\right) \\ 4\gamma_1 f^{(1)}\tau & -2\left(2\gamma_1 f^{(1)}(\tau) + \frac{2}{3}\right) \end{bmatrix},$$

$$C_2(\tau) = \begin{bmatrix} 0 & 0 \\ 4 & -4 \end{bmatrix} \tau, \quad B_0(\tau) = 3\begin{bmatrix} 4 + \eta_1 & -\left(4 + \frac{2}{3}\eta_1\right) \\ -\left(4 + \frac{2}{3}\eta_1\right) & 4 + \frac{4}{9}\eta_1 \end{bmatrix},$$

$$B_1(\tau) = \begin{bmatrix} -6 & 6 \\ 4 & -4 \end{bmatrix} \eta_1 \tau, \quad B_2(\tau) \equiv B_3(\tau) \equiv 0,$$

$$B_4(\tau) = \begin{bmatrix} -6 & 6 \\ 8 & -8 \end{bmatrix}, \quad P_0 = \frac{P_1}{K} \begin{bmatrix} -3 \\ 4 \end{bmatrix},$$

$$f^{(1)} = \frac{1}{\sqrt{v_0 C}}, \quad p_1 = l_1 q, \quad \eta_1 = \frac{p_1}{Q}. \tag{10.15}$$

The solution in this case takes the form

$$l_1\varphi = N_1^{(1)} e^{-(\beta_1^{(1)}t+\beta_2^{(1)}t^2)} \{[\mu_{11}^{(1)} - \mu_{21}^{(1)} + (\mu_{12}^{(1)} - \mu_{22}^{(1)})(\Delta_0^{(1)} + \Delta_1^{(1)}t^2)] \times$$
$$\times \sin(\delta_1^{(1)}t + \delta_2^{(1)}t^2 + \delta_3^{(1)}t^3 + \theta_1^{(1)}) + (\mu_{22}^{(1)} - \mu_{12}^{(1)})(\Delta_2^{(1)} + \Delta_3^{(1)}t) \times$$
$$\times \cos(\delta_1^{(1)}t + \delta_2^{(1)}t^2 + \delta_3^{(1)}t^3 + \theta_1^{(1)})\} +$$
$$+ N_2^{(1)} e^{-(\bar\beta_1 t+\bar\beta_2 t^2)} \{[\mu_{12}^{(1)} - \mu_{22}^{(1)} + (\mu_{11}^{(1)} - \mu_{21}^{(1)})(\bar\Delta_0^{(1)}t + \bar\Delta_1^{(1)}t^2)] \times$$
$$\times \sin(\bar\delta_1^{(1)}t + \bar\delta_2^{(1)}t^2 + \bar\delta_3^{(1)}t^3 + \theta_2^{(1)}) +$$
$$+ (\mu_{21}^{(1)} - \mu_{11}^{(1)})(\bar\Delta_2^{(1)} + \bar\Delta_3^{(1)}t)\cos(\bar\delta_1^{(1)}t + \bar\delta_2^{(1)}t^2 + \bar\delta_3^{(1)}t^3 + \theta_2^{(1)})\} - \frac{P_1}{2K}$$

$$\psi = N_1^{(1)} e^{-(\beta_1^{(1)}t+\beta_2^{(1)}t^2)} \left\{\left[\frac{4}{3}\mu_{21}^{(1)} - \mu_{11}^{(1)} +\right.\right.$$
$$\left. + \left(\frac{4}{3}\mu_{22}^{(1)} - \mu_{12}^{(1)}\right)(\Delta_0^{(1)}t + \Delta_1^{(1)}t^2)\right] \sin(\delta_1^{(1)}t + \delta_2^{(1)}t^2 + \delta_3^{(1)}t^3 + \theta_1^{(1)}) +$$
$$\left. + \left(\mu_{12}^{(1)} - \frac{4}{3}\mu_{22}^{(1)}\right)(\Delta_2^{(1)} + \Delta_3^{(1)}t)\cos(\delta_1^{(1)}t + \delta_2^{(1)}t^2 + \delta_3^{(1)}t^3 + \theta_1^{(1)})\right\} +$$
$$+ N_2^{(1)} e^{-(\bar\beta^{(1)}t+\bar\beta_2^{(1)}t^2)} \left\{\left[\frac{4}{3}\mu_{22}^{(1)} - \mu_{12}^{(1)} +\right.\right.$$
$$\left. + \left(\frac{4}{3}\mu_{21}^{(1)} - \mu_{11}^{(1)}\right)(\bar\Delta_0^{(1)}t + \bar\Delta_1^{(1)}t^2)\right] \sin(\bar\delta_1^{(1)}t + \bar\delta_2^{(1)}t^3 + \theta_2^{(1)}) +$$
$$\left. + \left(\mu_{11}^{(1)} - \frac{4}{3}\mu_{21}^{(1)}\right)(\bar\Delta_2^{(1)} + \bar\Delta_3^{(1)}t)\cos(\bar\delta_1^{(1)}t + \bar\delta_2^{(1)}t^2 + \bar\delta_3^{(1)}t^3 + \theta_2^{(1)})\right\} +$$
$$+ \frac{Q}{K}\left[1 + \eta_1\left(1 - \frac{v_0 t}{l_1}\right)\right], \tag{10.16}$$

where

$$\beta_1^{(1)} = \frac{ga\left[\frac{1}{3}(\omega_1^{(1)})^2 - 8\omega_1^{(1)} + 48 + 12\eta_1\right]}{2Ql_1(R_1^{(1)})^2} + \frac{v_0}{4l_1\omega_1^{(1)}(R_1^{(1)})^2} \times$$
$$\times \left[24\eta_1^2 + 12\eta_1\omega_1^{(1)} - 48\omega_1^{(1)} - \eta_1(\omega_1^{(1)})^2 + 8(\omega_1^{(1)})^2 - \frac{1}{3}(\omega_1^{(1)})^3\right],$$

$$\beta_2^{(1)} = \frac{v_0 g\alpha}{4l_1^2 Q (R_1^{(1)})^4}\left\{\left[\frac{1}{3}(\omega_1^{(1)})^2 - 8\omega_1^{(1)} + 48 + 12\eta_1^2\right]\left[\frac{1}{3}(\omega_1^{(1)})^2 - \right.\right.$$

$$\left. - \eta_1\omega_1^{(1)} - 8\omega_1^{(1)} + 48 + 12\eta_1 + 2\eta_1^2\right] - 2\eta_1 (R_1^{(1)})^2(\omega_1^{(1)} - 12)\Big\},$$

$$\Delta_0^{(1)} = \frac{v_0\eta_1 [(\omega_1^{(1)})^2 - 2\eta_1(\omega_1^{(1)} - \omega_2^{(1)}) - 24\eta_1]}{l_1 R_1^{(1)} R_2^{(1)}(\omega_2^{(1)} - \omega_1^{(1)})},$$

$$\Delta_1^{(1)} = -\frac{v_0^2\eta_1}{l_1^2 (R_1^{(1)})^3 (R_2^{(1)})^3 (\omega_2^{(1)} - \omega_1^{(1)})^2}\left\{12\eta_1\left[\frac{1}{3}(\omega_1^{(1)})^3 - (8+\eta_1)(\omega_1^{(1)})^2 + \right.\right.$$

$$\left. + 12(4+\eta_1)\omega_1^{(1)} + 24\eta_1^2\right](R_2^{(1)})^2 + [(\omega_1^{(1)})^2 - 2\eta_1(\omega_1^{(1)} - \omega_2^{(1)}) -$$

$$- 24\eta_1][4\eta_1\omega_2^{(1)} - 96\eta_1 + 12\omega_1^{(1)}(4+\eta_1)](R_1^{(1)})^2 +$$

$$+ \omega_1^{(1)}(\omega_2^{(1)} - \omega_1^{(1)})(12 + 2\eta_1 - \omega_2^{(1)})[R_2^{(1)}R_1^{(1)}]^2\Big\},$$

$$\Delta_2^{(1)} = -\frac{2v_0\omega_1^{(1)}\eta_1[(\omega_2^{(1)})^2 + 2(\omega_2^{(1)} - \omega_1^{(1)})(3+\eta_1)]}{l_1\nu^{(1)}(\omega_2^{(1)} - \omega_1^{(1)})^2 R_1^{(1)} R_2^{(1)}},$$

$$\Delta_3^{(1)} = \frac{v_0 g\alpha\omega_1^{(1)}}{l_1^2 Q\nu^{(1)}[R_1^{(1)}R_2^{(1)}]^3(\omega_2^{(1)} - \omega_1^{(1)})^2}\left\{12\eta_1^2(R_1^{(1)})^2\left[\frac{1}{3}(\omega_1^{(1)})^2 - \right.\right.$$

$$\left. - 8\omega_1^{(1)} + 48 + 12\eta_1\right] + \eta_1(R_1^{(1)})^2\left[\frac{1}{3}(\omega_2^{(1)})^2 - 8\omega_2^{(1)} + 48 + 12\eta_1\right]\times$$

$$\times[(\omega_1^{(1)})^2 - 2\eta_1(\omega_1^{(1)} - \omega_2^{(1)}) - 24\eta_1] - 2(\omega_2^{(1)} - \omega_1^{(1)})(R_1^{(1)})^2\times$$

$$\times(12 + 3\eta_1 - \omega_2^{(1)})(\omega_2^{(1)} - 12 - 4\eta_1)\Big\},$$

$$\delta_1^{(1)} = \nu^{(1)} - \frac{g^2\alpha^2\left[\frac{1}{3}(\omega_1^{(1)})^2 - 8\omega_1^{(1)} + 48 + 12\eta_1\right]^2}{8\nu^{(1)} l_1^2 Q^2 (R_1^{(1)})^4},$$

$$\delta_2^{(1)} = \frac{v_0\nu^{(1)}\left[\frac{1}{3}(\omega_1^{(1)})^3 - (8+\eta_1)(\omega_1^{(1)})^2 + (48 + 12\eta_1)\omega_1^{(1)} + 24\eta_1^2\right]}{4l_1^2\omega_1^{(1)}(R_1^{(1)})^2},$$

$$\delta_3^{(1)} = -\frac{v_0\nu^{(1)}}{24 l_1^2(\omega_1^{(1)})^2(R_1^{(1)})^4}\left\{\frac{1}{3}(\omega_1^{(1)})^3 - (8+\eta_1)(\omega_1^{(1)})^2 + \right.$$

$$+ 12(4+\eta_1)\omega_1^{(1)} + 24\eta_1^2 - 4\omega_1^{(1)}\left[\frac{1}{3}(\omega_1^{(1)})^3 - (8+\eta_1)(\omega_1^{(1)})^2 + \right.$$

$$\left. + 12(4+\eta_1)\omega_1^{(1)} + 24\eta_1^2\right]\left[\frac{1}{3}(\omega_1^{(1)})^2 - (8+\eta_1)\omega_1^{(1)} + \right.$$

$$\left. + 12(4+\eta_1) + 2\eta_1^2\right] + 4(\omega_1^{(1)})^2\eta_1(R_1^{(1)})^2(\omega_1^{(1)} - 12 - 2\eta_1) -$$

$$- \frac{4\omega_1^{(1)}\eta_1 (R_1^{(1)})^2 (12 + 3\eta_1 - \omega_1^{(1)})}{(R_2^{(1)})^2 (\omega_2^{(1)} - \omega_1^{(1)})} [16\eta_1 + 4\eta_1^2 - \eta_1 (\omega_2^{(1)} + 2\omega_1^{(1)}) -$$

$$- 4\omega_1^{(1)}] [(\omega_1^{(1)})^2 - 2\eta_1 (\omega_1^{(1)} - \omega_2^{(1)}) - 24\eta_1]\}, \tag{10.17}$$

$N_1^{(1)}$, $N_2^{(1)}$, $\theta_1^{(1)}$, $\theta_2^{(1)}$ are constants of integration, determined from the initial conditions, and the coefficients $\nu^{(1)}$, $\bar{\beta}_1^{(1)}$, $\bar{\beta}_2^{(1)}$, $\bar{\Delta}_0^{(1)}$, $\bar{\Delta}_1^{(1)}$, $\bar{\delta}_1^{(1)}$, $\bar{\delta}_2^{(1)}$, $\bar{\delta}_3^{(1)}$, $\bar{\Delta}_2^{(1)}$, $\bar{\Delta}_3^{(1)}$ coincide with the coefficients ν, $\beta_1^{(1)}$, $\beta_2^{(1)}$, $\Delta_0^{(1)}$, $\Delta_1^{(1)}$, $\delta_1^{(1)}$, $\delta_2^{(1)}$, $\delta_3^{(1)}$, $\Delta_2^{(1)}$, $\Delta_3^{(1)}$, respectively, provided in the latter we change the quantities l_0, $\omega_1^{(1)}$, $R_1^{(1)}$, p_0 to the quantities l_1, $\omega_2^{(1)}$, $R_2^{(1)}$; $\omega_2^{(1)}$, $R_2^{(1)}$ to $\omega_1^{(1)}$, $R_1^{(1)}$, here $\omega_1^{(1)}$, $\omega_2^{(1)}$, $\mu_{11}^{(1)}$, $\mu_{21}^{(1)}$, $\mu_{12}^{(1)}$, $\mu_{22}^{(1)}$, $R_1^{(1)}$, $R_2^{(1)}$ are determined from Eqs. (10.8) and (10.9), in which η_0 must be changed to

$$\eta_1 = \frac{p_1}{Q}, \quad p_1 = l_1 q. \tag{10.18}$$

3. In order to solve the system of differential equations (10.1) on the third segment of ascent of the weight Q, we must, as before, represent this system in the form (6.1).

For this we introduce the new variables

$$\varphi = \frac{x_1 - x_2}{l_2}, \quad \psi = \frac{4x_2 - 3x_1}{3},$$

$$T = \omega_{02} t, \quad \tau = \varepsilon T, \tag{10.19}$$

where

$$\omega_{02} = \frac{c}{l_2}, \quad \varepsilon = \sqrt{\frac{V_0}{c}}. \tag{10.20}$$

Then

$$A(\tau, \varepsilon) = \sum_{s=0} \varepsilon^s A_s(\tau), \quad C(\tau, \varepsilon) = \sum_{s=0}^{4} \varepsilon^s C_s(\tau),$$

$$B(\tau, \varepsilon) = \sum_{s=0}^{6} \varepsilon^s B_s(\tau), \quad P(\tau, \varepsilon) = P_0, \tag{10.21}$$

where

$$A_0(\tau) = \begin{bmatrix} 1 & -1 \\ -1 & \frac{4}{3} \end{bmatrix}, \quad A_1(\tau) = \begin{bmatrix} -2 & 2 \\ 1 & -\frac{4}{3} \end{bmatrix} \tau,$$

$$A_2(\tau) = \begin{bmatrix} 1 & -1 \\ 0 & 0 \end{bmatrix} \tau^2, \quad A_3(\tau) = 2\begin{bmatrix} -1 & 1 \\ 0 & 0 \end{bmatrix} \delta_3^* \tau^3,$$

$$A_4(\tau) = (\delta_3^*)^2 \begin{bmatrix} 1 & -1 \\ 0 & 0 \end{bmatrix} \tau^4,$$

$$C_0(\tau) = f^{(1)} \begin{bmatrix} 3\left(\frac{4\gamma}{l_2} + \gamma_1\right) & -3\left(\frac{4\gamma}{l_2} + \frac{2}{3}\gamma_1\right) \\ -3\left(\frac{4\gamma}{l_2} + \frac{2}{3}\gamma_1\right) & 2\left(\frac{6\gamma}{l_2} + \frac{2}{3}\gamma_1\right) \end{bmatrix}$$

$$C_1(\tau) = \begin{bmatrix} -3(1 + 2f^{(1)}\gamma_1\tau) & 3\left(2\gamma_1 f^{(1)}\tau + \frac{4}{3}\right) \\ 4\gamma_1 f^{(1)}\tau & -2\left(2\gamma_1 f^{(1)}\tau + \frac{2}{3}\right) \end{bmatrix},$$

$$C_2(\tau) = \begin{bmatrix} 6(\delta_3^*\gamma_1 f^{(1)}\tau^2 + \delta_3^*\tau) & -6\left(\delta_3^* f^{(1)}\tau^2 + \frac{4}{3}\delta_3^*\tau\right) \\ -2(2\gamma_1 f^{(1)}\delta_3^*\tau^2 - 2\tau) & 4\left(\gamma_1 f^{(1)}\delta_3^*\tau^2 - \tau + \frac{2}{3}\delta_3^*\tau\right) \end{bmatrix},$$

$$C_3(\tau) = 6\delta_3^* \begin{bmatrix} 0 & 0 \\ 1 & -1 \end{bmatrix} \tau^2, \quad C_4(\tau) = 4(\delta_3^*)^2 \begin{bmatrix} 0 & 0 \\ -1 & 1 \end{bmatrix} \tau^2,$$

$$B_0(\tau) = \begin{bmatrix} 3(4 + \eta_2) & -3\left(4 + \frac{2}{3}\eta_2\right) \\ -3\left(4 + \frac{2}{3}\eta_2\right) & 4\left(3 + \frac{1}{3}\eta_2\right) \end{bmatrix},$$

$$B_1(\tau) = 2\eta_2\tau \begin{bmatrix} -3 & 3 \\ 2 & -2 \end{bmatrix},$$

$$B_2(\tau) = 2\eta_2\delta_3^*\tau^2 \begin{bmatrix} 3 & -3 \\ -2 & 2 \end{bmatrix}, \quad B_4(\tau) = 2\begin{bmatrix} -3 & 3 \\ 4 & -4 \end{bmatrix}, \quad B_3(\tau) \equiv 0.$$

$$B_5(\tau) = 8\delta_3^*\tau \begin{bmatrix} -3 & 3 \\ 4 & -4 \end{bmatrix}, \quad B_6(\tau) = 8(\delta_3^*)^2\tau^2 \begin{bmatrix} -3 & 3 \\ 4 & -4 \end{bmatrix},$$

$$P_0 = \frac{p_2}{K}\left(1 - \frac{a}{g}\right)\begin{bmatrix} -3 \\ 4 \end{bmatrix}, \quad \eta_2 = \frac{p_2}{Q}, \quad p_2 = l_2 q, \quad \delta_3^* = \frac{a l_2}{2v_0^2}. \tag{10.22}$$

The solution to system **(10.1)** on the third segment, in the second approximation, has the form

$$l_2\varphi = N_1^{(2)} e^{-(\beta_1^{(2)}t+\beta_2^{(2)}t^2)} \{[\mu_{11}^{(2)} - \mu_{21}^{(2)} +$$

$$+ (\mu_{12}^{(2)} - \mu_{22}^{(2)})(\Delta_0^{(2)}t + \Delta_1^{(2)}t^2) \sin(\delta_1^{(2)}t + \delta_2^{(2)}t^2 + \delta_3^{(2)}t^3 + \theta_1^{(2)}) +$$

$$+ (\mu_{22}^{(2)} - \mu_{12}^{(2)})(\Delta_2^{(2)} + \Delta_3^{(2)}t)\cos(\delta_1^{(2)}t + \delta_2^{(2)}t^2 + \delta_3^{(2)}t^3 + \theta_1^{(2)})\} +$$

$$+ N_2^{(2)} e^{-(\bar\beta_1 t+\bar\beta_2 t^2)} \{[\mu_{12}^{(2)} - \mu_{22}^{(2)} + (\mu_{11}^{(2)} - \mu_{21}^{(2)})(\bar\Delta_0^{(2)}t + \bar\Delta_1^{(2)}t^2)] \times$$

$$\times \sin(\bar\delta_1^{(2)}t + \bar\delta_2^{(2)}t^2 + \bar\delta_3^{(2)}t^3 + \theta_2^{(2)}) +$$

$$+ (\mu_{21}^{(2)} - \mu_{11}^{(2)})(\bar\Delta_2^{(2)} + \bar\Delta_3^{(2)}t)\cos(\bar\delta^{(2)}t + \bar\delta_2^{(2)}t^2 + \bar\delta_3^{(2)}t^3 +$$

$$+ \theta_2^{(2)})\} - \frac{p_2}{2K}\left(1 - \frac{a}{g}\right),$$

$$\psi = N_1^{(2)} e^{-(\beta_1^{(2)}t+\beta_2^{(2)}t^2)} \left\{\frac{4}{3}\mu_{21}^{(2)} - \mu_{11}^{(2)} + \left(\frac{4}{3}\mu_{22}^{(2)} - \mu_{12}^{(2)}\right)(\Delta_0^{(2)}t + \Delta_1^{(2)}t^2) \times\right.$$

$$\times \sin(\delta_1^{(2)}t + \delta_2^{(2)}t^2 + \delta_3^{(2)}t^3 + \theta_1^{(2)}) + \left(\mu_{12}^{(2)} - \frac{4}{3}\mu_{22}^{(2)}\right)(\Delta_2^{(2)} + \Delta_3^{(2)}t) \times$$

$$\left.\times \cos(\delta_1^{(2)}t + \delta_2^{(2)}t^2 + \delta_3^{(2)}t^3 + \theta_1^{(2)})\right\} + N_2^{(2)} e^{-(\bar\beta_1^{(2)}t+\bar\beta_2^{(2)}t^2)} \times$$

$$\times \left\{\left|\frac{4}{3}\mu_{22}^{(2)} - \mu_{12}^{(2)} + \left(\frac{4}{3}\mu_{21}^{(2)} - \mu_{11}^{(2)}\right)(\bar\Delta_0^{(2)}t + \bar\Delta_1^{(2)}t^2)\right| \sin(\bar\delta_1^{(2)}t +\right.$$

$$+ \bar\delta_2^{(2)}t^2 + \bar\delta_3^{(2)}t^3 + \theta_2^{(2)}) + \left(\mu_{11}^{(2)} - \frac{4}{3}\mu_{21}^{(2)}\right)(\Delta_2^{(2)} + \bar\Delta_3^{(2)}t) \times$$

$$\left.\times \cos(\bar\delta_1^{(2)}t + \bar\delta_2^{(2)}t^2 + \bar\delta_3^{(2)}t^3 + \theta_2^{(2)})\right\} + \frac{Q}{K}\left(1 - \frac{a}{g}\right) \times$$

$$\times \left[1 + \eta_2\left(1 - \frac{v_0}{l_2}t + \frac{a}{2l_2}t^2\right)\right], \qquad (10.23)$$

where $N_1^{(2)}$, $N_2^{(2)}$, $\theta_1^{(2)}$, $\theta_2^{(2)}$ are constants of integration and the coefficients $\beta_1^{(2)}$, $\beta_2^{(2)}$, $\Delta_0^{(2)}$, $\delta_1^{(2)}$, $\delta_2^{(2)}$, $\Delta_2^{(2)}$, $\Delta_3^{(2)}$, $\bar\beta_1^{(2)}$, $\bar\beta_2^{(2)}$, $\bar\Delta_0^{(2)}$, $\bar\delta_1^{(2)}$, $\bar\delta_2^{(2)}$, $\bar\Delta_2^{(2)}$, $\bar\Delta_3^{(2)}$ coincide with the coefficients $\beta_1^{(1)}$, $\beta_2^{(1)}$, $\Delta_0^{(1)}$, $\delta_1^{(1)}$, $\delta_2^{(1)}$, $\Delta_2^{(1)}$, $\Delta_3^{(1)}$, $\bar\beta_1^{(1)}$, $\bar\beta_2^{(1)}$, $\bar\Delta_0^{(1)}$, $\bar\delta_1^{(1)}$, $\bar\delta_2^{(1)}$, $\bar\Delta_2^{(1)}$, $\bar\Delta_3^{(1)}$, respectively, provided, in the latter, we change the quantities η_1, $\omega_1^{(1)}$, $\omega_2^{(1)}$, $R_1^{(1)}$, $R_2^{(1)}$ to the quantities η_2, $\omega_1^{(2)}$, $\omega_2^{(2)}$, $R_1^{(2)}$, $R_2^{(2)}$, respectively; these latter quantities are determined from Eqs. (10.8) and (10.9) after we first change η_0 to η_2.

The coefficients $\Delta_1^{(2)}$, $\delta_3^{(2)}$ are of the form

$$\Delta_1^{(2)} = -\frac{v_0\eta_2}{l_2^2(R_1^{(2)}R_2^{(2)})^3(\omega_2^{(2)} - \omega_1^{(2)})^2}\left\{12\eta_2^2\left|\frac{1}{3}(\omega_1^{(2)})^3 -\right.\right.$$

$$- (8 + \eta_2)(\omega_1^{(2)})^2 + 12(4 + \eta_2)\,\omega_1^{(2)} + 24\eta_2^{(2)}](R_2^{(2)})^2 +$$

$$+(R_1^{(2)})^2[(\omega_1^{(2)})^2-2\eta_2(\omega_1^{(2)}-\omega_2^{(2)})-24\eta_2][4\eta_2\omega_2^{(2)}-96\eta_2+$$
$$+12\omega_1^{(2)}(4+\eta_2)]+\omega_1^{(2)}(R_1^{(2)}R_2^{(2)})^2(\omega_2^{(2)}-\omega_1^{(2)})(12+2\eta_2-\omega_2^{(2)})-$$
$$-\omega_1^{(2)}(R_1^{(2)}R_2^{(2)})^2\delta_3^*(\omega_2^{(2)}-\omega_1^{(2)})(2\omega_2^{(2)}\eta_2+\omega_1^{(2)}\eta_2-24\eta_2-6\eta_2^2)+$$
$$+2\delta_3^{*2}\eta_2^2(R_1^{(2)}R_2^{(2)})^2(\omega_2^{(2)}-\omega_1^{(2)})[4\omega_2^{(2)}+3\omega_1^{(2)}-36-12\eta_2]\}$$

$$\delta_3^{(2)}=-\frac{v_0^2\nu^2}{24l_2^2(\omega_1^{(2)})^2(R_1^{(2)})^4}\left\{\left[\frac{1}{3}(\omega_1^{(2)})^3-(8+\eta_2)(\omega_1^{(2)})^2+\right.\right.$$
$$\left.+12(4+\eta_2)\omega_1^{(2)}+24\eta_2^2\right]^2-4\omega_1^{(2)}\left[\frac{1}{3}(\omega_1^{(2)})^3-(8+\eta_2)(\omega_1^{(2)})^2+\right.$$
$$\left.+12(4+\eta_2)\omega_1^{(2)}+24\eta_2^2\right]\left[\frac{1}{3}(\omega_1^{(2)})^2-(8+\eta_2)\omega_1^{(2)}+12(4+\eta_2)+\right.$$
$$\left.+2\eta_2^2\right]+4\eta_2(\omega_1^{(2)}R_1^{(2)})^2(\omega_1^{(2)}-12-2\eta_2)-$$
$$-\frac{4\eta_2\omega_1^{(2)}(R_1^{(2)})^2(12+3\eta_2-\omega_1^{(2)})}{(R_2^{(2)})^2(\omega_2^{(2)}-\omega_1^{(2)})}[4\eta_2^2-\eta_2(\omega_2^{(2)}+2\omega_1^{(2)}-16)-4\omega_1^{(2)}]\times$$
$$\times[(\omega_1^{(2)})^2-2\eta_2(\omega_1^{(2)}-\omega_2^{(2)}+12)]+$$
$$+4\omega_1^{(2)}(R_1^{(2)})^2\delta_3^*\left[\frac{1}{3}(\omega_1^{(2)})^2-(8+\eta_2)\omega_1^{(2)}+12(4+\eta_2)+2\eta_2^2\right]-$$
$$\left.-8\omega_1^{(2)}\delta_3^*(\eta_2R_1^{(2)})^2(\omega_1^{(2)}-12)\right\}, \tag{10.24}$$

$\nu^{(2)}$ coincides with $\nu^{(1)}$, if in the latter we change the quantities $\omega_1^{(1)}$, l_1, p_1 to the quantities $\omega_1^{(2)}$, l_2, p_2.

In order to obtain the constant coefficients $\overline{\delta}_3^{(2)}$, $\overline{\Delta}_1^{(2)}$, we must, in the coefficients $\delta_3^{(2)}$, $\Delta_1^{(2)}$ substitute $\omega_2^{(2)}$, $R_2^{(2)}$ in place of $\omega_1^{(2)}$, $R_1^{(2)}$ and $\omega_1^{(2)}$, $R_1^{(2)}$ in place of $\omega_2^{(2)}$, $R_2^{(2)}$.

The characteristic functions $\mu_{11}^{(2)}$, $\mu_{21}^{(2)}$, $\mu_{12}^{(2)}$, $\mu_{22}^{(2)}$ are determined from the relationships (10.8), where η_0, ω_1, ω_2, R_1, R_2 are changed to the quantities η_2, $\omega_1^{(2)}$, $\omega_2^{(2)}$, $R_1^{(2)}$, $R_2^{(2)}$, respectively.

4. Beginning from the asymptotic solution (10.16) we can find, for a given coefficient α, the limiting value of the velocity $v_{\lim}(v<v_{\lim})$, at which the stresses T_1 will be damped out. This relationship is of the form

$$\alpha>\frac{vQ}{2g}\left\{1+\frac{\eta_1[(\omega_2^{(1)})^2-24\omega_2^{(1)}-24\eta_1]}{\frac{1}{3}(\omega_2^{(1)})^3+48\omega_2^{(1)}+12\eta_1\omega_2^{(1)}-8(\omega_2^{(1)})^2}\right\}. \tag{10.25}$$

As an illustration of the nature of the variation of the stresses in a visco-elastic thread during the first stage, we used the obtained formulas to calculate the stresses in the case of the following data:

$$Q = 20.10\ kG, \quad \eta_0 = 0.555, \quad \alpha = 3.10\ kG\cdot sec,$$
$$a = 0.1\ grams, \quad v_0 = 14.028 \quad K = 20{,}791{,}284\ kG$$
$$q = 11.5625\ kG/meter, \quad l_0 = 1200\ meters. \tag{10.26}$$

The nature of the variation of the stresses arising at the upper end of the thread during the first segment of motion of the weight Q is shown in Table 1, from which it is clear that

$$\max T_1 = 56{,}502\ kG.$$

According to the formula proposed by Savin [62], max T_1 for these numerical data is approximately equal to 56,300 kG.

Consequently, the deviation of the obtained numerical results does not exceed 0.36%.

11. The Boundary-Value Problem for a System of Second-Order Linear Differential Equations

In this section we will apply the asymptotic method discussed in Secs. 7 and 8 to finding the large characteristic values of the boundary-value problem defined by the system of differential equations

$$A(t,\lambda)\frac{d^2x}{dt_1^2} + C(t_1, \lambda)\frac{dx}{dt_1} + \lambda B(t_1, \lambda)x = 0 \tag{11.1}$$

and certain regular boundary conditions

$$\begin{aligned} G_1x'(1) + F_1x'(0) + G_0x(1) + F_0x(0) &= 0, \\ K_1x'(1) + M_1x'(0) + K_0x(1) + M_0x(0) &= 0, \end{aligned} \tag{11.2}$$

where $x(t_1)$ is an n-dimensional vector; G_i, F_i, K_i, M_i $(i = 0,1)$ are real constant nth order matrices.

Let

$$A(t_1, \lambda) = \sum_{s=0}^{\infty} \lambda^{-\frac{s}{2}} A_s(t_1), \quad B(t_1, \lambda) = \sum_{s=0}^{\infty} \lambda^{-\frac{s}{2}} B_s(t_1),$$

$$C(t_1, \lambda) = \sum_{s=0}^{\infty} \lambda^{-\frac{s}{2}} C_s(t_1).$$

Table 1

Time	Stresses	Time	Stresses	Time	Stresses
0	39352.620	4.8	30479.357	9.6	29210.112
0.1	42573.397	4.9	32284.290	9.7	28707.524
0.2	45788.894	5.0	34655.016	9.8	29087.609
0.3	49021.606	5.1	37592.388	9.9	30332.945
0.4	52001.039	5.2	40923.297	10.0	32281.005
0.5	54301.511	5.3	44309.865	10.1	34771.094
0.6	55731.732	5.4	47476.980	10.2	37717.260
0.7	56422.576	5.5	50332.247	10.3	40988.291
0.8	56501.583	5.6	52825.185	10.4	44377.104
0.9	55845.971	5.7	54769.648	10.5	47553.284
1.0	54266.623	5.8	55913.501	10.6	50343.786
1.1	51825.152	5.9	56154.410	10.7	52657.586
1.2	48965.116	6.0	55594.147	10.8	54366.837
1.3	45899.545	6.1	54355.548	10.9	55288.120
1.4	42687.063	6.2	52443.353	11.0	55342.510
1.5	39318.480	6.3	49849.307	11.1	54513.562
1.6	37279.770	6.4	46737.206	11.2	52985.818
1.7	33239.566	6.5	43417.648	11.3	50792.171
1.8	31179.940	6.6	40142.418	11.4	47994.059
1.9	29804.763	6.7	37012.561	11.5	44777.627
2.0	29030.267	6.8	34119.724	11.6	41421.415
2.1	28980.409	6.9	31683.526	11.7	38147.349
2.2	29860.796	7.0	29969.118	11.8	35088.577
2.3	31648.680	7.1	29090.894	11.9	32402.821
2.4	34056.040	7.2	28990.618	12.0	30320.574
2.5	36813.442	7.3	29611.300	12.1	29023.967
2.6	39868.327	7.4	30993.338	12.2	28549.198
2.7	43221.337	7.5	33151.370	12.3	28862.502
2.8	46660.444	7.6	35923.347	12.4	29972.424
2.9	49797.745	7.7	39030.001	12.5	31878.007
3.0	52361.788	7.8	42260.509	12.6	34447.935
3.1	54336.129	7.9	45517.610	12.7	37447.681
3.2	55753.387	8.0	48668.154	12.8	40678.168
3.3	56490.459	8.1	51453.105	12.9	44001.031
3.4	56313.671	8.2	53607.145	13.0	47226.009
3.5	55195.037	8.3	55020.619	13.1	50084.082
3.6	53352.077	8.4	55710.183	13.2	52354.948
3.7	51015.012	8.5	55656.230	13.3	53945.086
3.8	48238.108	8.6	54770.001	13.4	54796.801
3.9	45029.316	8.7	53041.559	13.5	54809.567
4.0	41562.733	8.8	50637.484	13.6	53926.561
4.1	38216.958	8.9	47792.571	13.7	52236.770
4.2	35269.503	9.0	44657.890	13.8	49905.672
4.3	32784.362	9.1	41327.916	13.9	47057.204
4.4	30770.061	9.2	37987.901	14.0	43812.225
4.5	29383.199	9.3	34929.004	14.1	40394.533
4.6	28861.296	9.4	32393.694	14.2	37086.889
4.7	29278.078	9.5	30474.617	14.3	34095.294

Setting

$$t_1 = \varepsilon t = \tau, \quad \varepsilon = \frac{1}{\sqrt{\lambda}},$$

we transform system (11.1) to the form (7.27):

$$A(\tau, \varepsilon)\frac{d^2x}{dt^2} + \varepsilon C(\tau, \varepsilon)\frac{dx}{dt} + B(\tau, \varepsilon)x = 0. \tag{11.3}$$

Here $A(\tau, \varepsilon), B(\tau, \varepsilon), C(\tau, \varepsilon)$ are matrices which satisfy the conditions of Sec. 6. On the basis of the calculations of Sec. 7, the particular solutions of the system of equations (11.3) are of the form

$$x_\nu(\tau, \varepsilon) = \Pi_\nu(\tau, \varepsilon)e^{\frac{1}{\varepsilon}\int_0^\tau D_\nu(\tau,\varepsilon)d\tau}\left[C_{1\nu}\cos\frac{1}{\varepsilon}\int_0^\tau \Omega_\nu(\tau, \varepsilon)\,d\tau + \right.$$

$$\left. + C_{2\nu}\sin\frac{1}{\varepsilon}\int_0^\tau \Omega_\nu(\tau, \varepsilon)\,d\tau\right], \tag{11.4}$$

where $C_{1\nu}, C_{2\nu}$ $(\nu = 1, 2, \ldots, n)$ are constants of integration.

The general solution of system (11.1) is written in the following way:

$$X(\tau,\varepsilon) = X_1(\tau, \varepsilon)C_1 + X_2(\tau, \varepsilon)C_2; \tag{11.5}$$

where $X_1(\tau, \varepsilon)$, $X_2(\tau, \varepsilon)$ are fundamental matrices of the solutions of the system (11.1); these matrices are of the form

$$X_1(\tau, \varepsilon) = \left[\Pi_\nu(\tau, \varepsilon)e^{\frac{1}{\varepsilon}\int_0^\tau D_\nu(\tau,\varepsilon)d\tau}\cos\frac{1}{\varepsilon}\int_0^\tau \Omega_\nu(\tau, \varepsilon)\,d\tau\right],$$

$$X_2(\tau, \varepsilon) = \left[\Pi_\nu(\tau, \varepsilon)e^{\frac{1}{\varepsilon}\int_0^\tau D_\nu(\tau,\varepsilon)d\tau}\sin\frac{1}{\varepsilon}\int_0^\tau \Omega_\nu(\tau,\varepsilon)\,d\tau\right] \quad (\nu=1, 2, \ldots, n), \tag{11.6}$$

C_1, C_2 are constant n-dimensional vectors which are determined from the boundary conditions (11.2).

Substituting the solution $X(\tau, \varepsilon)$ into the boundary conditions (11.2), we obtain a system of algebraic equations with respect to C_1 and C_2. As is well known, in order that there be a nontrivial solution to this system it is necessary and sufficient that its determinant be equal to zero. Setting the given determinant equal to zero, we find the trancendental equation for determining the characteristic values of the boundary-value problem.

As an example, we will consider a case which is often encountered in practice, i.e., when the boundary conditions (11.2) take the form

$$X(0) = 0, \quad X(1) = 0. \tag{11.7}$$

In this case, the characteristic values can be calculated very easily.

In fact, since, according to (11.6),

$$X_1(0, \varepsilon) \neq 0, \quad X_2(0, \varepsilon) = 0, \tag{11.8}$$

the first condition in (11.7) can be satisfied by setting $C_1 = 0$ in (11.5). Consequently,

$$X(\tau, \varepsilon) = X_2(\tau, \varepsilon)\, C_2. \tag{11.9}$$

Using the second condition in (11.7) we obtain

$$X_2(1, \varepsilon)\, C_2 = 0. \tag{11.10}$$

The system of equations (11.10) will have a nontrivial solution if and only if

$$\det |X_2(1, \varepsilon)| = \left| \Pi_\nu(\tau, \varepsilon)\, e^{\frac{1}{\varepsilon}\int_0^1 D_\nu(\tau,\varepsilon)d\tau} \sin \frac{1}{\varepsilon} \int_0^1 \Omega_\nu(\tau, \varepsilon)\, d\tau \right| = 0,$$

$$\nu = 1, 2, \ldots, n, \tag{11.11}$$

from which

$$\det [X_2(1, \varepsilon)] = e^{\frac{1}{\varepsilon}\int_0^1 \sum_{\nu=1}^{n} D_\nu(\tau,\varepsilon)d\tau} \prod_{\nu=1}^{n} \sin \frac{1}{\varepsilon} \int_0^1 \Omega_\nu(\tau, \varepsilon)\, d\tau \,|\, \Pi_\nu(\tau, \varepsilon)|_{\nu=1}^{n} = 0. \tag{11.12}$$

From Eq. (11.12) it follows that

$$\sin \frac{1}{\varepsilon} \int_0^1 \Omega_\nu(\tau, \varepsilon)\, d\tau = 0, \quad \nu = 1, 2, \ldots, n,$$

or

$$\int_0^1 \Omega_\nu(\tau, \varepsilon)\, d\tau = K_\nu \pi \varepsilon, \quad K_\nu = 1, 2, 3, \ldots .$$

Taking into consideration (7.3) we obtain

$$\int_0^1 [\Omega_{\nu 0}(\tau) + \varepsilon \Omega_{\nu 1}(\tau) + \ldots + \varepsilon^m \Omega_{\nu m}(\tau) + O(\varepsilon^{m+1})]\, d\tau = K_\nu \varepsilon \pi. \qquad (11.13)$$

Consequently, for the zero approximation we have

$$\lambda_{\nu,k}^{(0)} = \frac{[\pi K_\nu - O(1)]^2}{\left(\int_0^1 \sqrt{\omega_\nu(\tau)}\, d\tau \right)^2}. \qquad (11.14)$$

Setting $m = 1$ in (11.13), we find

$$\lambda_{\nu,k}^{(1)} = \frac{\left[\pi K_\nu - \int_0^1 \Omega_{\nu 1}(\tau)\, d\tau - O\left(\frac{1}{\sqrt{\lambda}} \right) \right]^2}{\left(\int_0^1 \sqrt{\omega_\nu(\tau)}\, d\tau \right)^2}$$

In this manner we can easily obtain the second approximation, and subsequent approximations, for the characteristic values $\lambda_{\nu,k}$.

We will illustrate the above with some examples.

Example. 1. We wish to find the characteristic values of the following boundary-value problem:

$$y'' + \lambda(1 + x) y = 0, \quad y(0) = y(1) = 0.$$

We seek a solution in the form

$$y = \xi, \quad \frac{d\xi}{dt} = [D(\tau, \varepsilon) + i\Omega(\tau, \varepsilon)]\, \xi, \quad x = \varepsilon t = \tau, \quad \varepsilon = \frac{1}{\sqrt{\lambda}}.$$

According to the formulas of Sec. 7, we find

$$\Omega_0(\tau) = \pm\sqrt{1+\tau}, \quad \Omega_1(\tau) = 0, \quad D_1(\tau) = -\frac{1}{8(1+\tau)},$$

$$\Omega_2(\tau) = \pm\frac{5}{32(1+\tau)^{5/2}}, \quad D_2(\tau) = 0.$$

From Eq. (11.13) we have $\varepsilon = 2.553$; $\lambda = 6.52$. The exact solution of this problem is $\lambda = 6.55$ (compare with the example in [26]).

Example 2. Find the characteristic values of the boundary-value problem

$$y^{(IV)} - \lambda(1+x)y = 0,$$

$$y(0) = y''(0) = 0, \quad y(1) = y''(1) = 0. \tag{11.15}$$

First, we must transform this equation to the form (11.3). We make the change of variables

$$y = u_1, \qquad \frac{d^2y}{dx^2} = u_2.$$

In addition, in order to obtain symmetric matrices, we introduce the matrix $V(x) = \begin{bmatrix} 1 & 0 \\ 0 & \sqrt{\lambda(1+x)} \end{bmatrix}$. Then, setting $u = V(x)z$, $x = \varepsilon t = \tau$, $\varepsilon = \frac{1}{\sqrt[4]{\lambda}}$,

where

$$u = \begin{bmatrix} u_1 \\ u_2 \end{bmatrix}, \qquad z = \begin{bmatrix} z_1 \\ z_2 \end{bmatrix},$$

we reduce problem (11.15) to the form

$$\frac{d^2z}{dt^2} + \varepsilon C(\tau, \varepsilon)\frac{dz}{dt} + B(\tau, \varepsilon)z = 0, \tag{11.16}$$

where

$$C(\tau, \varepsilon) = \begin{bmatrix} 0 & 0 \\ 0 & \frac{1}{1+\tau} \end{bmatrix}, \quad B(\tau, \varepsilon) = \begin{bmatrix} 0 & \sqrt{1+\tau} \\ \sqrt{1+\tau} & -\frac{\varepsilon^2}{4(1+\tau)^2} \end{bmatrix},$$

$$Z_1(0) = Z_2(0) = 0; \quad Z_1(1) = Z_2(1) = 0.$$

In the given case $\Omega_{\nu 0}(\tau) = \pm\sqrt{\omega_\nu(\tau)}$.

$$\omega_\nu(\tau) = \pm\sqrt{1+\tau}, \quad \Omega_1(\tau) = 0, \quad \nu = 1, 2,$$

$$D_1(\tau) = -\frac{1}{8(1+\tau)}, \quad \mu = \pm\frac{\sqrt{2}}{2}\begin{bmatrix} 1 & 1 \\ 1 & -1 \end{bmatrix}.$$

It is easy to see that in the first approximation $\lambda = 65.8$. This example is taken from [27], where in the first approximation $\underline{\lambda} = 63.2$, $\overline{\lambda} = 67.2$, mean value of $\lambda = 65.2$. Here $\underline{\lambda}$ and $\overline{\lambda}$ are, respectively, the upper and lower approximations to the solution, determined by Chaplygin's method.

Chapter 3

ASYMPTOTIC DECOMPOSITION OF A SYSTEM OF LINEAR DIFFERENTIAL EQUATIONS

12. Formulation of the Problem

In the previous chapters we considered the question of constructing asymptotic solutions to one second-order differential equation and to a system of n such equations in the case of simple characteristic values. However, the method which we discussed would be inapplicable if, among the roots of the characteristic equation, there appeared multiple roots on the whole interval $[0, L]$ or at separate points of the interval.

In such case, a given system of differential equations of higher order can be simplified by means of asymptotic decomposition of the original system into several subsystems of lower order. This will be the subject of the present chapter.

We consider a system of linear differential equations of the form

$$\frac{dx}{dt} = A(\tau, \varepsilon)\, x, \tag{12.1}$$

where $x(t, \varepsilon)$ is an n-dimensional vector; $A(\tau, \varepsilon)$ is a real square matrix of order n; $\tau = \varepsilon t$ and $\varepsilon > 0$ is a small parameter.

We will assume that the following conditions are fulfilled:

1. The matrix $A(\tau, \varepsilon)$ admits the expansion

$$A(\tau, \varepsilon) = \sum_{s=0}^{\infty} \varepsilon^s A_s(\tau) \tag{12.2}$$

and is infinitely differentiable (i.e., all of its elements are infinitely differentiable) with respect to τ on the closed interval $[0, L]$ where $L > 0$ is a fixed number.

In particular, the matrix $A(\tau, \varepsilon)$ can be some polynomial in ε.

2. The roots $\lambda_j(\tau)$ $(j = 1, 2, \ldots, n)$ of the characteristic equation of the matrix $A_0(\tau)$

$$D(\lambda) \equiv \det [A_0(\tau) - \lambda(\tau) E] = 0, \tag{12.3}$$

for $\tau \in [0, L]$ form two isolated groups, i.e., such that $\lambda_i(\tau) \neq \lambda_j(\tau)$, where $i = 1, 2, \ldots, r_1$; $j = r_1 + 1, r_1 + 2, \ldots, n$; $n - r_1 = r_2$. Within each group the roots can have an arbitrary multiplicity (and the multiplicity can be different for different values of τ).

We shall show that, given the above assumptions, the system (12.1) can be asymptotically decomposed into two independent systems; the sum of the orders of these two systems will be equal to the order of the original system.

In constructing an algorithm for the decomposition, we will have to use the nonsingular matrix $V(\tau)$, which transforms $A_0(\tau)$ to quasi-diagonal (block-diagonal) form

$$W_0(\tau) \equiv V^{-1}(\tau) A_0(\tau) V(\tau) = \begin{bmatrix} W_{10}(\tau) & 0 \\ 0 & W_{20}(\tau) \end{bmatrix}, \tag{12.4}$$

where $W_{10}(\tau)$ is a square matrix of order r_1 with characteristic values from the first group $\lambda_i(\tau)$; $W_{20}(\tau)$ is a square matrix of order r_2 with characteristic values from the second group $\lambda_j(\tau)$ $(i = 1, 2, \ldots, r_1; j = r_1 + 1, \ r_1 + 2, \ldots, n; \ r_1 + r_2 = n)$.

As is well known, if condition 2 is fulfilled then we can find an invertible matrix $V(\tau)$ for every $\tau \in [0, L]$. The construction and properties of the matrix $V(\tau)$ will be considered in detail in Sec. 14.

13. Formal Decomposition

The possibility of formal decomposition of a system of linear differential equations (12.1) into two independent subsystems is established by the following theorem.

Theorem III.1. *If the matrix $A(\tau, \varepsilon)$ satisfies conditions 1) and 2) of Sec. 12, then a formal solution of the system (12.1) can be represented in the form*

$$x(t, \varepsilon) = U(\tau, \varepsilon)\, \xi(t, \varepsilon), \tag{13.1}$$

where $U(\tau, \varepsilon)$ *is a square matrix of order n, and the n-dimensional vector* $\xi(t, \varepsilon)$ *satisfies the equation*

$$\frac{d\xi}{dt} = \mathfrak{A}(\tau, \varepsilon)\,\xi, \tag{13.2}$$

in which the matrix $\mathfrak{A}(\tau, \varepsilon)$ *has the quasi-diagonal structure*

$$\mathfrak{A}(\tau, \varepsilon) = \begin{bmatrix} \mathfrak{A}_1(\tau, \varepsilon) & 0 \\ 0 & \mathfrak{A}_2(\tau, \varepsilon) \end{bmatrix}, \tag{13.3}$$

and $\mathfrak{A}_k(\tau, \varepsilon)$ *are square matrices of order* r_k $(k = 1,2)$.

It is assumed that the matrices $U(\tau, \varepsilon)$, $\mathfrak{A}(\tau, \varepsilon)$ [*and consequently the matrices* $\mathfrak{A}_k(\tau, \varepsilon)$] *admit formal expansions of the form*

$$U(\tau, \varepsilon) = \sum_{s=0}^{\infty} \varepsilon^s U_s(\tau), \tag{13.4}$$

$$\mathfrak{A}(\tau, \varepsilon) = \sum_{s=0}^{\infty} \varepsilon^s \mathfrak{A}_s(\tau) \quad \text{and} \quad \mathfrak{A}_k(\tau, \varepsilon) = \sum_{s=0}^{\infty} \varepsilon^s \mathfrak{A}_{ks}(\tau). \tag{13.5}$$

Thus, in accordance with the structure of the matrix $\mathfrak{A}(\tau, \varepsilon)$, Eq. (13.2) can be considered as a system of two independent subsystems, where

$$\xi(t, \varepsilon) = \begin{bmatrix} \xi_1(t, \varepsilon) \\ \xi_2(t, \varepsilon) \end{bmatrix} \text{and } \frac{d\xi_1}{dt} = \mathfrak{A}_1(\tau, \varepsilon)\,\xi_1, \quad \frac{d\xi_2}{dt} = \mathfrak{A}_2(\tau, \varepsilon)\,\xi_2.$$

(The orders of the two subsystems are r_1 and r_2, respectively.)

The proof of Theorem III.1 will consist of constructing an algorithm whereby we can determine the terms of the expansions (13.4) and (13.5). Thus, we substitute expression (13.1) into system (12.1), taking account also of (13.2). In the identity obtained in this fashion, we equate the coefficients of the vector function $\xi(t, \varepsilon)$, as a result of which we obtain the matrix differential equation

$$\varepsilon\frac{dU}{d\tau} + U(\tau, \varepsilon)\,\mathfrak{A}(\tau, \varepsilon) = A(\tau, \varepsilon)\,U(\tau, \varepsilon), \tag{13.6}$$

which the desired matrices $U(\tau, \varepsilon)$ and $\mathfrak{A}(\tau, \varepsilon)$ must satisfy.

If in Eq. (13.6) we successively separate out the terms in front of like powers of the parameter ε, then we obtain an infinite system of algebraic matrix equations for determination of the unknown elements in the expansions (13.4), (13.5):

$$A_0(\tau)U_0(\tau) - U_0(\tau)\mathfrak{A}_0(\tau) = 0,$$

$$A_0(\tau)U_1(\tau) - U_1(\tau)\mathfrak{A}_0(\tau) = U_0(\tau)\mathfrak{A}_1(\tau) - A_1(\tau)U_0(\tau) + \\ + \frac{dU_0}{d\tau} \equiv U_0(\tau)\mathfrak{A}_1(\tau) + B_1(\tau),$$

. . . .

$$A_0(\tau)U_s(\tau) - U_s(\tau)\mathfrak{A}_0(\tau) = U_0(\tau)\mathfrak{A}_s(\tau) + B_s(\tau), \tag{13.7}$$

where

$$B_s(\tau) = \sum_{j=1}^{s-1} U_j(\tau)\mathfrak{A}_{s-j}(\tau) - \sum_{j=1}^{s} A_j(\tau)U_{s-j}(\tau) + \frac{dU_{s-1}}{d\tau}. \tag{13.8}$$

(The matrix $B_s(\tau)$ comprises unknown matrices with index numbers less than s, and derivatives with respect to τ of the matrix $U_{s-1}(\tau)$.)

We will henceforth assume that all the necessary derivatives with respect to τ of the elements of $U_s(\tau)$ exist. The question of proving the differentiability of the matrix $U_s(\tau)$ will be considered in Sec. 14.

Multiplying both sides of each of the equations of system (13.6) on the left by the matrix $V^{-1}(\tau)$ [see Sec. 12] and, introducing the new unknown matrix

$$Q(\tau) = V^{-1}(\tau)U_s(\tau), \tag{13.9}$$

we obtain, according to (13.7), the following system of equations

$$W_0(\tau)Q_0(\tau) - Q_0(\tau)\mathfrak{A}_0(\tau) = 0,$$

. . . .

$$W_0(\tau)Q_s(\tau) - Q_s(\tau)\mathfrak{A}_0(\tau) = Q_0(\tau)\mathfrak{A}_s(\tau) + F_s(\tau), \tag{13.10}$$

where

$$F_s(\tau) = V^{-1}(\tau)B_s(\tau), \qquad s = 1, 2, 3, \ldots . \tag{13.11}$$

Proceeding to the solution of system (13.10), we begin by considering the first equation.

Let

$$Q_0(\tau) = E, \tag{13.12}$$

where E is a unit matrix of order n.

Then, according to the first equation of system (13.10),

$$\mathfrak{A}_0(\tau) = W_0(\tau), \tag{13.13}$$

and the last equation of (13.10) can be rewritten in the form

$$W_0(\tau) Q_s(\tau) - Q_s(\tau) W_0(\tau) = \mathfrak{A}_s(\tau) + F_s(\tau), \quad s = 1, 2, \ldots. \tag{13.14}$$

Having determined the zero term of the expansion of the matrix $U(\tau, \varepsilon)$ in accordance with (13.9) and (13.12)

$$U_0(\tau) = V(\tau), \tag{13.15}$$

we can pass to solution of Eqs. (13.14) for $s \geqslant 1$. We note that, by (13.8) and (13.11), the matrix $F_s(\tau)$ consists only of those terms of the expansions (13.4), (13.5) whose index numbers are less than s. Thus, in successive solution ($s = 1, 2, \ldots$) of Eqs. (13.14), we should consider the matrix $F_s(\tau)$ as being known.

In constructing a solution of Eq. (13.14), we divide the matrices $Q_s(\tau)$ and $F_s(\tau)$ into blocks, corresponding to the quasi-diagonal structure (block-diagonal structure) of the known matrix $W_0(\tau)$ and the desired matrix $\mathfrak{A}(\tau, \varepsilon)$ [see (12.4) and (13.3)]:

$$Q_s(\tau) = \begin{bmatrix} Q_{11s}(\tau) & Q_{12s}(\tau) \\ Q_{21s}(\tau) & Q_{22s}(\tau) \end{bmatrix}, \qquad F_s(\tau) = \begin{bmatrix} F_{11s}(\tau) & F_{12s}(\tau) \\ F_{21s}(\tau) & F_{22s}(\tau) \end{bmatrix}, \tag{13.16}$$

where $Q_{ijs}(\tau)$ and $F_{ijs}(\tau)$ are matrices of the order (r_i, r_j) ($i = 1, 2$; $j = 1, 2$). Then Eq. (13.14) can be represented in the form of the following equivalent system of matrix equations:

$$W_{i0}(\tau) Q_{ijs}(\tau) - Q_{ijs}(\tau) W_{j0}(\tau) = \delta_{ij} \mathfrak{A}_{is}(\tau) + F_{ijs}(\tau), \tag{13.17}$$

where δ_{ij} is the Kronecker delta; $i, j = 1, 2$. Let us find the solution of this system.

Let $i = j$ and

$$Q_{iis} = E_{r_i} \tag{13.18}$$

(E_{r_i} is a unit matrix of order r_i).

In this case, by (13.17), we find

$$\mathfrak{A}_{is}(\tau) = -F_{iis}(\tau) \qquad (i = 1, 2). \tag{13.19}$$

For $i \neq j$ Eq. (13.17) can be presented in the form

$$W_{i0}(\tau)Q_{ijs}(\tau) - Q_{ijs}(\tau)W_{j0}(\tau) = F_{ijs}(\tau). \tag{13.20}$$

From Eq. (13.20) the unknown matrix $Q_{ijs}(\tau)$ $(i \neq j)$ is determined uniquely, since the corresponding homogeneous equation

$$W_{i0}(\tau)Q_{iis}(\tau) - Q_{ijs}(\tau)W_{j0}(\tau) = 0 \tag{13.21}$$

has only the zero solution.

This last assertion is a consequence of the fact that the matrices $W_{i0}(\tau)$ and $W_{j0}(\tau)$ $(i \neq j)$, for any $\tau \in [0, L]$, according to assumption 2) of Sec. 12, do not have any equal characteristic values (see Chap. VIII of [15]).

Thus, having determined from system (13.17) the square matrices (blocks) of matrix $Q_s(\tau)$, we can set up the matrix $Q_s(\tau)$ itself; consequently, we can determine the corresponding term of the expansion of the matrix $U(\tau, \varepsilon)$:

$$U_s(\tau) = V(\tau)Q_s(\tau). \tag{13.22}$$

Thus, the method of solution described here shows us how to find the elements of the formal expansions (13.4), (13.5),i.e., the matrices $U_s(\tau)$ and $\mathfrak{A}_s(\tau)$ for any number $s = 0, 1, 2, \ldots$.

To complete the description of the algorithm for formal decomposition of the system (12.1), we must show that when the conditions of Theorem III.1 are fulfilled, the matrices $U_s(\tau)$ are differentiable with respect to τ a sufficient number of times. We consider this question in detail in the next section.

14. Construction of the Transforming Matrix and Differentiability of the Formal Solution

Before proceeding to an investigation of the differentiability of the matrices $U_s(\tau)$ $(s = 0, 1, 2, \ldots)$ with respect to τ, we will prove the following lemma.

Lemma III.1. *If the matrix $A_0(\tau)$ has, on the closed interval [0, L], a certain number of derivatives with respect to τ, then we can choose the nonsingular transforming matrix $V(\tau)$ in such a way so that it, and consequently the block diagonal matrix $W_0(\tau)$ as well [see (12.4)], have the same number of derivatives on [0, L] as does the matrix $A_0(\tau)$.*

Proof. To construct the transforming matrix $V(\tau)$, we decompose the space R_n into the direct sum of two subspaces which are invariant with respect to the matrix $A_0(\tau)$, and which correspond to the two groups of characteristic values. The indicated decomposition, as is well known [68], can be accomplished by using the matrices $P_1(A_0)$ and $P_2(A_0)$, which are projections in the sense that

$$P_k^2(A_0) = P_k(A_0) \quad (k = 1, 2). \tag{14.1'}$$

These matrices have the following properties:

$$P_1(A_0) + P_2(A_0) = E, \qquad A_0 P_k = P_k A_0 \qquad (k = 1, 2),$$
$$P_1(A_0) P_2(A_0) = P_2(A_0) P_1(A_0) = 0. \tag{14.1''}$$

We shall recall the way in which the matrices $P_k(A_0)$ are constructed.

In accordance with assumption 2) of Sec. 12, we represent the characteristic polynomial $D(\lambda)$ of the matrix $A_0(\tau)$ in the form of a product of two relatively prime factors, each of which corresponds to one of the groups of characteristic values

$$D(\lambda) = D_1(\lambda) D_2(\lambda), \tag{14.2}$$

where $D_1(\lambda)$ is an r_1th-degree polynomial; $D_2(\lambda)$ is an r_2th-degree polynomial; $(r_1 + r_2 = n)$.

By (14.2) we have the formula

$$\frac{1}{D(\lambda)} = \frac{d_1(\lambda)}{D_1(\lambda)} + \frac{d_2(\lambda)}{D_2(\lambda)},$$

and consequently the identity

$$E = d_1(A_0) D_2(A_0) + d_2(A_0) D_1(A_0) \tag{14.3}$$

holds.

Here $d_k(\lambda)$ is a polynomial of degree no higher than $r_k - 1$, which is relatively prime with respect to $D_k(\lambda)$ $(k = 1, 2)$.

We denote

$$P_1(A_0) = d_1(A_0) D_2(A_0),$$
$$P_2(A_0) = d_2(A_0) D_1(A_0). \tag{14.4}$$

Using Eq. (14.3) and Cayley's identity $D(A_0) = 0$, it is not hard to convince oneself of the validity of Eqs. (14.1′) and (14.1″), i.e., the matrices $P_1(A_0)$ and $P_2(A_0)$ actually decompose the space R_n into a complete system of subspaces P_1R_n and P_2R_n, which are invariant with respect to $A_0(\tau)$; the sum of the dimensions of these two subspaces is equal to n.

Furthermore, we will show that the subspace P_kR_n, defined by the formula

$$x_k = P_k x, \qquad k = 1, 2, \tag{14.5}$$

can also be defined by an equation of the form

$$D_k(A_0)\, x_k = 0, \qquad k = 1, 2, \tag{14.6}$$

i.e., the subspace P_kR_n is the set of vectors which satisfies Eq. (14.6).

In fact, let us initially assume that we have a vector x_k which satisfies formula (14.5). Then substituting expression (14.5) in place of x_k into Eq. (14.6), we obtain

$$D_k(A_0)\, P_k x = d_k(A_0)\, D(A_0)\, x,$$

but $D(A_0) = 0$; consequently, the vectors (14.5) satisfy Eq. (14.6).

The converse is also true: a solution of Eq. (14.6) belongs to the subspace (14.5).

In fact, by (14.1), every vector in the space R_n, including any solution η_1 of the equation $D_1(A_0)\,\eta_1 = 0$, can be represented in the form

$$\eta_1 = (P_1 + P_2)\,\eta_1 \equiv d_1(A_0)\, D_2(A_0)\,\eta_1 + d_2(A_0)\, D_1(A_0)\,\eta_1. \tag{14.7}$$

But $D_1(A_0)\,\eta_1 = 0$, consequently,

$$\eta_1 = d_1(A_0)\, D_2(A_0)\,\eta_1 \equiv P_1(A_0)\,\eta_1,$$

i.e., the solution of Eq. (14.6) for $k = 1$ belongs to the subspace P_1R_n.

An analogous assertion holds in the case $k = 2$.

We note that the set of solutions of the equation $D_k(A_0)\, x = 0$ $(k = 1, 2)$ is not an empty subspace; it is easy to verify this if we write Eq. (14.6) in the form

$$D_1(A_0)\, x = \prod_{i=1}^{r_1} (A_0 - \lambda_i E)\, x = 0,$$

$$D_2(A_0)\, x = \prod_{j=r_1+1}^{n} (A_0 - \lambda_j E)\, x = 0.$$

Let the dimensions of the subspaces P_1R_n and P_2R_n be equal to α_1 and α_2, respectively ($\alpha_1 + \alpha_2 = n$). We choose as a new set of basis unit vectors of our n-dimensional space, the α_1 basis vectors of the subspace P_1R_n and the α_2 basis vectors of the substance P_2R_n.

Because of the invariance of the subspaces P_kR_n with respect to $A_0(\tau)$, the matrix $A_0(\tau)$ in this new basis will have a block-diagonal form; the indicated transformation is accomplished by using the matrix $T(\tau)$:

$$T^{-1}(\tau)\, A_0(\tau)\, T(\tau) = \Lambda(\tau),$$

where $T(\tau)$ is a square matrix of order n, consisting of the new basis vectors;

$$\Lambda(\tau) = \begin{bmatrix} \Lambda_1(\tau) & 0 \\ 0 & \Lambda_2(\tau) \end{bmatrix}; \qquad (14.8)$$

$\Lambda_1(\tau)$ is a matrix of order α_1; $\Lambda_2(\tau)$ is a matrix of order α_2.

We will show that $\alpha_1 = r_1$, $\alpha_2 = r_2$ and that the characteristic values μ_m ($m = 1, 2, \ldots, \alpha_1$) of the matrix $\Lambda_1(\tau)$ are the characteristic values of the first group $\lambda_i(\tau)$ ($i = 1, 2, \ldots, r_1$), while the characteristic values μ_l ($l = \alpha_1 + 1, \alpha_1 + 2, \ldots, n$) of the matrix $\Lambda_2(\tau)$ belong to the second group $\lambda_j(\tau)$ ($j = r_1 + 1, r_2 + 2, \ldots, n$) of roots of the characteristic polynomial of the matrix $A_0(\tau)$.

We take any vector y from the substance P_1R_n. This vector satisfies Eq. (14.6) for $k = 1$ and, consequently, in the new coordinates, it also satisfies the equation

$$T^{-1}(\tau)\, D_1(A_0)\, T(\tau)\, y = 0,$$

which, obviously, can be rewritten in the form

$$D_1(T^{-1}A_0T)\, y = 0. \qquad (14.9)$$

Since $y \in P_1R_n$, its last $\alpha_2 = n - \alpha_1$ components are equal to zero; consequently, Eq. (12.9) is equivalent to the equation

$$D_1(\Lambda_1)\, y_1 = 0, \qquad (14.10)$$

where y_1 is any α_1-dimensional vector.

Since Eq. (14.10) holds for any y_1, $D_1(\Lambda_1) \equiv 0$, which means that all the characteristic values of the matrix $D_1(\Lambda_1)$ are also equal to zero. But all of these characteristic values are formed from the characteristic values of the matrix Λ_1 by the formula $D_1(\mu_m)$; consequently, any characteristic value of the matrix Λ_1 is a root of the equation

$$D_1(\mu_m) = 0 \qquad (m = 1, 2, \ldots, \alpha_1).$$

By an analogous argument, we can convince ourselves that any characteristic value of the matrix Λ_2 is a root of the equation

$$D_2(\mu_l) = 0 \qquad (l = \alpha_1 + 1, \alpha_2 + 2, \ldots, n).$$

Since the similar matrices $A_0(\tau)$ and $\Lambda(\tau)$ have the same characteristic values, and, in addition, $D_1(\lambda)$ and $D_2(\lambda)$ are relatively prime polynomials, from these considerations it follows that $\alpha_1 = r_1$, $\alpha_2 = r_2$ and the characteristic values of the matrices $\Lambda_k(\tau)$ are equal to the roots of the corresponding polynomials $D_k(\lambda)$ $(k = 1, 2)$.

Thus, the matrix $T(\tau)$ which we have constructed can be taken as the desired transforming matrix.

It remains only to prove that this matrix has as many derivatives with respect to τ as does the matrix $A_0(\tau)$.

To prove this, we turn to the question of constructing the basis vectors which form the matrix T. It follows from the previous discussion that the vectors belonging to the subspaces P_1R_n and P_2R_n are solutions of the systems of algebraic equations

$$P_2(A_0(\tau))x_1 = d_2(A_0(\tau))D_1(A_0(\tau))x_1 = 0 \tag{14.11}$$

and

$$P_1(A_0(\tau))x_2 = d_1(A_0(\tau))D_2(A_0(\tau))x_2 = 0 \tag{14.12}$$

respectively.

Therefore, first of all, we should prove that the matrices $P_k(A_0(\tau))$ $(k = 1, 2)$ have as many derivatives with respect to τ as does the matrix $A_0(\tau)$. Obviously, to prove this, it is sufficient to show that the coefficients of the polynomial $P_k(\lambda)$ are differentiable with respect to τ at least as many times as are the elements of the matrix $A_0(\tau)$. We shall now prove this assertion.

As we have already noted, according to the decomposition

$$D(\lambda) = D_1(\lambda)D_2(\lambda), \tag{14.13}$$

we have the formula

$$\frac{1}{D(\lambda)} = \frac{d_1(\lambda)}{D_1(\lambda)} + \frac{d_2(\lambda)}{D_2(\lambda)}, \tag{14.14}$$

where $d_k(\lambda)$ is a polynomial of degree no higher than $r_k - 1$, and $d_k(\lambda)$ and $D_k(\lambda)$ are relatively prime $(k = 1, 2)$.

The roots of the polynomials $D_1(\lambda)$ and $D_2(\lambda)$ form two isolated groups on the complex plane, therefore we can construct on this plane two smooth nonintersecting contours Γ_1 and Γ_2, each of which encloses the roots of the corresponding polynomial.

Since the function $d_1(\lambda)/D_1(\lambda)$ is holomorphic in a closed region bounded by the contour Γ_2, Cauchy's formula holds:

$$\frac{d_1(\lambda)}{D_1(\lambda)} = \frac{1}{2\pi i} \int_{\Gamma_2} \frac{d_1(\mu)\,d\mu}{D_1(\mu)(\mu-\lambda)}, \tag{14.15}$$

where λ is any point within the contour Γ_2, which is transversed in the positive direction.

The function $d_2(\lambda)/D_2(\lambda)$ is holomorphic within the region bounded by Γ_2 and tends uniformly to zero as $\lambda \to \infty$. Therefore

$$0 = \frac{1}{2\pi i} \int_{\Gamma_2} \frac{d_2(\mu)\,d\mu}{D_2(\mu)(\mu-\lambda)}, \tag{14.16}$$

where λ is a point within the contour Γ_2, which is transversed in the same direction as in formula (14.15).

Adding Eqs. (14.15) and (14.16), we obtain, in accordance with (14.14),

$$\frac{d_1(\lambda)}{D_1(\lambda)} = \frac{1}{2\pi i} \int_{\Gamma_2} \frac{d\mu}{D(\mu)(\mu-\lambda)}. \tag{14.17}$$

On the basis of formula (14.17) we can assert that the function $d_1(\lambda)/D_1(\lambda)$ is differentiable with respect to the parameter τ as many times as is the characteristic polynomial $D(\lambda, \tau)$ of the matrix $A_0(\tau)$, i.e., as many times as are the elements of the matrix $A_0(\tau)$: the coefficients of the polynomial $D(\lambda, \tau)$ are multinomials formed from the elements of the matrix $A_0(\tau)$. Thus, the differentiability with respect to τ of the function $P_1(\lambda, \tau)$ is already obvious, since

$$P_1(\lambda) = \frac{d_1(\lambda)}{D_1(\lambda)} \cdot D(\lambda) = d_1(\lambda)\,D_2(\lambda),$$

and each of the functions $d_1(\lambda)/D_1(\lambda)$ and $D(\lambda)$ is differentiable with respect to τ as many times as is the matrix $A_0(\tau)$.

An analogous assertion is true for the polynomial

$$P_2(\lambda) = d_2(\lambda)\,D_1(\lambda).$$

We now turn to the proof of the differentiability with respect to τ of the solutions of Eqs. (14.11) and (14.12).

On the basis of previous considerations, we know that the system of n algebraic equations (14.11) has r_1 independent solutions, i.e., the rank of the matrix $P_2(A_0(\tau))$ is equal to r_2. Therefore, by excluding a nonzero minor of order r_2 from Eq. (14.11) and defining the corresponding values of r_1 arbitrary components of the vector x_1 (for example, by setting them equal to constants), we can differentiate Eq. (14.11) with respect to τ and verify the fact that the solution $x_1(\tau)$ is differentiable as many times as is the matrix $P_2(A_0(\tau))$, i.e., as many times as are the elements of the matrix $A_0(\tau)$. An analogous assertion with reference to differentiability is true for the r_2 independent solutions of system (14.12).

Thus, in constructing the transforming matrix, we can always find a space of differentiable solutions of Eqs. (14.11) and (14.12), which have as many derivatives as does the matrix $A_0(\tau)$.

If we take, as a new basis, the orthonormal (each one separately) systems of independent differentiable solutions of Eqs. (14.11) and (14.12) [which, as is well known, is always possible], then the transforming matrix $V(\tau) = [V_1, V_2]$ constructed from then will have all the properties indicated in Lemma III.1. In addition, the equation

$$V_k^*(\tau)\, V_k(\tau) = E_{r_k}, \qquad k = 1, 2, \tag{14.18}$$

will hold, where $V_k^*(\tau)$ is the transpose of the matrix $V_k(\tau)$. Obviously the matrix $W_0(\tau) = V^{-1}(\tau)\, A_0(\tau)\, V(\tau)$ will have as many derivatives as $V(\tau)$, i.e., as many as $A_0(\tau)$. Lemma III.1 is proved.

Now, by using the assertion of Lemma III.1, we will prove the differentiability of the matrices $U_s(\tau)$ $(s = 1, 2, 3, \ldots)$.

Since, by (13.22),

$$U_s(\tau) = V(\tau)\, Q_s(\tau),$$

the question of differentiability of the elements of $U_s(\tau)$ can be resolved after investigating the properties of the matrices $Q_s(\tau)$ $(s = 1, 2, \ldots)$.

The matrix $Q_s(\tau)$ will be differentiable if all of its square matrices (blocks) $Q_{ijs}(\tau)$ $(i = 1, 2;\ j = 1, 2;\ s = 1, 2, \ldots)$ are differentiable. The differentiability of the square matrices $Q_{iis}(\tau)$ follows directly from Eq. (13.18). The matrices $Q_{ijs}(\tau)$ for $i \neq j$ are the unique solutions of Eq. (13.20). Differentiating (13.20) with respect to τ, we conclude that the $Q_{ijs}(\tau)$ have as many derivatives as the matrices $W_{i0}(\tau)$ $(i = 1, 2)$, i.e., as the matrix $W_0(\tau)$, and the $F_{ijs}(\tau)$. We recall that the $F_{ijs}(\tau)$ are the blocks of the matrix $F_s(\tau)$, which is formed from the terms of the expansion (12.2) of the matrix $A(\tau, \varepsilon)$, the matrices $\mathfrak{A}_m(\tau)$, $U_m(\tau)$ $(m < s)$ and their derivatives.

Thus, if we assume the existence of a sufficient number of derivatives of the elements of $A_s(\tau)$, i.e., if condition 1) of Sec. 12 is fulfilled, then $F_s(\tau)$, and consequently the $Q_{ijs}(\tau)$ will have the necessary number of derivatives.

This assertion shows that all the derivatives with respect to τ of the matrices $U_s(\tau)$ $(s = 0, 1, 2, \ldots)$ with which we must work in the process of formal decomposition of the system (12.1), given the assumptions we have made, actually do exist.

Verification of the differentiability of the matrices $U_s(\tau)$ completes the proof of Theorem III.1.

15. Proof of Asymptotic Convergence

In Sec. 13 we developed an algorithm for formal decomposition of the system of differential equations (12.1) into two linearly independent systems.

In this section we will show that the formal solution (13.1) constructed by this algorithm converges asymptotically to the exact solution $x(t, \varepsilon)$ of the system (12.1). By this we mean that the norm of the difference between the exact solution and the mth approximation tends to zero for fixed m as $\varepsilon \to 0$. (The norm referred to here is the norm for ordinary unitary space $\|y\| = \sqrt{(y, y)}$, $\quad \|A\| = \max\limits_{i} \sum\limits_{j=1}^{n} |a_{ij}|$.)

As before, the term "mth order approximation" will refer to a vector $x^{(m)}(t, \varepsilon)$ of the form

$$x^{(m)}(t, \varepsilon) = U^{(m)}(\tau, \varepsilon)\, \xi^{(m)}(t, \varepsilon), \tag{15.1}$$

where $\xi^{(m)}(t, \varepsilon)$ is defined by Eq. (13.2), if in the formal expansions (13.4), (13.5) we limit ourselves to the first $m+1$ terms.

In order to obtain an estimate of the difference

$$z(t, \varepsilon) = x(t, \varepsilon) - x^{(m)}(t, \varepsilon) \tag{15.2}$$

we will need the following lemma.

Lemma III.2. *If the matrix* $A(\tau, \varepsilon) = A_0(\tau) + \varepsilon \bar{A}(\tau, \varepsilon)$, *where* $\bar{A}(\tau, \varepsilon) = \sum\limits_{s=1}^{\infty} \varepsilon^{s-1} A_s(\tau)$, *satisfies the conditions of Theorem III.1, and, in addition, for any n-dimensional vector y, the inequality*

$$\mathrm{Re}\,(A_0(\tau)\,y,\,y) \leqslant 0 \tag{15.3}$$

holds (this is equivalent to the characteristic values of the symmetric matrix $A_0 + A_0^*\,/2$ *being nonpositive), then for solution of the equation*

$$\frac{dx}{dt} = [A_0(\tau) + \varepsilon \bar{A}\,(\tau, \varepsilon)]\,x \tag{15.4}$$

with the initial condition $x\,(0, \varepsilon) = x_0$*, we have, on the closed interval* $[0,\ L/\varepsilon]$, $0 < \varepsilon \leqslant \varepsilon_0$*, the estimate*

$$\|\,x\,(t, \varepsilon)\,\| \leqslant C\,\|\,x_0\,\|, \tag{15.5}$$

where C *is some positive constant which does not depend on* ε *.*

Proof. Let $\Psi\,(t, \varepsilon) = (x\,(t, \varepsilon),\, x\,(t, \varepsilon))$, where $x\,(t, \varepsilon)$ is a solution of system (15.4), and $x\,(t, \varepsilon)\,|_{t=0} = x_0$. Then, on the strength of (15.3), we have

$$\begin{aligned}\frac{d\Psi}{dt} &= (A\,(\tau, \varepsilon)\,x,\, x) + (x,\, A\,(\tau, \varepsilon)\,x) = 2\mathrm{Re}\,(A\,(\tau, \varepsilon)\,x,\, x) = \\ &= 2\mathrm{Re}\,(A_0(\tau)\,x,\, x) + 2\varepsilon\,\mathrm{Re}\,(\bar{A}\,(\tau, \varepsilon)\,x,\, x) \leqslant \\ &\leqslant 2\varepsilon \sup_{\substack{0 \leqslant \tau \leqslant L,\\ 0 < \varepsilon \leqslant \varepsilon_0.}} \|\,\bar{A}\,(\tau, \varepsilon)\,\|\,\Psi\,(t, \varepsilon);\end{aligned} \tag{15.6}$$

or

$$\Psi\,(t, \varepsilon) \leqslant \Psi\,(0, \varepsilon) + 2\varepsilon \sup_{\substack{0 \leqslant \tau \leqslant L,\\ 0 < \varepsilon \leqslant \varepsilon_0.}} \|\,\bar{A}(\tau, \varepsilon)\,\| \int_0^t \Psi\,(t, \varepsilon)\,dt. \tag{15.7}$$

By Lemma I.1, from inequality (15.7) we obtain the estimate

$$\Psi\,(t, \varepsilon) \leqslant \Psi\,(0, \varepsilon)\, e^{\substack{2L\sup\|\bar{A}(\tau,\varepsilon)\|\\ 0 \leqslant \tau \leqslant L,\ 0 < \varepsilon \leqslant \varepsilon_0}},$$

which we rewrite in the form

$$\|\,x\,(t, \varepsilon)\,\| \leqslant C\,\|\,x_0\,\|, \quad \text{where} \quad C = e^{\substack{L\sup\|A(\tau,\varepsilon)\\ 0 \leqslant \tau \leqslant L,\ 0 < \varepsilon \leqslant \varepsilon_0}},$$

which completes the proof of our lemma.

On the basis of Lemma III.2 we can assert that an estimate of the form (15.5) also holds for the function $\xi_k^{(m)}(t, \varepsilon)$, $k = 1, 2$, since the system

$$\frac{d\xi_k^{(m)}}{dt} = \mathfrak{A}_k^{(m)}(\tau, \varepsilon)\, \xi^{(m)}, \quad k = 1, 2, \tag{15.8}$$

where

$$\mathfrak{A}_k^{(m)}(\tau, \varepsilon) = \mathfrak{A}_{k0}(\tau) + \varepsilon \sum_{s=0}^{m-1} \varepsilon^s \mathfrak{A}_{ks+1}(\tau)$$

satisfies the conditions of Lemma III.2.

In fact, in accordance with the definition of the matrix $\mathfrak{A}_0(\tau)$, (13.13), and the properties of the transforming matrix $V(\tau) = [V_1(\tau), V_2(\tau)]$, we can write

$$A_0(\tau)\, V_k(\tau) = V_k(\tau)\mathfrak{A}_{k0}(\tau),$$

or

$$\mathfrak{A}_{k0}(\tau) = V_k^*(\tau)\, A_0(\tau)\, V_k(\tau).$$

This obviously implies the inequality

$$\operatorname{Re}(\mathfrak{A}_{k0}(\tau)\, y_k, y_k) = \operatorname{Re}(V_k^*(\tau)\, A_0 V_k(\tau)\, y_k, y_k) = \operatorname{Re}(A_0 V_k(\tau)\, y_k, V_k(\tau) y_k) \leqslant 0,$$

where y_k is an arbitrary vector of dimension r_k.

Let us consider the difference (15.2).

On the basis of the definition of the matrices $U_s(\tau)$ and $\mathfrak{A}_s(\tau)$ $(s = 0, 1, 2, \ldots, m)$ [see (13.7)], the vector $x^{(m)}(t, \varepsilon)$ satisfies the equation

$$\frac{dx^{(m)}}{dt} = A^{(m)}(\tau, \varepsilon)\, x^{(m)} + \varepsilon^{m+1} f(t, \varepsilon), \tag{15.9}$$

where

$$A^{(m)}(\tau, \varepsilon) = \sum_{s=0}^{m} \varepsilon^s A_s(\tau),$$

$$f(t, \varepsilon) = \Phi(\tau, \varepsilon)\, \xi^{(m)}(t, \varepsilon),$$

in which

$$\Phi(\tau, \varepsilon) = \frac{dU_m}{d\tau} + \sum_{s=0}^{m-1} \varepsilon^s \sum_{p=s+1}^{m} [U_p(\tau)\mathfrak{A}_{m+s+1-p}(\tau) - A_{m+s+1-p}(\tau)\, U_p(\tau)].$$

Consequently, the vector $z(t, \varepsilon)$ is a solution of the system of equations

$$\frac{dz(t,\varepsilon)}{dt} = A(\tau,\varepsilon)z + \varepsilon^{m+1}F_1(t,\varepsilon), \tag{15.10}$$

where

$$F_1(t,\varepsilon) = \widetilde{A}(\tau,\varepsilon)\,x^{(m)}(t,\varepsilon) - f(t,\varepsilon), \quad \widetilde{A}(\tau,\varepsilon) = \sum_{s=m+1}^{\infty} \varepsilon^{s-m-1}A_s(\tau).$$

The vector $F_1(t,\varepsilon)$, on the basis of the assumptions of Sec. 12, Lemma III.2, and (15.1), is bounded on $[0, L/\varepsilon]$; the following estimate holds for $F_1(t,\varepsilon)$:

$$\|F_1(t,\varepsilon)\| \leqslant \|\widetilde{A}(\tau,\varepsilon)\|\,\|x^{(m)}(t,\varepsilon)\| + \|f(t,\varepsilon)\| \leqslant$$
$$\leqslant C[\|\widetilde{A}(\tau,\varepsilon)\|\,\|U^{(m)}(\tau,\varepsilon)\| + \|\Phi(\tau,\varepsilon)\|]\,\|\xi_0^{(m)}\|,$$

where C is some positive constant; $\xi_0^{(m)}$ is the initial value of the vector $\xi^{(m)}(t,\varepsilon)$.

As is known [1], the solution of Eq. (15.10) satisfying the initial condition $z(t,\varepsilon)|_{t=0} = z_0$, is determined by the formula

$$z(t,\varepsilon) = Y(t,\varepsilon)z_0 + \varepsilon^{m+1}\int_0^t Y(t,\varepsilon)Y^{-1}(t_1,\varepsilon)F(t_1,\varepsilon)\,dt_1, \tag{15.11}$$

where $Y(t,\varepsilon)$ is a solution of the problem

$$\frac{dY}{dt} = A(\tau,\varepsilon)Y, \quad Y(0,\varepsilon) = E. \tag{15.12}$$

In fact, let

$$z(t,\varepsilon) = Y(t,\varepsilon)u(t,\varepsilon). \tag{15.13}$$

Substituting expression (15.13) into Eq. (15.10), we obtain, by (15.12),

$$\frac{dz}{dt} = A(\tau,\varepsilon)z + Y(t,\varepsilon)\frac{du}{dt} = A(\tau,\varepsilon)z + \varepsilon^{m+1}F(t,\varepsilon),$$

from which it follows that

$$Y(t,\varepsilon)\frac{du}{dt} = \varepsilon^{m+1}F(t,\varepsilon)$$

or

$$u(t,\varepsilon) = u(0,\varepsilon) + \varepsilon^{m+1}\int_0^t Y^{-1}(t_1,\varepsilon)F(t_1,\varepsilon)\,dt_1. \tag{15.14}$$

Since $Y(0, \varepsilon) = E$ and, by (15.13), $z_0 = u(0, \varepsilon)$, then Eqs. (15.13) and (15.14) lead to the desired expression for the solution $z(t, \varepsilon)$ [see (15.11)].

Thus, according to (15.11), we have the following estimate for the vector $z(t, \varepsilon)$:

$$\| z(t, \varepsilon) \| \leqslant \| Y(t, \varepsilon) \| \, \| z_0 \| + \varepsilon^{m+1} \int_0^t \Psi(t, t_1, \varepsilon)\, dt_1,$$

where

$$\Psi(t, t_1, \varepsilon) = \| Y(t, \varepsilon) Y^{-1}(t_1, \varepsilon) F(t_1, \varepsilon) \|, \tag{15.15}$$

or

$$\| z(t, \varepsilon) \| \leqslant \| Y(t, \varepsilon) \| \, \| z_0 \| + \varepsilon^m M,$$

where

$$M = L \sup \Psi(t, t_1, \varepsilon),$$

$$0 \leqslant t, t_1 \leqslant \frac{L}{\varepsilon}, \quad 0 < \varepsilon \leqslant \varepsilon_0.$$

Now, on the basis of inequality (15.15), we can assert that we have proved the following theorem.

Theorem III.2. *Suppose that the exact solution $x(t, \varepsilon)$ of system (12.1) and the mth-order approximation $x^{(m)}(t, \varepsilon)$ (15.11) to this solution are taken for the same initial conditions. Then, provided that the conditions of Lemma III.2 are fulfilled, we can find a constant M, independent of ε, such that for all $t \in [0, L/\varepsilon]$ $0 < \varepsilon \leqslant \varepsilon_0$, the following estimate holds:*

$$\| x(t, \varepsilon) - x^{(m)}(t, \varepsilon) \| \leqslant \varepsilon^m M. \tag{15.16}$$

Inequality (15.16) indicates the asymptotic nature of the formal solution $x^{(m)}(t, \varepsilon)$; we have described the algorithm for obtaining this formal solution in Sec. 13.

16. Some Special Cases of Decomposition

The method expounded in this chapter can be applied to the case of division of the roots of the characteristic equation of the matrix $A_0(\tau)$ into p disjoint groups. In this case, we can decompose the original system of differential equations into p isolated subsystems of orders r_k $(k = 1, 2, \ldots, p;$

$$\sum_{k=1}^{p} r_k = n).$$

It is especially easy to obtain the decomposition of the given system in the case when the characteristic values of the matrix $A_0(\tau)$ are simple on the whole closed interval $[0, L]$.

In fact, according to the method developed in this chapter, we can, in this case, represent the general formal solution of the given system

$$\frac{dx}{dt} = A(\tau, \varepsilon)\, x \tag{16.1}$$

in the form

$$x(t, \varepsilon) = U(\tau, \varepsilon)\, \xi(t, \varepsilon) \equiv \sum_{k=1}^{n} U_k(\tau, \varepsilon)\, \xi_k(t, \varepsilon), \tag{16.2}$$

where the function $\xi_k(t, \varepsilon)$ is the general solution of the first-order equation

$$\frac{d\xi_k}{dt} = \omega_k(\tau, \varepsilon)\, \xi_k, \quad k = 1, 2, \ldots, n, \tag{16.3}$$

and $U_k(\tau, \varepsilon)$ is an n-dimensional vector which is the corresponding column of the transforming matrix $U(\tau, \varepsilon)$.

Thus, in this case, the nth-order system (16.1) is decomposed into n independent equations of first order (16.3), and its general solution can be written in the form

$$x(t, \varepsilon) = \sum_{k=1}^{n} c_k U_k(\tau, \varepsilon)\, e^{\int_{t_0}^{t} \omega_k(\tau, \varepsilon) dt},$$

where c_k are arbitrary constants, determined from the initial conditions.

During successive determination (by the algorithm described in Sec. 13) of the terms of the asymptotic expansion of the function $\omega_k(\tau, \varepsilon)$ and of the vector $U_k(\tau, \varepsilon)$, we find that $U_{k0}(\tau)$ is a characteristic vector of the matrix $A_0(\tau)$, corresponding to the characteristic value $\lambda_k(\tau)$, and $\omega_{k0}(\tau) \equiv \lambda_k(\tau)$.

Furthermore, in the case of simple characteristic values of the matrix $A_0(\tau)$, the elements of the matrix $Q_s(\tau)$ $(s \geqslant 1)$ [see (13.20)] are determined by the formula

$$q_{ijs}(\tau) = \frac{f_{ijs}(\tau)}{\lambda_i(\tau) - \lambda_j(\tau)}, \qquad i \neq j; \qquad i, j = 1, 2, \ldots, n,$$

where $f_{ijs}(\tau)$ is the corresponding element of the matrix $F_s(\tau)$ (13.20).

For $i=j$, we may set $q_{iis}(\tau) \equiv 0$, for $s \geqslant 1$ (but $q_{ii0} \equiv 1$!).

Knowing the columns of the matrix $Q_s(\tau)$ and using the formula $U_s(\tau) = V(\tau) Q_s(\tau)$, it is not difficult to determine the corresponding vectors $U_{ks}(\tau)$ as well.

This case shows that by using the algorithm described in Sec. 13, we can, for fixed conditions, rather easily determine the numerical values for the transforming matrix $U(\tau, \varepsilon)$, i.e., actually accomplish the asymptotic decomposition of the given system of differential equations into several subsystems of lower order.

We have an analogous situation in the case of p identically multiple roots of the characteristic polynomial on $[0, L]$, having simple elementary divisors (see the next chapter, Sec. 19).

However, in the general case, when the characteristic values of the matrix $A_0(\tau)$ have variable multiplicity for $\tau \in [0, L]$ and the order of the original system is sufficiently high, the described algorithm encounters significant computational difficulties. In particular, it is very difficult to construct the matrix $U_0(\tau) \equiv V(\tau)$, and also to solve, for each $s \geqslant 1$, the nonhomogeneous system of algebraic equations of the form (13.20). Therefore, in such cases, the calculation must be carried out on high-speed electronic computers, which requires the use of a special, simpler, algorithm. We will consider this question in Chap. V.

17. Decomposition of a Nonhomogeneous System of Linear Differential Equations

In this section, we will consider the question of decomposition of a system of differential equations of the form

$$\frac{dx}{dt} = A(\tau, \varepsilon) x + b(\tau, \varepsilon) e^{i\theta(t,\varepsilon)}, \tag{17.1}$$

where the matrix $A(\tau, \varepsilon)$ is the same as in Secs. 13-15, and the n-dimensional vector $b(\tau, \varepsilon)$ is infinitely differentiable with respect to τ on $[0, L]$ and admits the following representation:

$$b(\tau, \varepsilon) = \sum_{s=0}^{\infty} \varepsilon^s b_s(\tau). \tag{17.2}$$

As in the previous chapters, it is necessary to distinguish two cases:

a. resonance—when the values of the function $i\nu(\tau) \equiv i\, d\theta / dt$ ($i = \sqrt{-1}$) coincide with the values of a specific group of roots of the characteristic equation of the matrix $A_0(\tau)$ for certain $\tau \in [0, L]$, the above-mentioned roots form an isolated group, and the values of $i\nu(\tau)$ do not coincide with the other group of roots for any value of τ.

b. nonresonance—when the function $i\nu(\tau)$ does not take values coinciding with the characteristic values of the matrix $A_0(\tau)$ for any value of $\tau \in [0, L]$.

1. The resonance case. Let the values of the function $i\nu(\tau)$ coincide with the values of some of the characteristic roots from the first group for certain $\tau \in [0, L)$, i.e., with $\lambda_i(\tau)$, where $i = 1, 2, \ldots, r_1$.

Then we have the following theorem.

Theorem III.3. *If the conditions of Theorem III.1 are satisfied, and the vector $b(\tau, \varepsilon)$ and the function $\nu(\tau)$ are infinitely differentiable with respect to τ, then the formal general solution of the system (17.1) in the resonance case can be represented in the form*

$$x(t, \varepsilon) = U(\tau, \varepsilon)\,\xi(t, \varepsilon) + P(\tau, \varepsilon)\, e^{i\theta(t, \varepsilon)}, \tag{17.3}$$

where the matrix $U(\tau, \varepsilon)$ is the same as in Sec. 13; the n-dimensional vector $\xi(t, \varepsilon)$ is the general solution of the nonhomogeneous equation

$$\frac{d\xi}{dt} = \mathfrak{A}(\tau, \varepsilon)\,\xi + Z(\tau, \varepsilon)\, e^{i\theta(t, \varepsilon)}, \tag{17.4}$$

in which the matrix $\mathfrak{A}(\tau, \varepsilon)$ is the same as in Sec. 13,

$$\mathfrak{A}(\tau, \varepsilon) = \begin{bmatrix} \mathfrak{A}_1(\tau, \varepsilon) & 0 \\ 0 & \mathfrak{A}_2(\tau, \varepsilon) \end{bmatrix}, \tag{17.5}$$

and in the vector $Z(\tau, \varepsilon)$ only the first r_1 components are different from zero

$$Z(\tau, \varepsilon) = \begin{bmatrix} Z_1(\tau, \varepsilon) \\ 0 \end{bmatrix}. \tag{17.6}$$

The vector $P(\tau, \varepsilon)$ is n-dimensional and admits, as does the vector $Z(\tau, \varepsilon)$, the ordinary formal expansion

$$P(\tau, \varepsilon) = \sum_{s=0}^{\infty} \varepsilon^s P_s(\tau), \qquad Z(\tau, \varepsilon) = \sum_{s=0}^{\infty} \varepsilon^s Z_s(\tau). \tag{17.7}$$

In other words, by using the transformation (17.3), which can also be written in the form

$$x(t, \varepsilon) = U_1(\tau, \varepsilon)\xi_1(t, \varepsilon) + U_2(\tau, \varepsilon)\xi_2(t, \varepsilon) + P(\tau, \varepsilon)e^{i\theta(t,\varepsilon)}, \quad (17.8)$$

the nonhomogeneous nth-order system (17.1) can be asymptotically decomposed into two isolated systems of lower order, namely:

$$\frac{d\xi_1}{dt} = \mathfrak{A}_1(\tau, \varepsilon)\xi_1 + Z_1(\tau, \varepsilon)e^{i\theta(t,\varepsilon)}, \quad (17.9)$$

$$\frac{d\xi_2}{dt} = \mathfrak{A}_2(\tau, \varepsilon)\xi_2. \quad (17.10)$$

The system (17.9) is of order r_1; the system (17.10) is of order r_2 ($r_1 + r_2 = n$), in accordance with the number of roots in each of the isolated groups (see Sec. 12). We will not present the proof of Theorem III.3 in detail, since it is completely analogous to the proof of Theorem III.1. In addition, the formulas for determining the terms of the asymptotic expansions of the matrices $U(\tau, \varepsilon)$ and $\mathfrak{A}(\tau, \varepsilon)$ in this case are identical to the corresponding formulas in Sec. 13.

We will concern ourselves only with finding the terms of the expansion (17.7).

Following the procedure which we have already described in detail, we find that in order to prove Theorem III.3 [not concerning ourselves with the construction of the matrices $\mathfrak{A}(\tau, \varepsilon)$ and $U(\tau, \varepsilon)$], it is sufficient to choose the vectors $P(\tau, \varepsilon)$ and $Z(\tau, \varepsilon)$ so that they satisfy the equation

$$\varepsilon\frac{dP}{d\tau} + U(\tau, \varepsilon)Z(\tau, \varepsilon) = [A(\tau, \varepsilon) - i\nu(\tau)E]P(\tau, \varepsilon) + b(\tau, \varepsilon). \quad (17.11)$$

In Eq. (17.11) we successively separate out the coefficients of the powers ε^s ($s = 0, 1, 2, \dots$); we obtain recurrent relationships for determination of the vectors $Z_s(\tau)$ and $P_s(\tau)$:

$$[A_0(\tau) - i\nu(\tau)E]P_s(\tau) = U_0(\tau)Z_s(\tau) + G_s(\tau), \quad (17.12)$$

where

$$G_s(\tau) = \frac{dP_{s-1}}{d\tau} + \sum_{k=0}^{s-1}[U_{s-k}(\tau)Z_k(\tau) - A_{s-k}(\tau)P_k(\tau)] - b_s(\tau)$$

$$s = 0, 1, 2, \dots . \quad (17.13)$$

Multiplying (17.12) from the left by $V^{-1}(\tau)$ and introducing the vector $R_s(\tau)$ according to the formula

$$V^{-1}P_s(\tau) = R_s(\tau), \qquad s = 0, 1, 2, \dots, \quad (17.14)$$

we obtain

$$[W_0(\tau) - i\nu(\tau)E]R_s(\tau) = Z_s(\tau) + \Phi_s(\tau), \qquad (17.15)$$

where

$$\Phi_s(\tau) = V^{-1}(\tau)G_s(\tau), \quad V^{-1}(\tau)U_0(\tau) = Q_0(\tau) \equiv E.$$

Due to the structure of the matrix W_0 and the vector $Z_s(\tau)$, the system (17.15) decomposes into two independent systems

$$[W_{k0}(\tau) - i\nu(\tau)E_{r_k}]R_{ks}(\tau) = Z_{ks}(\tau) + \Phi_{ks}(\tau) \quad (k = 1, 2) \qquad (17.16)$$

of lower order. Here we adopt the notation:

$$R_s(\tau) = \begin{bmatrix} R_{1s}(\tau) \\ R_{2s}(\tau) \end{bmatrix}, \qquad \Phi_s(\tau) = \begin{bmatrix} \Phi_{1s}(\tau) \\ \Phi_{2s}(\tau) \end{bmatrix}. \qquad (17.17)$$

Let $k = 2$. Then (17.16) takes the form

$$[W_{20}(\tau) - i\nu(\tau)E_{r_2}]R_{2s}(\tau) = \Phi_{2s}(\tau). \qquad (17.18)$$

Since the values of $i\nu(\tau)$ and $\tau \in [0, L]$ do not coincide with the roots in the second group, the matrix $[W_{20}(\tau) - i\nu(\tau)E_{r_2}]$ is nonsingular and Eq. (17.18) has a unique solution $R_{2s}(\tau)$:

$$R_{2s}(\tau) = [W_{20}(\tau) - i\nu(\tau)E_{r_2}]^{-1}\Phi_{2s}(\tau), \quad s = 0, 1, 2, \ldots. \qquad (17.19)$$

For $k = 1$ the system (17.16) takes the form

$$[W_{10}(\tau) - i\nu(\tau)E_{r_1}]R_{1s}(\tau) = Z_{1s}(\tau) + \Phi_{1s}(\tau), \qquad (17.20)$$

from which it is necessary to determine the unknown vectors $R_{1s}(\tau)$ and $Z_{1s}(\tau)$.

On the basis of our assumptions, the matrix $[W_{10}(\tau) - i\nu(\tau)E_r]$ becomes singular at certain points of the closed interval

$$\det[W_{10}(\tau) - i\nu(\tau)E] = 0. \qquad (17.21)$$

Therefore, here we must again make use of the necessary and sufficient condition for solvability of a nonhomogeneous algebraic system whose determinant is equal to zero (see Sec. 7). And, although the determinant (17.21) becomes zero only at certain points $\tau \in [0, L]$, we choose the (as yet unknown) vector $Z_{1s}(\tau)$ in such a way that on the entire closed interval $[0, L]$ we fulfill the cited condition of solvability; namely, we make this choice in such a way that the right-hand side of Eq. (17.20) $f_s(\tau) = Z_{1s}(\tau) + \Phi_{1s}(\tau)$ is orthogonal to all the solutions of the algebraic system

$$[W_{10}^*(\tau) + i\nu(\tau) E_{r_1}] y = 0.$$

The formulated condition will be necessarily satisfied if we choose $Z_{1s}(\tau)$ in such a way that

$$Z_{1s}(\tau) + \Phi_{1s}(\tau) = 0,$$

i.e.,

$$Z_{1s}(\tau) = -\Phi_{1s}(\tau), \quad s = 0, 1, 2, \ldots.$$

On the basis of our choice of the vector $Z_{1s}(\tau)$, we must restrict ourselves, on the closed interval $[0, L]$, to the trivial solution for the vector $R_{1s}(\tau)$; namely, we must set

$$R_{1s}(\tau) \equiv 0, \quad s = 0, 1, 2 \ldots.$$

Thus, by sequential solution of the system (17.16) we can determine, by taking account of (17.14), any term of the expansions of the desired vectors $Z(\tau, \varepsilon)$ and $P(\tau, \varepsilon)$. This, in conjunction with Theorem III.1, proves Theorem III.3.

2. Decomposition of system (17.1) in the nonresonance case is even simpler. Here we can formulate and prove a theorem which is analogous to Theorem III.3; this theorem asserts that in the nonresonance case the general formal solution of system (17.1) can be represented in the form

$$x(t, \varepsilon) = U(\tau, \varepsilon)\xi(t, \varepsilon) + H(\tau, \varepsilon) e^{i\theta(t, \varepsilon)},$$
$$\frac{d\xi}{dt} = \mathfrak{A}(\tau, \varepsilon)\xi, \tag{17.22}$$

where the matrices $U(\tau, \varepsilon)$ and $\mathfrak{A}(\tau, \varepsilon)$ are the same as in Theorems III.1 and III.3, and the n-dimensional vector $H(\tau, \varepsilon)$ admits the formal expansion

$$H(\tau, \varepsilon) = \sum_{s=0}^{\infty} \varepsilon^s H_s(\tau). \tag{17.23}$$

The recurrent formulas for determination of the terms of the series (17.23) can be obtained if we seek a particular solution of the nonhomogeneous system (17.1) in the form

$$X(\tau, \varepsilon) = H(\tau, \varepsilon) e^{i\theta} \tag{17.24}$$

In fact, substituting (17.24) into system (17.1), we find an equation which must be satisfied by the desired vector $H(\tau, \varepsilon)$:

$$[A(\tau, \varepsilon) - i\nu(\tau) E] H(\tau, \varepsilon) = \varepsilon \frac{dH}{d\tau} - b(\tau, \varepsilon). \tag{17.25}$$

From this, by using the formal expansions which hold for all of the terms of Eq. (17.25), we obtain the following recurrent formulas for determining the terms of the series (17.23):

$$[A_0(\tau) - i\nu(\tau) E] H_s(\tau) = \Psi_s(\tau), \quad s = 0, 1, 2, \ldots, \tag{17.26}$$

where

$$\Psi_s(\tau) = \frac{dH_{s-1}}{d\tau} - b_s(\tau) - \sum_{k=0}^{s-1} A_{s-k}(\tau) H_k(\tau). \tag{17.26'}$$

In the nonresonance case, the system (17.26) for each $s \geqslant 0$ defines a unique solution

$$H_s(\tau) = [A_0(\tau) - i\nu(\tau) E]^{-1} \Psi_s(\tau). \tag{17.27}$$

Thus, in the case of the absence of resonance as well, obtaining a formal solution (17.22) of the nonhomogeneous system (17.1) reduces to the solution of two independent differential systems of lower order:

$$\frac{d\xi_1}{dt} = \mathfrak{A}_1(\tau, \varepsilon)\xi_1, \qquad \xi(t, \varepsilon) = \begin{bmatrix} \xi_1(t, \varepsilon) \\ \xi_2(t, \varepsilon) \end{bmatrix}$$
$$\frac{d\xi_2}{dt} = \mathfrak{A}_2(\tau, \varepsilon)\xi_2$$

and the determination of the vector $H(\tau, \varepsilon)$ by using the recurrent formulas (17.26).

Just as we have done in Sec. 15, we can show that the formal solutions for the nonhomogeneous system (17.1) which we have constructed are, in fact, asymptotic (in both the resonance and nonresonance cases). In the resonance case, the estimate will be of the form

$$\| x(t, \varepsilon) - x^{(m)}(t, \varepsilon) \| \leq C\varepsilon^{m-1},$$

and in the nonresonance case

$$\| x(t, \varepsilon) - x^{(m)}(t, \varepsilon) \| \leq C_1\varepsilon^{m}.$$

The latter, better, estimate is true in both cases if $b_0(\tau) \equiv 0$.

Note 1. It is not difficult to see that all the constructions of this section will also remain valid in the case of division of the roots of the characteristic equation of the matrix $A_0(\tau)$ into p isolated groups. The modifications in the structure of the matrix $\mathfrak{A}(\tau, \varepsilon)$ and the vector $Z(\tau, \varepsilon)$ (in the case of resonance) are obvious.

Note 2. The asymptotic decomposition of a system of higher order into several isolated subsystems, which we have constructed in this section, does not always make it possible to write down directly the asymptotic solution of the original system of differential equations. This is explained by the fact that the "decomposed" systems, although they are of lower order than the given system, may not always be solvable in closed form. Only in the case of simple characteristic values of the matrix $A_0(\tau)$ (see Sec. 16) is a solution by quadrature necessarily possible. In the presence of multiple roots of the characteristic equation, construction of asymptotic solutions becomes possible only in special cases, and, in general, is significantly more complicated.

Chapter IV will be devoted to a consideration of the abovementioned special cases.

18. Asymptotic Decomposition of a System of Ordinary Linear Differential Equations in the Case of Multiple Roots of the Characteristic Equation

In the preceding sections of Chapter III we proved that, given certain conditions, we can carry out an asymptotic decomposition of a system of linear differential equations of higher order into several independent subsystems of lower order.

Here, when we speak of an asymptotic decomposition, we refer to the asymptotic nature of the convergence of the approximate solution $x^{(m)}(t, \varepsilon)$ to the exact solution $x(t, \varepsilon)$ of the original system.

However, there exists another approach to establishing the possibility of asymptotic decomposition of a system of linear differential equations, namely: We can prove the asymptotic convergence of the transforming matrix to a certain "exact" matrix which realizes the decomposition of the given system.

Such an approach is taken, for example, in [126, 29, 30]. In this section, the results of which were obtained by Ilyukhin, we will consider the basic propositions of the second approach.

1. We again consider the system of linear differential equations (12.1)

$$\frac{dx}{dt} = A(\tau, \varepsilon)\, x. \tag{18.1}$$

We will assume that the matrix $A(\tau, \varepsilon)$ satisfies condition 1) of Sec. 12; we will change condition 2) to the following:

The roots $\lambda_1(\tau)$, $\lambda_2(\tau)$, ..., $\lambda_n(\tau)$ of the characteristic equation (12.3) can be divided into p classes, $p \leqslant n$; in each of these classes there are n_j $(j = 1, 2, \ldots, p;\ \sum_{j=1}^{p} n_j = n)$ multiple roots, the multiplicity of the roots being preserved on the entire closed interval $0 \leqslant \tau \leqslant L$. In addition, we will assume that the matrix $A_0(\tau)$ retains its canonical structure on the entire interval $[0, L]$, i.e., for any $\tau \in [0, L]$ the matrix $A_0(\tau)$ reduces to normal form with one and the same number of Jordan blocks along its principal diagonal.

Then we can construct a nonsingular matrix $V(\tau)$ of order n which transforms the matrix $A_0(\tau)$ to the canonical Jordan form [which we shall denote by $W_0(\tau)$]

$$W_0(\tau) = V^{-1}(\tau)\, A_0(\tau)\, V(\tau), \tag{18.2}$$

where

$$W_0(\tau) = \begin{bmatrix} W_{10}(\tau) & 0 & \ldots & 0 \\ 0 & W_{20}(\tau) & \ldots & 0 \\ \cdot & \cdot & \cdot & \cdot \\ 0 & 0 & & W_{p0}(\tau) \end{bmatrix}, \tag{18.3}$$

and the $W_{j0}(\tau)$ $(j = 1, 2, \ldots, p)$ are square matrices of the form

$$W_{j0}(\tau) = \begin{bmatrix} \lambda_j(\tau) & \alpha_{j1} & 0 & 0 \\ 0 & \lambda_j(\tau) \ \ldots & 0 & 0 \\ \cdot\ \cdot\ \cdot & \cdot\ \cdot\ \cdot & \cdot\ \cdot\ \cdot & \cdot\ \cdot\ \cdot \\ 0 & 0 & \lambda_j(\tau) & \alpha_{j,n_j-1} \\ 0 & 0 & 0 & \lambda_j(\tau) \end{bmatrix}, \tag{18.4}$$

where the numbers $\alpha_{j1}, \ldots, \alpha_{j,n_j-1}$ can be either zero or one for all $\tau \in [0, L]$, according to the assumption which we have made above. Thus, in the $W_{j0}(\tau)$ $(j = 1, 2, \ldots, p)$ are collected all the Jordan blocks corresponding to the root $\lambda_j(\tau)$ of multiplicity n_j $(j = 1, 2, \ldots, p)$.

In this case, the matrix $V(\tau)$ is differentiable as many times as is the matrix $A_0(\tau)$. In fact, in Sec. 14 we proved that if the spectrum of the matrix $A_0(\tau)$ decomposes into p isolated parts for $\tau \in [0, L]$, then we can find a certain matrix $T(\tau)$, which reduces $A_0(\tau)$ to block-diagonal form $\Lambda(\tau)=[\Lambda_1(\tau), \Lambda_2(\tau), \ldots \Lambda_p(\tau)]$, where the $\Lambda_j(\tau)$ are diagonal square matrices whose orders are determined by the dimensions of the invariant subspaces corresponding to the isolated parts of the spectrum of the matrix $A_0(\tau)$. There we also proved that $T(\tau)$ and the $\Lambda_j(\tau)$ $(j = 1, 2, \ldots, n)$ have as many derivatives with respect to τ as does the matrix $A_0(\tau)$.

Now, by an analogous method, we will show that we can construct a matrix $\tilde{V}(\tau)$ which, given the assumptions we have made relative to $A_0(\tau)$, reduces the block-diagonal matrix $\Lambda(\tau)$ to the form (18.3). Here, $\tilde{V}(\tau)$ will be differentiable as many times as the matrices $\Lambda_j(\tau)$ $(j = 1, 2, \ldots, p)$, i.e., in the final analysis, as many times differentiable as the matrix $A(\tau)$.

Indeed, as a particular example, let us consider the invariant subspace E_1, corresponding to the first diagonal block $\Lambda_1(\tau)$ of the matrix $\Lambda(\tau)$. The subspace E_1 of dimension n_1 will be, in the given case, a "root subspace" (see [49]) corresponding to the root $\lambda_1(\tau)$. Then, as is known from linear algebra (see [68]), we can define a basis for which the matrix $\Lambda_1(\tau)$ will be reduced to the canonical Jordan form (18.4). To do this, we find the smallest number $l < n_1$, for which the following matrix equation holds:

$$(\Lambda_1(\tau) - \lambda_1(\tau) E_{n_1})^l = 0. \tag{18.5}$$

To simplify the calculations we adopt the notation

$$\Lambda_1(\tau) - \lambda_1(\tau) E_{n_1} = B(\tau). \tag{18.6}$$

We find all the nonzero solutions of the homogeneous system of linear algebraic equations

$$B^{l-1}(\tau) x = 0. \tag{18.7}$$

Since the matrix $A_0(\tau)$ has a constant canonical structure for all $\tau \in [0, L]$, the obtained vector solutions of the system (18.7) will have the same differentiability properties as the matrix $B(\tau)$, i.e., in the final analysis, the same differentiability properties as $\Lambda_1(\tau)$ and the characteristic value $\lambda_1(\tau)$.

In fact, since the multiplicity of $\lambda_1(\tau)$ remains the same for any value of τ, the matrix $\Lambda_1(\tau)$, as we showed above, is as many times differentiable as the matrix $A_0(\tau)$. We can also show that the roots $\lambda_j(\tau)$ $(j = 1, 2, \ldots, p)$ have the same number of derivatives as the elements of the matrix $A_0(\tau)$. Then, from equality (18.6) it follows that $B(\tau)$ has the same differentiability properties as the matrix $A_0(\tau)$.

For the vector solution of the homogeneous system (18.7) to be as many times differentiable as the matrix $A_0(\tau)$, it is necessary, in addition, that the matrix $B^{l-1}(\tau)$ have the same rank for all $\tau \in [0, L]$. In turn, the rank of the matrix $B^{l-1}(\tau)$ will be preserved under variation of τ, if the canonical form of the matrix

$\Lambda_1(\tau)$ is preserved, i.e., if the multiplicity of the elementary divisors corresponding to the root $\lambda_1(\tau)$ is preserved.

We will illustrate the above with a simple example. Suppose that the matrix $\Lambda_1(\tau)$ has the following canonical form for all $\tau \in [0, L]$:

$$\begin{bmatrix} \lambda_1(\tau) & 1 & 0 & 0 \\ 0 & \lambda_1(\tau) & 1 & 0 \\ 0 & 0 & \lambda_1(\tau) & 1 \\ 0 & 0 & 0 & \lambda_1(\tau) \end{bmatrix}. \tag{18.8}$$

Then, by (18.6), the matrix $B(\tau)$ will be equivalent to the matrix

$$\begin{bmatrix} 0 & 1 & 0 & 0 \\ 0 & 0 & 1 & 0 \\ 0 & 0 & 0 & 1 \\ 0 & 0 & 0 & 0 \end{bmatrix} \tag{18.9}$$

everywhere on the interval $[0, L]$. In this case, for any $\tau \in [0, L]$, the rank of the matrix $B^3(\tau)$ will be equal to one.

If, for example, for one value $\tau_1 \in [0, L]$ the matrix $\Lambda_1(\tau_1)$ has the canonical form (18.8), and for another value $\tau_2 \in [0, L]$ the canonical form of $\Lambda_1(\tau_2)$ is

$$\begin{bmatrix} \lambda_1(\tau_2) & 1 & 0 & 0 \\ 0 & \lambda_1(\tau_2) & 0 & 0 \\ 0 & 0 & \lambda_1(\tau_2) & 1 \\ 0 & 0 & 0 & \lambda_1(\tau_2) \end{bmatrix}, \tag{18.10}$$

then the matrix $B^3(\tau_2)$ will already have rank zero. Consequently, in this case, not all of the vector-solutions of the homogeneous system of equations

$$B^3(\tau)\, x = 0$$

will be continuous, if only one of these solutions has a discontinuity in the interval $\tau_1 < \tau < \tau_2$.

Thus, in order for the vector solution of system (18.7) to be infinitely differentiable, two conditions are essential: that the matrix $A_0(\tau)$ be infinitely differentiable; and that the canonical structure of the matrix $A_0(\tau)$ be constant on the whole interval $[0, L]$. That is why we assumed that these conditions held from the very beginning.

In constructing the transforming matrix $V_1(\tau)$, which reduces the matrix $\Lambda_1(\tau)$ to canonical Jordan form, it becomes necessary to find, not the solutions of the homogeneous system (18.7), but vectors which do not belong to the subspace of solutions of this system. Since the above vector-solutions are infinitely differentiable, we can choose, in the orthogonal complement to the subspace of solutions of system (18.7), a basis which also consists of arbitrarily smooth functions. Applying to the vectors of this basis the linear transformation defined by the matrix (18.6), we construct the columns of the matrix $V_1(\tau)$ by the well-known rule [68]. We will describe this process briefly; a more detailed treatment is given in [68].

Thus, we will find the columns of the matrix $V_1(\tau)$ which reduces the matrix $\Lambda_1(\tau)$ to canonical Jordan form. The number of linearly independent vectors which do not satisfy the system (18.7) is obviously equal to the rank of the matrix $B^{l-1}(\tau)$. We will denote this number by r_1. Then the r_1 linearly independent vectors in the subspace orthogonal to the subspace of solutions of system (18.7) can be taken as the columns of the matrix $V_1(\tau)$. We apply to each of these vectors the transformation defined by the matrix $B(\tau)$. Then we again obtain r_1 vectors, some of which may possibly be identically equal to zero, while the remainder will be different from zero. To these latter vectors we again apply the matrix $B(\tau)$, and so on, until such time as, after a series of successive applications of the matrix $B(\tau)$, all the vectors have become identically equal to zero.

Thus, each of the r_1 initially chosen linearly independent vectors $x^{(k)}(\tau)$ $(k = 1, 2, \ldots, r_1)$ together with the vectors $B(\tau)x^{(k)}(\tau)$, $B^2(\tau)x^{(k)}(\tau), \ldots$ $(k=1, 2, \ldots, r_1)$ form a series of unit vectors in the orthogonal completion to the subspace of solutions of the system (18.7). The series of linearly independent vectors constructed in this way [there will be n_1 vectors in all, where n_1 is the order of the matrix $\Lambda_1(\tau)$] form the n_1 columns of the desired matrix $V_1(\tau)$.

In the same way we construct the nonsingular square matrices $V_2(\tau), V_3(\tau), \ldots, V_p(\tau)$ of dimension $n_2, n_3, \ldots, n_p$, respectively, which reduce the matrices $\Lambda_2(\tau), \Lambda_3(\tau), \ldots, \Lambda_p(\tau)$ to normal Jordan form.

Next we construct the square block-diagonal matrix $\widetilde{V}(\tau)$ of order $n = n_1 + n_2 + \ldots + n_p$, whose diagonal blocks are the matrices $V_1(\tau), V_2(\tau), \ldots, V_p(\tau)$. Then the obtained matrix $\widetilde{V}(\tau) = [V_1(\tau), V_2(\tau), \ldots, V_p(\tau)]$ reduces the block-diagonal matrix $\Lambda(\tau) = [\Lambda_1(\tau), \Lambda_2(\tau), \ldots, \Lambda_p(\tau)]$ to normal Jordan form, i.e., we have the equality

$$\widetilde{V}^{-1}(\tau)\,\Lambda(\tau)\widetilde{V}(\tau) = W_0(\tau),$$

where $W_0(\tau)$ is of the form (18.3).

The described process of constructing $V_1(\tau)$, $V_2(\tau), \ldots, V_p(\tau)$ shows that the matrix $\widetilde{V}(\tau)$, and, consequently, the matrix $V(\tau) = T(\tau)\widetilde{V}(\tau)$, which reduces the matrix $A_0(\tau)$ to the Jordan form (18.3), are as many times differentiable with respect to τ as is the matrix $A_0(\tau)$. Hence, we have verified the required property.

2. We shall, as in Sec. 13, seek a solution of the system (18.1) in the form

$$x = U(\tau, \varepsilon)\zeta, \tag{18.11}$$

where $\zeta(t, \varepsilon)$ is an n-dimensional vector determined from the system of equations

$$\frac{d\zeta}{dt} = \mathfrak{A}(\tau, \varepsilon)\zeta. \tag{18.12}$$

Here $U(\tau, \varepsilon)$ and $\mathfrak{A}(\tau, \varepsilon)$ are nth-order matrices, infinitely differentiable with respect to τ, and representable in the form of the formal series

$$U(\tau, \varepsilon) = \sum_{s=0}^{\infty} \varepsilon^s U_s(\tau), \tag{18.13}$$

$$\mathfrak{A}(\tau, \varepsilon) = \sum_{s=0}^{\infty} \varepsilon^s \mathfrak{A}_s(\tau). \tag{18.14}$$

In accordance with the structure of $W_0(\tau)$, we seek the matrix $\mathfrak{A}(\tau, \varepsilon)$ in the form

$$\mathfrak{A}(\tau, \varepsilon) = \begin{bmatrix} \mathfrak{A}_1(\tau, \varepsilon) & 0 & \ldots & 0 \\ 0 & \mathfrak{A}_2(\tau, \varepsilon) & \ldots & 0 \\ \cdot & \cdot & \cdot\,\cdot\,\cdot & \cdot \\ 0 & 0 & \ldots & \mathfrak{A}_p(\tau, \varepsilon) \end{bmatrix}, \tag{18.15}$$

where $\mathfrak{A}_j(\tau, \varepsilon)$ $(j = 1, 2, \ldots, p)$ are square matrices of the same orders as the matrices $W_{j0}(\tau, \varepsilon)$, respectively; expansions of the form (18.14) hold for the $\mathfrak{A}_j(\tau, \varepsilon)$ $(j = 1, 2, \ldots, p)$.

As in Sec. 13, for determination of the matrices $U(\tau, \varepsilon)$ and $\mathfrak{A}(\tau, \varepsilon)$ we obtain the matrix equation

$$\varepsilon \frac{dU(\tau, \varepsilon)}{d\tau} + U(\tau, \varepsilon)\mathfrak{A}(\tau, \varepsilon) - A(\tau, \varepsilon)U(\tau, \varepsilon) = 0. \tag{18.16}$$

We introduce the matrices $Q(\tau, \varepsilon)$ and $W(\tau, \varepsilon)$ defined by the equations

$$Q(\tau, \varepsilon) = V^{-1}(\tau)U(\tau, \varepsilon), \tag{18.17}$$

$$W(\tau, \varepsilon) = V^{-1}(\tau) A(\tau, \varepsilon) V(\tau). \tag{18.18}$$

Since, by assumption, the matrices $A(\tau, \varepsilon)$ and $U(\tau, \varepsilon)$ are represented as power series in ε, the matrices $Q(\tau, \varepsilon)$ and $W(\tau, \varepsilon)$ obviously also have this property

$$Q(\tau, \varepsilon) = \sum_{s=0}^{\infty} \varepsilon^s Q_s(\tau), \tag{18.19}$$

$$W(\tau, \varepsilon) = \sum_{s=0}^{\infty} \varepsilon^s W_s(\tau). \tag{18.20}$$

Multiplying (18.16) from the left by $V^{-1}(\tau)$, we obtain the matrix equation

$$\varepsilon V^{-1}(\tau) \frac{dV}{d\tau} Q(\tau, \varepsilon) + \varepsilon \frac{dQ(\tau, \varepsilon)}{d\tau} + Q(\tau, \varepsilon)\mathfrak{A}(\tau, \varepsilon) - W(\tau, \varepsilon) Q(\tau, \varepsilon) = 0, \tag{18.21}$$

from which, by the method described in Sec. 13, we can determine the terms of the expansions of the desired matrices $Q(\tau, \varepsilon)$ and $\mathfrak{A}(\tau, \varepsilon)$.

3. In the subsequent discussion, formulas (13.12)-(13.14) will be essential; these formulas can also be obtained from (18.21).

We divide each of the matrices $Q_s(\tau)$ and $F_s(\tau)$ occurring in Eq. (13.14) into blocks in such a way that on the principal diagonal we have square matrices of the orders $n_1, n_2, \ldots, n_p \left(\sum_{j=1}^{p} n_j = n\right)$, equal to the orders of the corresponding diagonal blocks of the matrices $\mathfrak{A}_s(\tau)$ $(s = 1, 2, \ldots)$.

As a result we obtain block matrices of a somewhat more general form in comparison with (13.16) (in this case the matrices will consist of p^2 blocks). We note that the matrices $\mathfrak{A}_s(\tau)$ $(s = 1, 2, \ldots)$, and also $W_0(\tau)$, already have the required block structure, as is obvious from (18.15) and (18.3).

Now we can carry out all the considerations of Sec. 13 concerning solution of the matrix equation (13.14), i.e., finding the matrices $Q_s(\tau)$ and $\mathfrak{A}_s(\tau)$ $(s = 1, 2, \ldots)$.

However, in contrast to (13.18), it will be convenient here to set

$$Q_{iis}(\tau) \equiv 0 \quad (i = 1, 2, \ldots, p; \ s = 1, 2, \ldots). \tag{18.22}$$

This is entirely admissible, since in the definition of the diagonal blocks of the matrix $Q_s(\tau)$ $(s = 1, 2, \ldots)$, as follows from system (13.17), there is a certain arbitrariness.

Then the remaining blocks $Q_{ijs}(\tau)(i, j=1, 2, \ldots, p, i \neq j; s=1, 2, \ldots)$, and also the $\mathfrak{A}_s(\tau)$ $(s = 1, 2, \ldots)$ are uniquely determined from the matrix equations (13.14).

Thus, by (18.19), we obtain the transforming matrix $Q(\tau, \varepsilon)$ in the form of a formal matrix series, whose asymptotic convergence will be proved below.

4. In the subsequent discussion, we will need certain preliminary constructions.

Taking account of (18.19) and (18.20), and also of (13.12) and (13.13), we represent each of the matrices $W(\tau, \varepsilon)$, $\mathfrak{A}(\tau, \varepsilon)$ and $Q(\tau, \varepsilon)$ as the sum of two terms

$$W(\tau, \varepsilon) = W_0(\tau) + \widetilde{W}(\tau, \varepsilon), \tag{18.23}$$

$$\mathfrak{A}(\tau, \varepsilon) = W_0(\tau) + \widetilde{\mathfrak{A}}(\tau, \varepsilon), \tag{18.24}$$

$$Q(\tau, \varepsilon) = E + \widetilde{Q}(\tau, \varepsilon), \tag{18.25}$$

where

$$\widetilde{W}(\tau, \varepsilon) = \sum_{s=1}^{\infty} \varepsilon^s W_s(\tau), \tag{18.26}$$

$$\widetilde{\mathfrak{A}}(\tau, \varepsilon) = \sum_{s=1}^{\infty} \varepsilon^s \mathfrak{A}_s(\tau), \tag{18.27}$$

$$\widetilde{Q}(\tau, \varepsilon) = \sum_{s=1}^{\infty} \varepsilon^s Q_s(\tau). \tag{18.28}$$

We write $\widetilde{W}(\tau, \varepsilon)$ as a block matrix, on whose principal diagonal we have the matrices $\widetilde{W}_{ii}(\tau, \varepsilon)$ of order n_i $(i = 1, 2, \ldots, p)$:

$$\widetilde{W}(\tau, \varepsilon) = \begin{bmatrix} \widetilde{W}_{11}(\tau, \varepsilon) & \widetilde{W}_{12}(\tau, \varepsilon) & \ldots & \widetilde{W}_{1p}(\tau, \varepsilon) \\ \widetilde{W}_{21}(\tau, \varepsilon) & \widetilde{W}_{22}(\tau, \varepsilon) & \ldots & \widetilde{W}_{2p}(\tau, \varepsilon) \\ \ldots & \ldots & \ldots & \ldots \\ \widetilde{W}_{p1}(\tau, \varepsilon) & \widetilde{W}_{p2}(\tau, \varepsilon) & \ldots & \widetilde{W}_{pp}(\tau, \varepsilon) \end{bmatrix}. \tag{18.29}$$

According to condition (18.22) (assumed earlier), which must be satisfied by the matrices $Q_s(\tau)$ $(s = 1, 2, \ldots)$, the matrix $\widetilde{Q}(\tau, \varepsilon)$ can be divided into blocks in the following way:

$$\widetilde{Q}(\tau, \varepsilon) = \begin{bmatrix} 0 & \widetilde{Q}_{12}(\tau, \varepsilon) & \ldots & \widetilde{Q}_{1p}(\tau, \varepsilon) \\ \widetilde{Q}_{21}(\tau, \varepsilon) & 0 & \ldots & \widetilde{Q}_{2p}(\tau, \varepsilon) \\ \ldots & \ldots & \ldots & \ldots \\ \ldots & \ldots & \ldots & \ldots \\ \widetilde{Q}_{p1}(\tau, \varepsilon) & \widetilde{Q}_{p2}(\tau, \varepsilon) & \ldots & 0 \end{bmatrix}; \tag{18.30}$$

where the zeros on the principal diagonal denote zero matrices of order n_j $(j = 1, 2, \ldots, p)$.

The matrix $V^{-1}(\tau)\, dV(\tau)\,/d\tau$ can also be represented as a block matrix, in a manner similar to (18.29) and (18.30). Its blocks will be denoted by

$$\left(V^{-1}(\tau)\frac{dV(\tau)}{d\tau}\right)_{jk} \quad (j, k = 1, 2, \ldots, p). \tag{18.31}$$

Taking into consideration Eqs. (18.23) - (18.25), we write the matrix equation (18.21) in a slightly different form

$$\varepsilon V^{-1}(\tau)\frac{dV(\tau)}{d\tau}[E + \widetilde{Q}(\tau, \varepsilon)] + \varepsilon\frac{d\widetilde{Q}(\tau,\varepsilon)}{d\tau} +$$
$$+ [E + \widetilde{Q}(\tau, \varepsilon)][W_0(\tau) + \widetilde{\mathfrak{A}}(\tau, \varepsilon)] - [W_0(\tau) + \widetilde{W}(\tau, \varepsilon)][E + \widetilde{Q}(\tau, \varepsilon)] = 0. \tag{18.32}$$

All the matrices occurring in Eq. (18.32) are divided up, in an identical fashion, into p^2 blocks; therefore in (18.32) we can carry out multiplication of the block matrices.

Writing out the result of this multiplication for the diagonal and nondiagonal blocks, we obtain the following relationships:

$$\widetilde{\mathfrak{A}}_j(\tau, \varepsilon) = \widetilde{W}_{jj}(\tau, \varepsilon) + \sum_{k=1}^{p}\widetilde{W}_{jk}(\tau, \varepsilon)\widetilde{Q}_{kj}(\tau, \varepsilon) -$$
$$- \varepsilon\left(V^{-1}(\tau)\frac{dV(\tau)}{d\tau}\right)_{jj} - \varepsilon\sum_{k=1}^{p}\left(V^{-1}(\tau)\frac{dV(\tau)}{d\tau}\right)_{jk}\widetilde{Q}_{kj}(\tau, \varepsilon),\ j = 1, 2, \ldots, p, \tag{18.33}$$

and

$$\varepsilon\frac{d\widetilde{Q}_{jk}(\tau, \varepsilon)}{d\tau} = W_{j0}(\tau)\widetilde{Q}_{jk}(\tau, \varepsilon) - \widetilde{Q}_{jk}(\tau, \varepsilon)W_{k0}(\tau) +$$
$$+ \widetilde{W}_{jk}(\tau, \varepsilon) - \widetilde{Q}_{jk}(\tau,\varepsilon)\widetilde{\mathfrak{A}}_k(\tau,\varepsilon) + \sum_{l=1}^{p} W_{jl}(\tau, \varepsilon)\widetilde{Q}_{lk}(\tau, \varepsilon) -$$
$$- \varepsilon\left(V^{-1}(\tau)\frac{dV(\tau)}{d\tau}\right)_{jk} - \varepsilon\sum_{l=1}^{p}\left(V^{-1}(\tau)\frac{dV(\tau)}{d\tau}\right)_{jk}\widetilde{Q}_{lk}(\tau, \varepsilon) \tag{18.34}$$

for $j \neq k$ $(j, k = 1, 2, \ldots, p)$.

Substituting the value of $\widetilde{\mathfrak{A}}_k(\tau, \varepsilon)$ from Eq. (18.33) into (18.34) we obtain

$$\varepsilon \frac{d\widetilde{Q}_{jk}(\tau, \varepsilon)}{d\tau} = W_{j0}(\tau)\,\widetilde{Q}_{jk}(\tau, \varepsilon) - \widetilde{Q}_{jk}(\tau, \varepsilon)\,W_{k0}(\tau) +$$

$$+ \sum_{l=1}^{p} W_{jl}(\tau,\varepsilon)\widetilde{Q}_{lk}(\tau, \varepsilon) - \varepsilon \sum_{l=1}^{p} \left(V^{-1}(\tau)\frac{dV(\tau)}{d\tau}\right)_{jl} \widetilde{Q}_{lk}(\tau, \varepsilon) +$$

$$+ \widetilde{W}_{jk}(\tau, \varepsilon) - \varepsilon \left(V^{-1}(\tau)\frac{dV(\tau)}{d\tau}\right)_{jk} - \widetilde{Q}_{jk}(\tau, \varepsilon)\,\widetilde{W}_{kk}(\tau, \varepsilon) -$$

$$- \widetilde{Q}_{jk}(\tau, \varepsilon) \sum_{l=1}^{p} \widetilde{W}_{kl}(\tau, \varepsilon)\,\widetilde{Q}_{lk}(\tau, \varepsilon) +$$

$$+ \varepsilon\,\widetilde{Q}_{jk}(\tau, \varepsilon) \sum_{l=1}^{p} \left(V^{-1}(\tau)\frac{dV(\tau)}{d\tau}\right)_{kl} \widetilde{Q}_{lk}(\tau, \varepsilon) +$$

$$+ \varepsilon\widetilde{Q}_{jk}(\tau,\varepsilon)\left(V^{-1}(\tau)\frac{dV(\tau)}{d\tau}\right)_{kk} \quad (j \neq k;\ j, k = 1, 2, \ldots, p). \tag{18.35}$$

Thus, we have obtained a system (18.35) of ordinary nonlinear differential equations, which must be satisfied by the k elements of the matrices $\widetilde{Q}_{jk}(\tau, \varepsilon)$ $(j \neq k;\ j, k = 1, 2, \ldots, p)$. If we write system (18.35) in expanded form, it is easy to see that the order of this system will be equal to $n^2 - \sum_{j=1}^{p} n_j^2$; in addition, the right-hand sides of the system will be second-degree multinomials with respect to the unknown functions [the elements of the matrix $\widetilde{Q}(\tau, \varepsilon)$] with coefficients which are functions of τ and ε. Since these coefficients are constructed from the elements of the matrices $\widetilde{W}(\tau, \varepsilon)$ and $V^{-1}(\tau)\, dV(\tau)/d\tau$ (see [18.35)], they can be expanded in powers series in ε, just like the elements of the matrix $\widetilde{W}(\tau, \varepsilon)$.

5. The formal solution

$$\widetilde{Q}_{jk}(\tau, \varepsilon) = \sum_{s=1}^{\infty} \varepsilon^s \widetilde{Q}_{jks}(\tau) \quad (j \neq k;\ j, k = 1, 2, \ldots p), \tag{18.36}$$

obtained by using the recurrent process (13.14) described in Sec. 13 obviously satisfies system (18.35), since in deriving system (18.35) we started out from Eqs. (13.14). Now we will show that this formal solution is an asymptotic expansion of a certain exact solution of the system of differential equations (18.35). This will also prove the asymptotic convergence of the formal series (18.36) to a certain exact transforming matrix $Q(\tau, \varepsilon)$.

Before we formulate the basic theorem of this section concerning the asymptotic convergence of the series (18.36), let us consider the system (18.35) in greater detail. From this point on, we will, for brevity, denote the unknown elements of the matrices $\widetilde{Q}_{jk}(\tau, \varepsilon)$ $(j \neq k;\ j, k = 1, 2, \ldots, p)$ by $u_1, u_2, \ldots, u_m$. We noted above that the order of system (18.35) is equal to

$$m = n^2 - \sum_{j=1}^{p} n_j^2. \tag{18.37}$$

The first two matrix terms on the right-hand sides of (18.35) play the dominant role (in a certain sense), since they are linear with respect to $u_1, u_2, \ldots, u_m$ and the coefficients of the unknown functions in these terms do not depend on ε. The remaining terms (linear as well as nonlinear) on the right-hand sides of Eqs. (18.35) are of the order of ε. In fact each of these terms, by (18.26) and (18.35), is of the form

$$\varepsilon F_k(\tau, \varepsilon) u_k \quad \text{or} \quad \varepsilon G_{jk}(\tau, \varepsilon) u_j u_k \quad (j, k = 1, \ldots, p),$$

where $F_k(\tau, \varepsilon)$ and $G_{jk}(\tau, \varepsilon)$ are certain functions of τ and ε, infinitely differentiable with respect to τ on the closed interval $[0, L]$, which are majorized by constants which are independent of ε.

We will call the expressions

$$W_{j0}(\tau)\widetilde{Q}_{jk}(\tau, \varepsilon) - \widetilde{Q}_{jk}(\tau, \varepsilon) W_{k0}(\tau) \qquad (j \neq k;\ j, k = 1, 2, \ldots, p) \tag{18.38}$$

the dominant linear part of system (18.35). For simplicity, we will illustrate that transformation of system (18.35) with an example. All the considerations which relate to the example can be carried over directly to the general case.

6. Thus, let the original system of differential equations (18.1) be of order $n = 5$, and let the corresponding matrix (18.3) consist of the two Jordan blocks

$$W_{10} = \begin{bmatrix} \lambda_1(\tau) & 1 & 0 \\ 0 & \lambda_1(\tau) & 1 \\ 0 & 0 & \lambda_1(\tau) \end{bmatrix}, \quad W_{20}(\tau) = \begin{bmatrix} \lambda_2(\tau) & 1 \\ 0 & \lambda_2(\tau) \end{bmatrix}. \tag{18.39}$$

In this case the unknown elements ($\widetilde{Q}_{12}$ and $\widetilde{Q}_{21}$) of the matrix $\widetilde{Q}(\tau, \varepsilon)$ in system (18.35) will be of the form

$$\tilde{Q}_{12}(\tau, \varepsilon) = \begin{bmatrix} u_1 & u_4 \\ u_2 & u_5 \\ u_3 & u_6 \end{bmatrix}, \qquad \tilde{Q}_{21}(\tau, \varepsilon) = \begin{bmatrix} u_7 & u_8 & u_9 \\ u_{10} & u_{11} & u_{12} \end{bmatrix}. \tag{18.40}$$

Lemma III.2. *By using a linear change of variables with constant coefficients, the system of differential equations (18.35) can be reduced to the form*

$$\varepsilon \frac{dv_j}{d\tau} = f_j(v_1, v_2, \ldots, v_m; \tau, \varepsilon) \qquad (j = 1, 2, \ldots, m), \tag{18.41}$$

where the $f_j(v_1, v_2, \ldots, v_m; \tau, \varepsilon)$ *are polynomials of second degree with respect to* $v_1, v_2, \ldots, v_m$ *with coefficients depending on* τ *and* ε*; the coefficients are expanded in series in powers of* ε *and are infinitely differentiable with respect to* τ*. In this case, the matrix of the dominant linear part of system (18.41) is of the form*

$$P(\tau) = \begin{cases} \mu_j(\tau) & (j = k) \\ \delta_j & (j = k-1) \\ 0 & (j \neq k, k-1) \end{cases} \qquad (j, k = 1, 2, \ldots, m), \tag{18.42}$$

where

$$\mu_j(\tau) = \lambda_r(\tau) - \lambda_s(\tau) \quad (r \neq s;\ r, s = 1, 2, \ldots, p;\ j = 1, \ldots, m),$$

and the numbers δ_j $(j = 1, 2, \ldots, m)$ *are either equal to zero or to a number* δ, *which can be chosen to be as small as we wish. In addition, if* $\delta_j = \delta$, *then* $\mu_{j-1}(\tau) = \mu_j(\tau)$.

Proof. We will first carry out the proof for the matrices (18.39)-(18.40), after which the proof can easily be extended to the general case.

In conformity with our example, the dominant linear part (18.38) of system (18.35) will consist of the matrices

$$W_{10}(\tau)\tilde{Q}_{12}(\tau, \varepsilon) - \tilde{Q}_{12}(\tau, \varepsilon) W_{20}(\tau) \tag{18.43}$$

and

$$W_{20}(\tau)\tilde{Q}_{21}(\tau, \varepsilon) - \tilde{Q}_{21}(\tau, \varepsilon) W_{10}(\tau). \tag{18.44}$$

In this case, performing the mentioned operations with matrices (18.39) and (18.40), we find that the system (18.35) takes the form

$$\varepsilon \frac{du}{d\tau} = R(\tau) u + \ldots, \tag{18.45}$$

where the dots denote terms which are proportional to ε, ε^2 etc., $u = \{u_1, u_2, \ldots, u_{12}\}$, and the matrix of the dominant linear part is of the form

$$R(\tau) = \begin{bmatrix} R_1(\tau) & 0 \\ 0 & R_2(\tau) \end{bmatrix}, \tag{18.46}$$

where, in turn,

$$R_1 = \begin{bmatrix} \mu_1(\tau) & 1 & 0 & 0 & 0 & 0 \\ 0 & \mu_1(\tau) & 1 & 0 & 0 & 0 \\ 0 & 0 & \mu_1(\tau) & 0 & 0 & 0 \\ -1 & 0 & 0 & \mu_1(\tau) & 1 & 0 \\ 0 & -1 & 0 & 0 & \mu_1(\tau) & 1 \\ 0 & 0 & -1 & 0 & 0 & \mu_1(\tau) \end{bmatrix}, \tag{18.47}$$

$$R_2(\tau) = \begin{bmatrix} \mu_2(\tau) & 0 & 0 & 1 & 0 & 0 \\ -1 & \mu_2(\tau) & 0 & 0 & 1 & 0 \\ 0 & -1 & \mu_2(\tau) & 0 & 0 & 1 \\ 0 & 0 & 0 & \mu_2(\tau) & 0 & 0 \\ 0 & 0 & 0 & -1 & \mu_2(\tau) & 0 \\ 0 & 0 & 0 & 0 & -1 & \mu_2(\tau) \end{bmatrix}, \tag{18.48}$$

$$\mu_1(\tau) = \lambda_1(\tau) - \lambda_2(\tau), \qquad \mu_2(\tau) = \lambda_2(\tau) - \lambda_1(\tau), \tag{18.49}$$

the zero on the secondary diagonal of matrix (18.46) denote zero matrices of order six.

The matrices (18.47) and (18.48) have a very simple structure. It is easy to see directly that $R_1(\tau)$ has a characteristic value $\mu_1(\tau)$ of multiplicity six, and $R_2(\tau)$ has a characteristic value $\mu_2(\tau)$ of multiplicity six.

The fact that the characteristic values of the matrices $R_1(\tau)$ and $R_2(\tau)$ lie on the principal diagonal, and that the nondiagonal elements do not depend on τ, is also valid in the general case of the system (18.35). This circumstance allows us to reduce system (18.35) by using a linear change of variables with constant coefficients; we reduce system (18.35) to the form (18.41) with matrix $P(\tau)$ of the dominant linear part [see (18.42)]. We shall demonstrate this on our example. In system (18.45) we perform the linear change of variables

$$u = S\tilde{u}, \tag{18.50}$$

where the constant matrix S is very simply constructed:

$$S=\begin{bmatrix} S_1 & 0 \\ 0 & S_2 \end{bmatrix}, \tag{18.51}$$

$$S_1=\begin{bmatrix} -\frac{1}{3} & 0 & 0 & 1 & 0 & 0 \\ 0 & -\frac{1}{3} & 0 & 0 & 1 & 0 \\ 0 & 0 & 0 & 0 & 0 & 1 \\ 0 & 0 & -3 & 0 & 0 & 0 \\ -\frac{1}{3} & 0 & 0 & -2 & 0 & 0 \\ 0 & -\frac{2}{3} & 0 & 0 & -1 & 0 \end{bmatrix}, \tag{18.52}$$

$$S_2=\begin{bmatrix} 0 & \frac{2}{3} & 0 & 0 & 1 & 0 \\ -\frac{1}{3} & 0 & 0 & -2 & 0 & 0 \\ 0 & 0 & 3 & 0 & 0 & 0 \\ 0 & 0 & 0 & 0 & 0 & 1 \\ 0 & \frac{1}{3} & 0 & 0 & -1 & 0 \\ -\frac{1}{3} & 0 & 0 & 1 & 0 & 0 \end{bmatrix}. \tag{18.53}$$

After such a conversion, the system (18.45) will look like this

$$\varepsilon\frac{d\tilde{u}}{d\tau}=S^{-1}R(\tau)S\tilde{u}+\ldots. \tag{18.54}$$

We leave it to the reader to verify that the matrix $S^{-1}R(\tau)S$ is of canonical Jordan form.

Finally, we carry out, in system (18.54), the linear transformation

$$\tilde{u}=Dv, \qquad v=(\{v_1, v_2, \ldots, v_m\}) \tag{18.55}$$

with the matrix

$$D=\begin{bmatrix} D_1 & 0 \\ 0 & D_1 \end{bmatrix}; \tag{18.56}$$

$$D_1 = \begin{bmatrix} 1 & 0 & 0 & 0 & 0 & 0 \\ 0 & \delta & 0 & 0 & 0 & 0 \\ 0 & 0 & \delta^2 & 0 & 0 & 0 \\ 0 & 0 & 0 & \delta^3 & 0 & 0 \\ 0 & 0 & 0 & 0 & \delta^4 & 0 \\ 0 & 0 & 0 & 0 & 0 & \delta^5 \end{bmatrix}, \tag{18.57}$$

where $\delta \neq 0$ is some number. Then system (18.54) is transformed to the following:

$$\varepsilon \frac{dv}{d\tau} = D^{-1}S^{-1}R(\tau)SDv + \ldots. \tag{18.58}$$

We introduce the notation

$$D^{-1}S^{-1}R(\tau)SD = P(\tau). \tag{18.59}$$

Thus, by using the linear change of variables defined by the constant matrix SD [see formulas (18.41)-(18.57)], the system of differential equations (18.35) corresponding to the matrices (18.39) and (18.40) is transformed to the system

$$\varepsilon \frac{dv}{d\tau} = P(\tau)v + \ldots \tag{18.60}$$

with a matrix of the dominant linear part of the form

$$P(\tau) = \begin{bmatrix} P_1(\tau) & 0 \\ 0 & P_2(\tau) \end{bmatrix}, \tag{18.61}$$

where

$$P_1(\tau) = \begin{bmatrix} \mu_1(\tau) & \delta & 0 & 0 & 0 & 0 \\ 0 & \mu_1(\tau) & 0 & 0 & 0 & 0 \\ 0 & 0 & \mu_1(\tau) & \delta & 0 & 0 \\ 0 & 0 & 0 & \mu_1(\tau) & \delta & 0 \\ 0 & 0 & 0 & 0 & \mu_1(\tau) & \delta \\ 0 & 0 & 0 & 0 & 0 & \mu_1(\tau) \end{bmatrix}. \tag{18.62}$$

The matrix $P_2(\tau)$ differs from $P_1(\tau)$ only along the principal diagonal where instead of $\mu_1(\tau)$ we have $\mu_2(\tau)$. The zeros on the right-hand side of (18.61), as in formulas (18.51) and (18.46), denote zero matrices of the corresponding order.

The remarks made above about the general character of the linear transformations performed here, which can be directly carried over to system (18.35), allow us to consider Lemma III.2 proved.

We must emphasize that the characteristic values $\mu_j(\tau)$ of the matrix of the dominant linear part of system (18.35) are equal to all possible pairwise differences (18.43) of the various characteristic values $\lambda_s(\tau)$ $(s = 1, 2, \ldots, p)$, therefore the values $\mu_j(\tau)$ $(j = 1, 2, \ldots, m)$ do not become equal to zero for any $\tau \in [0, L]$.

We also note that system (18.35) is equivalent to system (18.41) in the sense that any solution of system (18.35) corresponds to a solution of (18.41) and vice versa; knowing, for example, a solution of system (18.35), we can find the solution of system (18.41) which corresponds to it. In particular, to the formal solution (18.36) of system (18.35) there corresponds some formal solution of the system (18.41).

Therefore, if we prove the asymptotic convergence of the formal solution of system (18.41) which corresponds to the formal solution (18.36) of system (18.35), this will be equivalent to proving the asymptotic convergence of the formal solution (18.36).

We not turn to the proof of this assertion.

7. Theorem III.4. *Suppose we are given a system of differential equations (18.41), satisfying the conditions of Lemma III.2; let*

$$\mu_j(\tau) \neq 0 \qquad (j = 1, 2, \ldots, m), \qquad 0 \leqslant \tau \leqslant L. \tag{18.63}$$

We will assume that

$$v_j(\tau, \varepsilon) = \sum_{s=1}^{\infty} p_{js}(\tau)\, \varepsilon^s$$

$$(j = 1, 2, \ldots, m) \tag{18.64}$$

is a formal solution of system (18.41) with coefficients $p_{js}(\tau)$ $(j = 1, 2, \ldots, m;\ s = 1, 2, \ldots)$, *infinitely differentiable with respect to* τ.

Then we can find an $\varepsilon_1 < \varepsilon_0$, *such that in the region*

$$0 \leqslant \tau \leqslant L, \qquad 0 < \varepsilon \leqslant \varepsilon_1 \qquad (\varepsilon_1 \leqslant \varepsilon_0) \tag{18.65}$$

there exists a unique solution of system (18.41)

$$v_j = p_j(\tau, \varepsilon) \qquad (j = 1, 2, \ldots, m), \tag{18.66}$$

which is at least continuous with respect to τ, *and the series (18.64) will be the asymptotic expansions of the solution (18.66) in the region (18.65).*

Before turning to the proof of this theorem, we note that the $\mu_j(\tau)$ $(j = 1, 2, \ldots, m)$, generally speaking, are complex-valued functions of τ, and we can select complex constants $c_j = c_j' + ic_j''$ $(j = 1, 2, \ldots, m)$ such that the quantities

$$\sup_{\tau \in [0, L_1]} |\mu_j(\tau) - c_j| \qquad (j = 1, 2, \ldots, m) \tag{18.67}$$

will be as small as we like, provided the region of the approximation

$$0 \leqslant \tau \leqslant L_1 \qquad (L_1 \leqslant L) \tag{18.68}$$

is sufficiently small.

What is more, we can approximate the functions $\mu_j(\tau)$ $(j = 1, 2, \ldots, m)$ on $[0, L]$ by certain piecewise-constant functions of the form

$$C_j(\tau) = \begin{cases} c_{j0} = c_j, & 0 \leqslant \tau \leqslant L_1, \\ c_{j1}, & L_1 < \tau \leqslant L_2, \\ \cdots\cdots\cdots & \\ c_{j,q-1}, & L_{q-1} < \tau \leqslant L_q = L \\ & (j = 1, 2, \ldots, m). \end{cases} \tag{18.69}$$

Such a subdivision of the closed interval $[0, L]$ and such an approximation of the functions $\mu_j(\tau)$ $(j = 1, 2, \ldots, m)$ by the piecewise-constant functions (18.69) are completely feasible for any continuous function; however, since the $\mu_j(\tau)$ are not only continuous, but also infinitely differentiable, they certainly can be approximated very well by step functions.

We will first consider the functions $\mu_j(\tau)$ $(j = 1, 2, \ldots, m)$ on the first interval of approximation $0 \leqslant \tau \leqslant L_1$. The subsequent discussion can be extended, with a few small changes, to the successive intervals $[L_i, L_{i+1}]$ $(i = 0, 1, 2, \ldots, q-1)$ which form the whole interval $[0, L]$.

Without loss of generality we can assume that the first m' $(m' < m)$ functions $\mu_j(\tau)$ $(j = 1, 2, \ldots, m')$ have, on the interval $[0, L_1]$, a nonnegative real part, while the remaining functions $\mu_j(\tau)$ $(j = m' + 1, m' + 2, \ldots, m)$ have a negative real part. In choosing the closed interval $[0, L_1]$ we set up the condition that the real part of each of the functions $\mu_j(\tau)$ $(j = 1, 2, \ldots, m)$ does not change sign within the interval $[0, L_1]$. Thus, it follows that we must choose the partition points $L_1, L_2, \ldots, L_{q-1}, L$ in formula (18.69) in such a way that all the values $\tau \in [0, L]$, for which any of the functions $\mu_j(\tau)$ $(j = 1, 2, \ldots, m)$ changes the sign of its real part are included in the set of partition points L_i $(i = 1, 2, \ldots, p)$. Thus, the number p will always be greater than or equal to the number of changes of sign of the functions $\operatorname{Re}\mu_j(\tau)$ $(j = 1, 2, \ldots, m)$.

We note that among the first m' functions $\mu_j(\tau)$ $(j = 1, 2, \ldots, m')$ there may be some for which $\operatorname{Re}\mu_j(\tau) \equiv 0$ $(j = 1, 2, \ldots, l,\ l \leqslant m')$.

Lemma III.3. *If ε and τ vary in the region*

$$0 \leqslant \tau \leqslant L_1, \qquad 0 < \varepsilon \leqslant \varepsilon_0 \qquad (L_1 \leqslant L), \tag{18.70}$$

then we can always find a positive constant c, independent of ε, such that the following inequality

$$\left| \int_{\tau_j}^{\tau} \exp\left(-\frac{c_j(\tau - \tau_j)}{\varepsilon}\right) d\tau \right| \leqslant c\varepsilon \left| \exp\left(-\frac{c_j(\tau - \tau_j)}{\varepsilon}\right) \right|, \tag{18.71}$$

will hold, where

$$\tau_j = \begin{cases} L_1 \text{ for } j = 1, 2, \ldots, m';\ c_j' \geqslant 0; \\ 0 \text{ for } j = m' + 1,\ m' + 2, \ldots, m;\ c_j' < 0. \end{cases} \tag{18.72}$$

Proof. The proof of the lemma becomes obvious if we consider the following sequence of inequalities:

$$\left| \int_{\tau_j}^{\tau} \exp\left(-\frac{c_j(\tau - \tau_j)}{\varepsilon}\right) d\tau, \quad \varepsilon \left| \frac{1}{c_j} \left[1 - \exp\left(-\frac{c_j(\tau - \tau_j)}{\varepsilon}\right)\right] \right| = \right.$$

$$= \varepsilon \left| \frac{1}{c_j} \left[\exp\left(\frac{c_j(\tau - \tau_j)}{\varepsilon}\right) - 1\right] \right| \left| \exp\left(-\frac{c_j(\tau - \tau_j)}{\varepsilon}\right) \right| \leqslant$$

$$\leqslant c\varepsilon \left| \exp\left(-\frac{c_j(\tau - \tau_j)}{\varepsilon}\right) \right| \qquad (j = 1, 2, \ldots, m), \tag{18.73}$$

where

$$c = \max_{j=1,\ldots,m} \left\{ \frac{1}{|c_j|} \sup_{\substack{\tau \in [0, L_2] \\ 0 < \varepsilon \leqslant \varepsilon_0}} \left| \exp\left(\frac{c_j(\tau - \tau_j)}{\varepsilon} \right) - 1 \right| \right\} = \max_{j=1,\ldots,m} \left\{ \frac{2}{|c_j|} \right\}. \tag{18.74}$$

In the proof of the theorem we will be interested in the parts of the functions $f_j(v; \tau, \varepsilon)$ $(j = 1, 2, \ldots, m)$ in system (18.41) which are linear with respect to v:

$$a_j(\tau, \varepsilon) + \sum_{k=1}^{m} a_{jk}(\tau, \varepsilon) v_k \qquad (j = 1, 2, \ldots, m). \tag{18.75}$$

According to the conditions of the theorem, the coefficients of the v_j $(j = 1, \ldots, m)$ can be expanded in asymptotic series

$$a_{jk}(\tau, \varepsilon) = \sum_{s=0}^{\infty} a_{jks}(\tau) \varepsilon^s \qquad (j = 1, 2, \ldots, m). \tag{18.76}$$

Then the first terms of the expansions (18.76), which do not contain ε, form the matrix $P(\tau) = [a_{jk0}(\tau)]_{j,k=1}^{j,k=m}$, which is of the form (18.42).

8. Proof of Theorem III.4. In system (13.41) we carry out the change of variables

$$v_j = p_j^{(N)}(\tau, \varepsilon) + y_j \qquad (j = 1, 2, \ldots, m), \tag{18.77}$$

where

$$p_j^{(N)}(\tau, \varepsilon) = \sum_{s=1}^{N-1} p_{js}(\tau) \varepsilon^s$$
$$(j = 1, 2, \ldots, m;\ N > 1), \tag{18.78}$$

i.e.,a partial sum of the series (18.64).

As a result of this conversion, system (18.41) takes the form

$$\frac{dy_j}{dt} = g_j^{(N)}(y_1, y_2, \ldots, y_m; \tau, \varepsilon)$$
$$(j = 1, 2, \ldots, m), \tag{18.79}$$

where the right-hand sides, as before, are polynomials in y_j $(j = 1,2, \ldots, m)$ of second degree with coefficients which are infinitely differentiable with respect to τ ; the coefficients can be expanded in asymptotic series in powers of the parameter ε in the region $0 \leqslant \tau \leqslant L$, $0 < \varepsilon \leqslant \varepsilon_0$.

By analogy with (18.75) the linear parts $g_j^{(N)}(y; \tau, \varepsilon)$ are of the form

$$b_j^{(N)}(\tau, \varepsilon) + \sum_{k=1}^{m} b_{jk}^{(N)}(\tau, \varepsilon)\, y_k \quad (j = 1, 2, \ldots, m). \tag{18.80}$$

In addition, we have the expansions of the coefficients

$$b_{jk}^{(N)}(\tau, \varepsilon) = \sum_{s=0}^{\infty} b_{jks}^{(N)}(\tau)\, \varepsilon^s \quad (j, k = 1, 2, \ldots, m). \tag{18.81}$$

Then, by substituting (18.77) directly into (18.75) and (18.41), we can easily verify that the matrix of the coefficients of the dominant linear part of system (18.79) coincides with (18.42), i.e.,

$$b_{jk0}^{(N)}(\tau) = a_{jk0}(\tau) = \begin{cases} \mu_j(\tau) & (k = j), \\ \delta_j & (k = j+1), \\ 0 & (k \neq j,\ j+1). \end{cases} \tag{18.82}$$

On the other hand, the system (18.79) has the formal solution

$$y_j = \sum_{s=N}^{\infty} p_{js}(\tau)\, \varepsilon^s \qquad (j = 1, 2, \ldots, m), \tag{18.83}$$

which follows from the change of variables (18.77) and the conditions of the theorem.

Therefore, the expansions of the free terms $b_j^{(N)}(\tau, \varepsilon)$ $(j=1, 2, \ldots, m)$ do not contain powers of ε lower than N; consequently, we can find a constant B_N, such that the inequality

$$|b_j^{(N)}(\tau, \varepsilon)| \leqslant B_N \varepsilon^N \qquad (j = 1, 2, \ldots, m) \tag{18.84}$$

holds for $0 \leqslant \tau \leqslant L$, $0 < \varepsilon \leqslant \varepsilon_0$, in which B_N is independent of ε. We adopt the notation

$$\| y \| = \max \{ |y_1|, |y_2|, \ldots, |y_m| \}. \tag{18.85}$$

We note that δ in (18.42) can be chosen as small as we like.

Then we can find a δ, an $\varepsilon_1 \leqslant \varepsilon_0$ and an $L_1 \leqslant L$, such that the following inequalities hold:

$$|b_{jj}^{(N)}(\tau, \varepsilon) - c_j| \leqslant A_1 \qquad (j = 1, 2, \ldots, m), \tag{18.86}$$

$$|b_{jk}^{(N)}(\tau, \varepsilon)| \leqslant A_1 \qquad (j \neq k;\ j, k = 1, 2, \ldots, m), \tag{18.87}$$

provided

$$0 \leqslant \tau \leqslant L_1, \qquad 0 < \varepsilon \leqslant \varepsilon_1. \tag{18.88}$$

The constant A_1 can be chosen to be sufficiently small, provided ε, δ and L_1 are also sufficiently small. We will again return to the question of the choice of these constants.

We make the following change of variables in system (18.79), setting

$$y_j = z_j \exp\left[\frac{c_j(\tau - \tau_j)}{\varepsilon}\right] \qquad (j = 1, 2, \ldots, m). \tag{18.89}$$

Then, from system (18.79), we obtain a system of equations with respect to the z_j $(j = 1, 2, \ldots, m)$:

$$\varepsilon \frac{dz_j}{d\tau} = g_j^{(N)}\left[z_1 \exp\left(\frac{c_1(\tau - \tau_1)}{\varepsilon}\right), \ldots, z_m \exp\left(\frac{c_m(\tau - \tau_m)}{\varepsilon}\right); \tau, \varepsilon\right] \times$$
$$\times \exp\left(-\frac{c_j(\tau - \tau_j)}{\varepsilon}\right) - c_j z_j \qquad (j = 1, 2, \ldots, m). \tag{18.90}$$

In order to obtain an estimate of the right-hand sides of system (18.90) it is convenient to partially retain the old variables y_j $(j = 1, 2, \ldots, m)$ in system (18.90). By comparing (18.89) and (18.90), it is not difficult to see that system (18.90) can be written in the form

$$\varepsilon \frac{dz_j}{d\tau} = \{g_j^{(N)}(y_1, \ldots, y_m; \tau, \varepsilon) - c_j y_j\} \exp\left(-\frac{c_j(\tau - \tau_j)}{\varepsilon}\right) \qquad (j = 1, 2, \ldots, m), \tag{18.91}$$

where the τ_j are chosen in accordance with (18.72).

Let us estimate the expression in brackets in system (18.91).

The functions $g_j^{(N)}(y; \tau, \varepsilon)$ $(j = 1, \ldots, m)$ consist of linear terms of the form (19.80) and nonlinear terms whose structure can be clarified by considering the right-hand sides of the system (18.35), where they are obtained after linear changes of variables. We already noted above that the coefficients of the nonlinear terms in system (18.35) are of the order of ε. We can say the same thing about the right-hand sides of system (18.79). Then, taking into account the inequalities (18.84), (18.86) and (18.87), we obtain

$$|g_j^{(N)}(y;\ \tau,\ \varepsilon)-c_jy_j|\leqslant B_N\varepsilon^N+A_1m\,\|y\|+\varepsilon Hm^2\,\|y\|^2 \quad (j=1,\ 2,\ \ldots,m), \tag{18.92}$$

where the first term on the right-hand side corresponds to the estimate (18.84), and the second term corresponds to the estimates (18.86) and (18.87); by means of the constant H we estimate the maximum coefficient of the nonlinear (quadratic with respect to y) terms in system (18.79). For sufficiently small ε and $\|y\|$, the term on the right-hand side of inequality (18.92) can be made as small as we like. We write

$$A_1m\,\|y\|+\varepsilon Hm^2\,\|y\|^2=m\,\|y\|\,(A_1+\varepsilon Hm\,\|y\|)=Am\,\|y\|, \tag{18.93}$$

where

$$A=A_1+\varepsilon Hm\,\|y\|. \tag{18.94}$$

Consequently,

$$|g_j^{(N)}(y;\ \tau,\ \varepsilon)-c_jy_j|\leqslant B_N\varepsilon^N+Am\,\|y\| \quad (j=1,\ 2,\ \ldots,\ m) \tag{18.95}$$

for

$$0\leqslant\tau\leqslant L_1,\qquad 0<\varepsilon\leqslant\varepsilon_1.$$

We choose L_1, δ and ε_1 small enough so that the inequality

$$Amc<1, \tag{18.96}$$

holds, where c is determined by formula (18.74). Inequalities (18.95) and (18.96) will be important in the subsequent discussion.

Let $\psi_j(\varepsilon)$ $(j=1,\ 2,\ \ldots.\ m)$ be certain function of ε $(0<\varepsilon\leqslant\varepsilon_0)$, which can be expanded in power series in ε:

$$\psi_j(\varepsilon)=\sum_{s=1}^{\infty}p_{js}(\tau_j)\,\varepsilon^s \qquad (j=1,\ 2,\ \ldots,\ m). \tag{18.97}$$

We set

$$\psi_j^{(N)}(\varepsilon) = \psi_j(\varepsilon) - p_j^{(N)}(\tau_j, \varepsilon) \qquad (j = 1, 2, \ldots, m), \tag{18.98}$$

where the τ_j are constants which are determined in accordance with (18.72), and the $p_j^{(N)}(\tau_j, \varepsilon)$ are defined by (18.78).

Then we have the inequalities

$$|\psi_j^{(N)}(\varepsilon)| \leqslant R_N \varepsilon^N \qquad (j = 1, 2, \ldots, m), \tag{18.99}$$

$$|\psi_j^{(N)}(\varepsilon_2) - \psi_j^{(N)}(\varepsilon_1')| \leqslant k_N |\varepsilon_2 - \varepsilon_1'| \varepsilon^{N-1} \qquad (\varepsilon_1', \varepsilon_2 \in [0, \varepsilon_1]),$$

which follow from the differentiability of the $p_j(\tau, \varepsilon)$ $(j = 1, \ldots, m)$ with respect to ε; R_N and k_N are constants, independent of ε, which are common for all $j = 1, 2, \ldots, m$.

Now we will prove the existence and uniqueness of the solutions

$$z_j = \psi_j^{(N)}(\tau, \varepsilon) \qquad (j = 1, 2, \ldots, m) \tag{18.100}$$

of system (18.90), continuous in τ, and satisfying the conditions

$$\psi_j^{(N)}(\tau_j, \varepsilon) = \psi_j^{(N)}(\varepsilon) \qquad (j = 1, 2, \ldots, m) \tag{18.101}$$

and the inequalities

$$|\psi_j^{(N)}(\tau, \varepsilon)| \leqslant K_N \varepsilon^N \left| \exp\left(- \frac{c_j(\tau - \tau_j)}{\varepsilon} \right) \right| \qquad (j = 1, 2, \ldots, m) \tag{18.102}$$

in the region (18.88): $0 \leqslant \tau \leqslant L_1$, $0 < \varepsilon \leqslant \varepsilon_1$. The constant K_N does not depend on ε and, as will be shown below, can be defined in the following way:

$$K_N = \frac{R_N + cB_N}{1 - Amc}. \tag{18.103}$$

Because of (18.89), verification of the existence and uniqueness of solution (18.100) of system (18.90), satisfying conditions (18.101) and (18.102), is equivalent to proof of the existence and uniqueness of the solution of system (18.79), satisfying the conditions

$$|y_j(\tau, \varepsilon)| \leqslant K_N \varepsilon^N \qquad (j = 1, 2, \ldots, m) \tag{18.104}$$

and conditions analogous to (18.101). If we take into account formulas (18.77), (18.78) and (18.64), then we can understand why the above assertion about the solution (18.100) is equivalent to a proof of Theorem III.4 for the region (18.88).

The proof reduces, in essence, to application of the fixed-point principle for Banach spaces (Shauder's principle [33]). We can also refer to a theorem of similar content, formulated for linear topological spaces in [135]. Here we will use the concepts of convexity and compactness as applied to sets in Banach (or in topological) spaces. The reader can find the definitions, and other relevant material, in the book by Kantorovich and Akilov [33], for example.

Continuing the proof of Theorem III.4, we consider sets Φ_j $(j = 1, 2, \ldots, m)$ of functions $\varphi_j(\tau, \varepsilon)$, defined in the region (18.88), infinitely differentiable with respect to τ, having a continuous derivative with respect to ε, and satisfying, in the given region, the inequalities

$$|\varphi_j(\tau, \varepsilon)| \leqslant K_N \varepsilon^N \left| \exp\left(-\frac{c_j(\tau - \tau_j)}{\varepsilon}\right)\right|, \tag{18.105}$$

$$\left|\varphi_j(\tau, \varepsilon_2)\exp\left(\frac{c_j(\tau-\tau_j)}{\varepsilon_2}\right) - \varphi_j(\tau, \varepsilon_1)\exp\left(\frac{c_j(\tau-\tau_j)}{\varepsilon_1}\right)\right| \leqslant$$
$$\leqslant h_N \varepsilon^{N-2} |\varepsilon_2 - \varepsilon_1'|, \tag{18.106}$$

$$\left|\varphi_j(\tau_2, \varepsilon)\exp\left(\frac{c_j(\tau_2-\tau_j)}{\varepsilon}\right) - \varphi_j(\tau_1, \varepsilon)\exp\left(\frac{c_j(\tau-\tau_j)}{\varepsilon}\right)\right| \leqslant$$
$$\leqslant M_N \varepsilon^{N-1} |\tau_2 - \tau_1| \tag{18.107}$$
$$(j = 1, 2, \ldots, m;\ \tau_1, \tau_2 \in [0, L_1],\ 0 < \varepsilon \leqslant \varepsilon_1),$$

where the constant K_N was defined above by formula (18.103), and h_N and M_N are certain constants which are independent of ε. In particular, we can set

$$M_N = R_N c^* + (1 + c^* c)(B_N + A_m K_N), \tag{18.108}$$

where

$$c^* = \max_{1 \leqslant j \leqslant m} |c_j|. \tag{18.109}$$

With each set Φ_j $(j = 1, 2, \ldots, m)$ we associate a set F_j $(j = 1, 2, \ldots, m)$ of functions $f_j(\tau, \varepsilon)$, defined in the same region (18.88) and related to the functions $\varphi_j \in \Phi_j$ by the relationships

$$f_j(\tau, \varepsilon) = \varphi_j(\tau, \varepsilon)\exp\left(\frac{c_j(\tau - \tau_j)}{\varepsilon}\right)$$
$$(j = 1, 2, \ldots, m). \tag{18.110}$$

Equations (18.110) obviously correspond to the change of variables (18.89) and establish a one-to one correspondence between the elements of the sets Φ_j and F_j $(j = 1, \ldots, m)$.

Then from inequalities (18.105)-(18.107), by the relationship (18.110), we obtain directly the following inequalities for the functions $f_j(\tau, \varepsilon) \in F_j$ $(j = 1, 2, \ldots, m)$:

$$| f_j(\tau, \varepsilon)| \leqslant K_N \varepsilon^N, \tag{18.111}$$

$$| f_j(\tau, \varepsilon_2) - f_j(\tau, \varepsilon_1')| \leqslant h_N \varepsilon^{N-2} | \varepsilon_2 - \varepsilon_1' |, \tag{18.112}$$

$$| f_j(\tau_2, \varepsilon) - f_j(\tau_1, \varepsilon)| \leqslant M_N \varepsilon^{N-1} | \tau_2 - \tau_1 | \tag{18.113}$$

$$(j = 1, 2, \ldots, m;\ \tau_1, \tau_2 \in [0, L],\ 0 < \varepsilon \leqslant \varepsilon_1),$$

where

$$0 < \varepsilon_1' \leqslant \varepsilon_2 \leqslant \varepsilon_1. \tag{18.114}$$

We introduce in the sets F_j $(j = 1, 2, \ldots, m)$ the topology of uniform convergence, i.e., the topology of the space C of continuous functions. In other words, we will say that the two functions $f_j^{(1)}, f_j^{(2)} \in F_j$ lie close to one another, provided that the "distance" between them, defined by the formula

$$\varrho(f_j^{(1)}, f_j^{(2)}) = \max_{\substack{\tau \in [0, L_1] \\ 0 < \varepsilon \leqslant \varepsilon_1}} | f_j^{(1)}(\tau, \varepsilon) - f_j^{(2)}(\tau, \varepsilon) |$$

$$(j = 1, 2, \ldots, m), \tag{18.115}$$

is small enough. Thus, we can consider that $F_j \subset C$. We will show that the inequalities (18.111) and (18.113) ensure the compactness of the sets F_j $(j = 1, 2, \ldots, m)$.

According to Arzela's theorem, a set of functions in the space C is compact if the functions of this set are uniformly bounded and equicontinuous. The uniform boundedness of the functions in F_j follows from inequality (18.111). The requirement of equicontinuity can be replaced by a Lipschitz condition (see [33]). Thus, we must show that the functions $f_j \in F_j$ satisfy a Lipschitz condition with respect to τ and ε in the region (18.88):

$$| f_j(\tau_2, \varepsilon_2) - f_j(\tau_1, \varepsilon_1')| \leqslant k_1 | \tau_2 - \tau_1 | + k_2 | \varepsilon_2 - \varepsilon_1' |$$

$$(j = 1, 2, \ldots, m), \tag{18.116}$$

where τ_1, τ_2, ε_1' and ε_2 are any values of τ and ε from (18.88), and k_2 and k_1 are constants which do not depend on τ and ε.

In fact, (18.112) and (18.113) imply an inequality which is even stronger than (18.116):

$$|f_j(\tau_2, \varepsilon_2) - f_j(\tau_1, \varepsilon_1')| = |f_j(\tau_2, \varepsilon_2) - f_j(\tau_1, \varepsilon_2) + f_j(\tau_1, \varepsilon_2) -$$

$$- f_j(\tau, \varepsilon_1')| \leqslant |f_j(\tau_2, \varepsilon_2) - f_j(\tau_1, \varepsilon_2)| + |f_j(\tau_1, \varepsilon_2) - f_j(\tau_1, \varepsilon_1')|$$

$$(j = 1, 2, \ldots, m;\ \tau_1, \tau_2 \in [0, L_1];\ \varepsilon_1', \varepsilon_2 \in (0, \varepsilon_1]). \qquad (18.117)$$

In estimating the first term on the right-hand side of (18.117) we rely on inequality (18.113), whereas in estimating the second term we use (18.112). Then we obtain

$$|f_j(\tau_2, \varepsilon_2) - f_j(\tau_1, \varepsilon_1')| \leqslant M_N \varepsilon^{N-1} |\tau_2 - \tau_1| + h_N \varepsilon^{N-2} |\varepsilon_2 - \varepsilon_1'|$$

$$(j = 1, 2, , \ldots, m;\ 0 < \varepsilon_1' \leqslant \varepsilon_2 \leqslant \varepsilon_1;\ \varepsilon_1' \leqslant \varepsilon \leqslant \varepsilon_2). \qquad (18.118)$$

Obviously, inequality (18.118) is even stronger than (18.116). Thus, on the basis of (18.111) and (18.118), we have proved that the sets F_j $(j = 1, \ldots, m)$ are compact in the metric space C of continuous functions. But then the sets Φ_j $(j = 1, 2, \ldots, m)$ are also compact, but in the metrics which are defined, in accordance with (18.115) and (18.110), by the equalities:

$$\tilde{\varrho}_j(\varphi_j^{(1)}, \varphi_j^{(2)}) = \max_{\substack{\tau \in [0, L_1] \\ 0 < \varepsilon \leqslant \varepsilon_1}} \left| \exp\left(\frac{c_j(\tau - \tau_j)}{\varepsilon}\right) [\varphi_j^{(1)}(\tau, \varepsilon) - \varphi_j^{(2)}(\tau, \varepsilon)] \right|$$

$$(j = 1, 2, \ldots, m). \qquad (18.119)$$

We note that the sets Φ_j $(j = 1, 2, \ldots, m)$ are convex. This follows directly from inequalities (18.105) (18.107). Indeed, if we take two positive numbers α and β, such that $\alpha + \beta = 1$, and take any two functions $\varphi_j^{(1)}, \varphi_j^{(2)} \in \Phi_j$, then from inequality (18.105) it follows that

$$|\alpha\varphi_j^{(1)} + \beta\varphi_j^{(2)}| \leqslant \alpha |\varphi_j^{(1)}| + \beta |\varphi_j^{(2)}| \leqslant$$

$$\leqslant (\alpha + \beta) K_N \varepsilon^N \left| \exp\left(-\frac{c_j(\tau - \tau_j)}{\varepsilon}\right) \right| = K_N \varepsilon^N \left| \exp\left(-\frac{c_j(\tau - \tau_j)}{\varepsilon}\right) \right|$$

$$(j = 1, 2, \ldots, m). \qquad (18.120)$$

In a completely similar manner, we can show that the function $\varphi_j^{(3)}(\tau, \varepsilon) = \alpha\varphi_j^{(1)}(\tau, \varepsilon) + \beta\varphi_j^{(2)}(\tau, \varepsilon)$ satisfies both inequalities (18.106) and (18.107). Consequently, $\varphi_j^{(3)}(\tau, \varepsilon) \in \Phi_j$. But this implies that the sets Φ_j $(j = 1, 2, \ldots, m)$ are convex.

Let us consider the direct product of the sets Φ_j $(j = 1, \ldots, m)$:

$$F = \Phi_1 \times \Phi_2 \times \ldots \times \Phi_m. \qquad (18.121)$$

The elements of the set F are all possible ordered m-tuples of functions: $\{\varphi_1(\tau, \varepsilon), \ldots, \varphi_m(\tau, \varepsilon)\}$, where $\varphi_j(\tau, \varepsilon) \in \Phi_j$ $(j = 1, 2, \ldots, m)$.

From the convexity and compactness of the sets Φ_j ($j = 1, 2, \ldots, m$), it follows that the set F is also convex and compact in the metric defined by an m-tuple of the distances (18.119). This follows from the properties of a direct product of metric or topological spaces [33].

The system of differential equations (18.90) with the conditions (18.101) can be written in the following integral form:

$$z_j(\tau, \varepsilon) = \psi_j^{(N)}(\varepsilon) + \frac{1}{\varepsilon}\int_{\tau_j}^{\tau} G_j(z_1, \ldots, z_m; \tau, \varepsilon)\, d\tau$$

$$(j = 1, 2, \ldots, m), \qquad (18.122)$$

where the $G_j(z; \tau, \varepsilon)$ denote the right-hand sides of Eqs. (18.90). Proceeding from system (18.122), we can consider that the equations

$$\Psi_j(\tau, \varepsilon) = \psi_j^{(N)}(\varepsilon) + \frac{1}{\varepsilon}\int_{\tau_j}^{\tau} G_j(\varphi_1, \ldots, \varphi_m; \tau, \varepsilon)\, d\tau$$

$$(j = 1, 2, \ldots, m) \qquad (18.123)$$

define an operator T on the set F; this operator maps each element of the set F, i.e., each ordered m-tuple of functions $\{\varphi_1(\tau, \varepsilon), \varphi_2(\tau, \varepsilon), \ldots, \varphi_m(\tau, \varepsilon)\}$, into a new completely determined m-tuple of functions $\{\Psi_1(\tau, \varepsilon), \ldots, \Psi_m(\tau, \varepsilon)\}$.

We recall that the $G_j(\varphi_1, \ldots, \varphi_m; \tau, \varepsilon)$ are second-degree polynomials with respect to $\varphi_1, \ldots, \varphi_m$ with coefficients which are infinitely differentiable with respect to τ, multiplied by $(-c_j(\tau - \tau_j)/\varepsilon)$. Then, from the form of the right-hand side of (18.123) it follows that the operator T preserves infinite differentiability with respect to τ. It is easy to show that T is a continuous operator, i.e., that T transforms close elements to close elements (in the given metric).

Now we must show that the operator T maps the set F into itself, i.e., that

$$T\{F\} \subseteq F. \qquad (18.124)$$

This means that the functions $\Psi_j(\tau, \varepsilon)$, found by (18.123), must satisfy inequalities (18.105)-(18.107). If we can prove this, then we will simultaneously prove the compactness of $T\{F\}$ and the inclusion (18.124).

Let us exhibit for $\Psi_j(\tau, \varepsilon)$ ($j = 1, 2, \ldots, m$) an estimate of the type (18.105). We note that the inequalities (18.111) can be collected into one inequality

$$\|f\| \leqslant K_N \varepsilon^N, \qquad (18.125)$$

if we set

$$\| f \| = \max \{ | f_1(\tau, \varepsilon) |, \ldots, | f_m(\tau, \varepsilon) | \}. \quad (18.126)$$

Recalling the relationship between systems (18.90) and (18.91), as well as relationships (18.89) and (18.110), we can estimate (18.123) as follows:

$$| \Psi_j(\tau, \varepsilon) | \leqslant | \psi_j^{(N)}(\varepsilon) | + \frac{1}{\varepsilon} \left| \int_{\tau_j}^{\tau} \{ g_j^{(N)}(f_1, \ldots, f_m; \tau, \varepsilon) - c_j f_j \} \times \right.$$

$$\left. \times \exp\left(- \frac{c_j(\tau - \tau_j)}{\varepsilon} \right) d\tau \right| \qquad (j = 1, 2, \ldots, m). \quad (18.127)$$

The estimates (18.95) and (18.99) remain valid when we replace y_j by f_j $(j = 1, \ldots, m)$ in them. This follows from (18.85), (18.126) and (18.125). If we use these estimates and Lemma III.3, then from inequality (18.127) we obtain

$$| \Psi_j(\tau, \varepsilon) | \leqslant R_N \varepsilon^N + \frac{1}{\varepsilon} (B_N \varepsilon^N + Am \| f \|) \left| \int_{\tau_j}^{\tau} \exp\left(- \frac{c_j(\tau - \tau_j)}{\varepsilon} \right) d\tau \right| \leqslant$$

$$\leqslant R_N \varepsilon^N + (B_N \varepsilon^N + Am \| f \|) c \left| \exp\left(- \frac{c_j(\tau - \tau_j)}{\varepsilon} \right) \right| =$$

$$= \varepsilon^N (R_N + cB_N) \left[1 + \frac{Am \| f \|}{(R_N + B_N c) \varepsilon^N} \right] \left| \exp\left(- \frac{c_j(\tau - \tau_j)}{\varepsilon} \right) \right| =$$

$$= \varepsilon^N (R_N + cB_N) \left[1 + \frac{Amc \| f \|}{(1 - Amc) \dfrac{R_N + cB_N}{1 - Amc} \varepsilon^N} \right] \left| \exp\left(- \frac{c_j(\tau - \tau_j)}{\varepsilon} \right) \right|$$

$$(j = 1, 2, \ldots, m). \quad (18.128)$$

Using the notation (13.103) and inequality (18.125), we find from this

$$| \Psi_j(\tau, \varepsilon) | \leqslant K_N \varepsilon^N \left| \exp\left(\frac{- c_j(\tau - \tau_j)}{\varepsilon} \right) \right| \qquad (j = 1, 2, \ldots, m), \quad (18.129)$$

which was to be proved.

To obtain inequalities of the form (18.106) for the functions $\Psi_j(\tau, \varepsilon)$ $(j = 1, 2, \ldots, m)$, we introduce the notation

$$\left| \Psi_j(\tau, \varepsilon_2) \exp \frac{c_j(\tau - \tau_j)}{\varepsilon_2} - \Psi_j(\tau, \varepsilon_1') \exp \frac{c_j(\tau - \tau_j)}{\varepsilon_1'} \right| = \Delta(\Psi_j, \varepsilon_1', \varepsilon_2)$$
$$(j = 1, 2, \ldots, m). \tag{18.130}$$

Then, on the basis of Eq. (18.123), we find

$$\Delta(\Psi_j, \varepsilon_1', \varepsilon_2) \leqslant \left| \Psi_j^N(\varepsilon_2) \exp \frac{c_j(\tau - \tau_j)}{\varepsilon_2} - \Psi_j^{(N)}(\varepsilon_1') \exp \frac{c_j(\tau - \tau_j)}{\varepsilon} \right| +$$
$$+ \left| \frac{1}{\varepsilon_2} \exp\left(\frac{c_j(\tau - \tau_j)}{\varepsilon_2} \right) \int_{\tau_j}^{\tau} G_j(\varphi; \tau, \varepsilon_2)\, d\tau - \frac{1}{\varepsilon_1'} \exp\left(\frac{c_j(\tau - \tau_j)}{\varepsilon} \right) \times \right.$$
$$\left. \times \int_{\tau_j}^{\tau} G_j(\varphi; \tau, \varepsilon_1')\, d\tau \right| \qquad (j = 1, 2, \ldots, m). \tag{18.131}$$

In order to estimate the first term on the right-hand side of inequality (18.131), we can add and subtract the expression $\psi_j^{(N)}(\varepsilon_1')$ exp $c_j(\tau - \tau_j)/\varepsilon$. Then from relationships (18.89) and (18.109) it is easy to obtain the inequality

$$\left| \psi_j^{(N)}(\varepsilon_2) \exp \frac{c_j(\tau - \tau_j)}{\varepsilon_2} - \psi_j^{(N)}(\varepsilon_1') \exp \frac{c_j(\tau - \tau_j)}{\varepsilon_1'} \right| \leqslant$$
$$\leqslant k_N' \varepsilon^{N-2} |\varepsilon_2 - \varepsilon_1'| \qquad (j = 1, 2, \ldots, m; \quad \varepsilon_1' \leqslant \varepsilon \leqslant \varepsilon_2), \tag{18.132}$$

where

$$k_N' = k_N \varepsilon_1 + R_N c^*. \tag{18.133}$$

The second term on the right-hand side of (18.131) will be denoted, for brevity, by $\Delta_2(\Psi_j, \varepsilon_1', \varepsilon_2)$. For this term, by using the mean-value theorem, the inequality (18.131), and system (18.91), we obtain the estimate

$$\Delta_2(\Psi_j, \varepsilon_1', \varepsilon_2) = \left| \frac{d}{d\varepsilon} \frac{1}{\varepsilon} \int_{\tau_j}^{\tau} \{ g_j^{(N)}(f_1, \ldots, f_m; \tau, \varepsilon) - c_j f_j \}\, d\tau \right|_{\varepsilon = \varepsilon_j^*} |\varepsilon_2 - \varepsilon_1'|, \tag{18.134}$$

where $\varepsilon_1' \leqslant \varepsilon_j^* \leqslant \varepsilon_2$; $j = 1, 2, \ldots, m$.

In estimating the derivative of the integral term in (18.134) we use the differentiability with respect to ε of the functions $f_j(\tau, \varepsilon)$ and the coefficients of the original system (18.90); we repeat inequalities of the type used in (18.128). As a result we obtain the estimate

$$\Delta_2(\Psi_j, \varepsilon_1', \varepsilon_2) \leqslant H_N \varepsilon^{N-2} |\varepsilon_2 - \varepsilon_1'| \qquad (j = 1, 2, \ldots, m;\ \varepsilon_1' \leqslant \varepsilon \leqslant \varepsilon_2), \tag{18.135}$$

where the constant H_N does not depend on ε.

Then, from the inequalities (18.132) and (18.135), we have the following estimate for the expression (18.130):

$$\Delta(\Psi_j, \varepsilon_1', \varepsilon_2) \leqslant (H_N + k_N') \varepsilon^{N-2} |\varepsilon_2 - \varepsilon_1'|$$
$$(j = 1, 2, \ldots, m; \quad \varepsilon \in [\varepsilon_1', \varepsilon_2] \subset (0, \varepsilon_1]). \tag{18.136}$$

Thus, if, in inequality (18.106), we set the constant h_N equal to $h_N = H_N + k_N'$ (up to this time h_N has remained arbitrary), then the inequalities (18.106) will be satisfied not only by the functions $\varphi_j(\tau, \varepsilon) \in \Phi_j$, but also by the functions $\Psi_j(\tau, \varepsilon)$ $(j = 1, \ldots, m)$ constructed according to formulas (18.123).

It remains to prove that the functions $\Psi_j(\tau, \varepsilon)(j = 1, 2, \ldots, m)$ satisfy the conditions (18.107). Substituting Eqs. (18.123) on the left-hand sides of (18.107) together with the $\varphi_j(\tau, \varepsilon)$ and carrying out the corresponding estimates, we obtain

$$\left| \Psi_j(\tau_2, \varepsilon) \exp\left(\frac{c_j(\tau_2 - \tau_j)}{\varepsilon}\right) - \Psi_j(\tau_1, \varepsilon) \exp\left(\frac{c_j(\tau_1 - \tau_j)}{\varepsilon}\right) \right| \leqslant$$
$$\leqslant \left| \psi_j^{(N)}(\varepsilon) \left[\exp\left(\frac{c_j(\tau_2 - \tau_j)}{\varepsilon}\right) - \exp\left(\frac{c_j(\tau_1 - \tau_j)}{\varepsilon}\right) \right] \right| +$$
$$+ \frac{1}{\varepsilon} \left| \exp\left(\frac{c_j(\tau_2 - \tau_j)}{\varepsilon}\right) \int_{\tau_j}^{\tau_2} G_j(\varphi; \tau, \varepsilon)\, d\tau - \exp\left(\frac{c_j(\tau_2 - \tau_j)}{\varepsilon}\right) \int_{\tau_j}^{\tau_1} G_j(\varphi; \tau, \varepsilon)\, d\tau \right|$$
$$(j = 1, \ldots, m; \quad \tau_1, \tau_2 \in [0, L_1], \ 0 < \varepsilon \leqslant \varepsilon_1). \tag{18.137}$$

Because of (18.99), the first term on the right-hand side of (18.137) is majorized by the quantity $R_N c^* |\tau_2 - \tau_1| \varepsilon^{N-1}$; $c^* = \max_{1 \leqslant j \leqslant m} |c_j|$. To estimate the second term in inequality (18.137), we add and subtract from it the quantity

$$\exp\left(\frac{c_j(\tau - \tau_j)}{\varepsilon}\right) \int_{\tau_j}^{\tau_1} G_j(\varphi; \tau, \varepsilon)\, d\tau. \tag{18.138}$$

After this we carry out the estimates analogous to (18.128). Omitting the intermediate calculations, which are very easy to carry out, we write down the final result

$$\left| \Psi_j(\tau_2, \varepsilon) \exp\left(\frac{c_j(\tau_2 - \tau_j)}{\varepsilon}\right) - \Psi_j(\tau_1, \varepsilon) \exp\left(\frac{c_j(\tau_1 - \tau_j)}{\varepsilon}\right) \right| \leqslant$$

$$\leqslant [R_N c^* + (1 + cc^*)(B_N + AmK_N)]\, \varepsilon^{N-1} |\tau_2 - \tau_1| = M_N \varepsilon^{N-1} |\tau_2 - \tau_1|$$

$$(j = 1, 2, \ldots, m), \qquad (18.139)$$

where the constant M_N obviously coincides with the constant M_N on the right-hand side of (18.107), (18.108).

Thus, the comparison of inequalities (18.105), (18.106), and (18.107), with inequalities (18.129), (18.136), and (18.139), respectively, and the fact that the operator T defined above does not reduce the smoothness of the functions, allows us to conclude that the image $T\{F\}$ of the set F is contained within F itself, i.e., the inclusion (18.124) is valid.

Now the only remaining concern is Shauder's principle or the fixed-point theorem, which is proved in a paper by Hukuhara [135]: if a continuous operator T maps a convex compact set F into a subset of itself, i.e., if $T\{F\} \subseteq F$, then the set F contains at least one point x which is invariant with respect to the operator T, i.e., for which

$$Tx = x. \qquad (18.140)$$

In other words, there exists at least one m-tuple of functions $\psi_1^{(N)}(\tau, \varepsilon), \psi_2^{(N)}(\tau, \varepsilon), \ldots, \psi_m^{(N)}(\tau, \varepsilon)$ in F which transforms the system of equations (18.122) into a system of identities

$$\psi_j^{(N)}(\tau, \varepsilon) \equiv \psi_j^{(N)}(\varepsilon) + \varepsilon^{-1} \int_{\tau_j}^{\tau} G_j(\psi_1^{(N)}, \ldots, \psi_m^{(N)}; \tau, \varepsilon)\, d\tau$$

$$(j = 1, 2, \ldots, m). \qquad (18.141)$$

Consequently, the existence of a solution of the system of differential equations (18.90) satisfying the conditions (18.101) and (18.102) is proved.

Let us prove the uniqueness of this solution. Suppose that there exists another solution

$$z_j = \chi_j^{(N)}(\tau, \varepsilon) \qquad (j = 1, 2, \ldots, m), \qquad (18.142)$$

satisfying conditions of the form (18.101) and (18.102) and differing from solution (18.100). We set

$$M(\varepsilon) = \max_{\tau, j} \left| [\chi_j^{(N)}(\tau, \varepsilon) - \psi_j^{(N)}(\tau, \varepsilon)] \exp \frac{c_j(\tau - \tau_j)}{\varepsilon} \right|. \qquad (18.143)$$

Then, taking into account inequalities (18.86), (18.92) and (18.95), we obtain the following estimate for $M(\varepsilon)$:

$$M(\varepsilon)=\max_{\tau,j}\left|\left\{\frac{1}{\varepsilon}\int_{\tau_j}^{\tau}[G_j(\chi^{(N)};\tau,\varepsilon)-G_j(\psi^{(N)};\tau,\varepsilon)]d\tau\right\}\exp\frac{c_j(\tau-\tau_j)}{\varepsilon}\right|<$$
$$<\max_{\tau,j}\left\{Amc\,|\chi_j^{(N)}(\tau,\varepsilon)-\psi_j^{(N)}(\tau,\varepsilon)|\left|\exp\frac{c_j(\tau-\tau_j)}{\varepsilon}\right|\right\}=AmcM(\varepsilon), \tag{18.144}$$

i.e.,

$$M(\varepsilon)<AmcM(\varepsilon), \tag{18.145}$$

provided ε is small enough. However, inequality (18.145) contradicts condition (18.96). Consequently, $\chi_j^{(N)}(\tau,\varepsilon)\equiv\psi_j^{(N)}(\tau,\varepsilon)$ $(j=1,2,\ldots,m)$. The uniqueness is proven.

Thus, the initially considered system (18.41) has the unique solution

$$v_j(\tau,\varepsilon)=p_j^{(N)}(\tau,\varepsilon)+\psi_j^{(N)}(\tau,\varepsilon)\exp\frac{c_i(\tau-\tau_i)}{\varepsilon}$$
$$(j=1,2,\ldots,m;\ \ N>1) \tag{18.146}$$

in the region $0\leqslant\tau\leqslant L_1$, $0<\varepsilon\leqslant\varepsilon_1$. Therefore, from relationships (18.64), (18.77), (18.89) and (18.102) it follows that the formal series (18.64) is an asymptotically convergent series in this region.

Thus, we have proved Theorem III.4 only for $\tau\in[0,L_1]$ $(L_1\leqslant L)$. However, this proof can now be extended to the whole original interval $[0,L]$. In fact, in accordance with (18.69) we divide the given interval $[0,L]$ into partial intervals $[L_i,L_{i+1}]$ $(i=0,1,\ldots,q-1)$ in such a way that the end of each subinterval corresponds to the beginning of the next. Then, obviously, $L_0=0$, $L_q=L$.

From the preceding discussion it is easy to see that the proof of Theorem III.4 for $0\leqslant\tau\leqslant L_1$ essentially rests upon the inequalities (18.86), (18.87), and (18.96), and upon Lemma III.3, from which all the basic estimates were derived. These inequalities, in turn, are satisfied for a sufficiently good approximation of the functions $\mu_j(\tau)$ $(j=1,2,\ldots,m)$ by the constants c_j $(j=1,2,\ldots,m)$.

We subject the partition of the interval $[0,L]$ into the subintervals $[L_i,L_{i+1}]$ $(i=0,1,\ldots,q-1)$ to two conditions:

1. The approximation of the functions $\mu_j(\tau)$ by constants c_{ji} $(j = 1, 2, \ldots, m;\quad i = 0, 1, \ldots, q-1)$ [see (18.69)] should guarantee that inequalities of the type (18.86) and (18.87) are fulfilled

$$
\begin{gathered}
|b_{jj}^{(N)}(\tau, \varepsilon) - c_{ji}| \leqslant A, \\
|b_{jk}^{(N)}(\tau, \varepsilon)| \leqslant A \quad (j \neq k) \\
L_i \leqslant \tau \leqslant L_{i+1},\ 0 < \varepsilon \leqslant \varepsilon_1,\ c_{j0} = c_j \\
(j, k = 1, 2, \ldots, m;\ i = 0, 1, \ldots, q-1);
\end{gathered}
\tag{18.147}
$$

2. Those points in the interval $[0, L]$ at which the real part of any of the functions $\mu_j(\tau)$ $(j = 1, 2, \ldots, m)$ changes sign, i.e., those points at which the graphs of the functions $\operatorname{Re}\mu_j(\tau)$ $(j = 1, 2, \ldots, m)$ cross the abscissa axis, must not lie within any of the intervals $[L_i, L_{i+1}]$.

Then all the considerations which were presented above for the case $\tau \in [0, L_1]$ can be carried over to all the subsequent subintervals. Here we seek, on each subinterval $[L_i, L_{i+1}]$, a solution of the system (18.90) satisfying the condition

$$
\begin{gathered}
\psi_j^{(N)}(\tau_{ji}, \varepsilon) = \psi_j^{(N)}(\varepsilon), \\
\psi_j^{(N)}(\varepsilon) = \sum_{s=N}^{\infty} p_{js}(\tau_{ji})\varepsilon^s,
\end{gathered}
\tag{18.148}
$$

where, by analogy with (18.72),

$$
\tau_{ji} = \begin{cases} L_{i+1}, & \text{if } c'_{ji} \geqslant 0; \\ L_i, & \text{if } c'_{ji} < 0, \end{cases}
\tag{18.149}
$$

where

$$
\begin{gathered}
j = 1, 2, \ldots, m;\ i = 0, 1, \ldots, q-1; \\
c'_{ji} = \operatorname{Re} c_{ji} \text{ [see (18.69)]}.
\end{gathered}
$$

Thus, the existence and uniqueness of a solution of system (18.90) satisfying conditions of the form (18.101) and (13.102) is proved for each of the subintervals $[L_i, L_{i+1}]$ $(i = 0, 1, \ldots, q-1)$. Now it is necessary to show that the solution on each preceding subinterval develops into the solution on the subsequent subinterval, which will then imply the existence and uniqueness of a solution with the required properties on the whole interval $[0, L]$.

As a matter of fact, the partition of the interval $[0, L]$ which guarantees the approximation of the functions $\mu_j(\tau)$ $(j = 1, 2, \ldots, m)$ by the constants c_{ji} $(j = 1, 2, \ldots, m;\ i = 0, 1, \ldots, q-1)$, with the condition that inequality (18.147) is satisfied, is not unique. Together with the above partition of the interval $[0, L]$ into subintervals $[L_i, L_{i+1}]$ $(i = 0, 1, \ldots, q-1)$, let us consider a new partition into subintervals $[\bar{L}_k, \bar{L}_{k+1}]$ $(k = 0, 1, \ldots, q'-1;\ q' > q;\ \bar{L}_0 = 0, L_{q'} = L)$. This latter partition should have the following properties: first of all, the approximating functions $\bar{c}_j(\tau)$ defined analogously to (18.69) should guarantee that inequalities of the form (18.147) hold for each of the $[\bar{L}_k, \bar{L}_{k+1}]$ $(k = 0, 1, 2, \ldots, q'-1)$ (this allows us to carry out the proof of the existence theorem, as was done above). Second, the system of subintervals $[\bar{L}_k, \bar{L}_{k+1}]$ $(k = 0, 1, \ldots, q'-1)$ should overlap the original system of subintervals in such a way that all the points L_{i+1} $(i=0, 1, \ldots, p)$ lie within certain of the subintervals of the second system. In other words, the inequalities: $0 < \bar{L}_1 < L_1 < \bar{L}_2 < L_2 < \ldots < L$ should hold. We note that in this case certain of the functions $\operatorname{Re}\mu_j(\tau)$ $(j=1, 2, \ldots, m)$ may change sign within the subintervals $[\bar{L}_k, \bar{L}_{k+1}]$ $(k = 0, 1, \ldots, q'-1;\ q' > q)$. However, then we can choose the subintervals of sufficiently small length such that in approximating the functions $\mu_j(\tau)$ by step functions $\bar{c}_j(\tau)$ of form (18.69), the real parts of the constants of the approximation can be taken as equal to zero:

$$c'_{jk} = \operatorname{Re} c_{jk} = 0.$$

The imaginary parts of these constants will then necessarily be different from zero, since according to the condition of the theorem $\mu_j(\tau) \neq 0$ $(j=1, 2, \ldots, m)$ everywhere on $[0, L]$. Such a choice of the constants approximating the function $\mu_j(\tau)$ $(j = 1, 2, \ldots, m]$ allows us, as before, to rely on Lemma III.3 [by using τ_{ji} from (18.148)] and apply a change of variables of the form (18.89) in proving the existence and uniqueness theorem for the solution of system (18.90) on each of the subintervals $[\bar{L}_k, L_{k+1}]$ $(k = 0, 1, \ldots, q'-1)$.

Now, the existence and uniqueness theorem has been proved for the intervals $[0, L_1]$ and $[L_1, L_2]$ and also for the intervals $[0, \bar{L}_1]$ and $[\bar{L}_1, \bar{L}_2]$ The solution of system (18.90) coincides on the common portion of the intervals $[0, L_1]$ and $[0, \bar{L}_1]$, i.e., on $[0, \bar{L}_1]$, since the initial conditions (18.101) are the same. Then, if, as initial conditions for the solution of system (18.90) on $[\bar{L}_1, \bar{L}_2]$ we take the value (at the point $\tau = \bar{L}_1$) of the solution found on the interval $[0, L_1] \supset [0, \bar{L}_1]$, then the solution of system (18.90) will be continued on the interval $[0, L_2]$, and so on. Thus, we can glue together the solutions obtained on the neighboring intervals

$[0, L_1]$ and $[L_1, L_2]$. Repeating the above argument the necessary number of times, we prove that the solution of system (18.90) satisfying the conditions

$$\psi_j^{(N)}(0, \varepsilon) = \psi_j^{(N)}(\varepsilon) \qquad (j = 1, 2, \ldots, m) \tag{18.150}$$

and

$$|\psi_j^{(N)}(\tau, \varepsilon)| \leqslant K_N \varepsilon^N \exp \frac{|\xi_j(\tau)|}{\varepsilon}, \tag{18.151}$$

where

$$\xi_j(\tau) = \operatorname{Re} \mu_j(\tau) \qquad (j=1, 2, \ldots, m)$$

exists and is unique on $[0, L]$.

Condition (18.151) is obtained in the following manner. On each of the intervals $[L_k, L_{k+1}]$ the solution of system (18.90) constructed by the method described above satisfies the inequalities

$$|\psi_j^{(N)}(\tau,\varepsilon)| \leqslant K_N \varepsilon^N \left| \exp\left(-\frac{c_{jk}(\tau-\tau_{jk})}{\varepsilon}\right)\right|$$
$$(j = 1, 2, \ldots, m; \quad k = 0, 1, \ldots, q-1; \; L_k < \tau \leqslant L_{k+1}), \tag{18.152}$$

where the τ_{jk} are chosen in accordance with (18.149). Then, for a sufficiently fine partition of the interval $[0, L]$ the right-hand side of inequality (18.152) will be majorized by the quantity $K_N \varepsilon^N \exp|\xi_j(\tau)|/\varepsilon$ for any $\tau \in [0, L]$ and $j = 1, 2, \ldots, m$.

Thus, by continuous continuation of the solution of system (18.90) from one subinterval to the next, as described above, we have obtained a unique solution, continuous with respect to τ, satisfying the initial conditions (18.150) and the conditions (18.151).

Proceeding from this "glued" solution satisfying conditions (18.150) and (18.151) we now carry out two changes of variables which are inverse to the changes of variables with which we transformed the system of differential equations (18.41) to the form (18.90). Then, as the final result, inequality (18.151) gives us the required asymptotic estimate for the remainder of the formal series (18.64):

$$|p_j(\tau, \varepsilon) - p_j^{(N)}(\tau, \varepsilon)| \leqslant K_N \varepsilon^N$$
$$(j = 1, 2, \ldots, m; \; N > 1; \; 0 \leqslant \tau \leqslant L; \; 0 < \varepsilon \leqslant \varepsilon_1). \tag{18.153}$$

Thus, the series (18.64) is not only the formal solution of the system of differential equations (18.41), but is also an asymptotic expansion, in powers of the parameter ε, of the solution of the above system in the region $0 \leqslant \tau \leqslant L$, $0 < \varepsilon \leqslant \varepsilon_1$.

The theorem is proved.

Chapter 4

CONSTRUCTION OF AN ASYMPTOTIC SOLUTION IN THE CASE OF MULTIPLE ROOTS OF THE CHARACTERISTIC EQUATION

19. General Remarks

The method explained in the preceding chapter permits the asymptotic reduction of a system of linear differential equations (12.1) or (17.1) to the systems (13.2), (17.4), which decompose into isolated subsystems of lower order than the original one. In the case when the roots of the characteristic equation (12.3) are simple on the closed interval $[0, L]$, such a decomposition, as shown in Sec. 16, leads to scalar differential equations which are integrable by quadrature. Thus, in this latter case, we can obtain an asymptotic solution of the systems (12.1), (17.1) by the decomposition method.

In the more complicated case when there are multiple roots among the roots of the characteristic equation (12.3), we cannot obtain an asymptotic solution of the given systems by using the algorithm presented in Chap. 3, since the systems of differential equations (13.2), (17.4) obtained by the process of decomposition are generally not integrable by quadrature [the matrices occurring in the given systems have the same structure as the matrices in the systems (12.1), (17.1)]. In fact, only in the easiest case when simple elementary divisors can be associated with the multiple roots, as will be shown in Sec. 20, does asymptotic decomposition make possible the construction of a solution to the original systems by subjecting the "decomposed" systems to supplementary investigation. In the general case, when along with multiple roots we also have multiple elementary divisors, solution of the decomposed systems becomes extremely complicated. Certain methods which make use of the specific structure of the decomposed systems can be applied in this latter case. We will discuss these methods in Secs. 21 and 23. We should, however, note here that the theorems on asymptotic decomposition were obtained for the assumption that condition (15.3) holds; this condition certainly does not hold if, among the roots of the characteristic equation, we have pure imaginary roots which have multiple elementary divisors. In fact, let the matrix $A_0(\tau)$ be of the form

$$A_0(\tau)=\begin{bmatrix} i\alpha(\tau) & 1 \\ 0 & i\alpha(\tau) \end{bmatrix}, \tag{19.1}$$

where $\alpha(\tau)$ is a real positive function on the closed interval $[0, L]$. Then in order for condition (15.3) to hold, as we have already noted above, it is necessary that the matrix

$$\Delta(\tau)=\frac{1}{2}[A_0(\tau)+A_0^*(\tau)] \tag{19.2}$$

not have characteristic values with positive real parts. In that case

$$\Delta(\tau)=\frac{1}{2}\begin{bmatrix} 0 & 1 \\ 1 & 0 \end{bmatrix}, \tag{19.3}$$

from which it follows that the characteristic values of the matrix are equal to $\pm 1/2$.

This chapter is devoted to an investigation of the case of multiple roots of the characteristic equation where we assume that the multiplicity of the roots and the multiplicity of the corresponding elementary divisors does not change on the closed interval $[0, L]$. In this case, the method explained here allows us to construct the asymptotic solution for the original systems of linear differential equations directly, without using the preliminary decomposition.

Thus, let the roots of the characteristic equation (12.3), denoted, as before, by $\lambda_1(\tau), \lambda_2(\tau), \ldots, \lambda_p(\tau)$ $(p<n)$, have on the interval $[0, L]$ the constant multiplicity $k_1, k_2, \ldots, k_p$ $\left(\sum_{j=1}^{p} k_j = n\right)$.

Then, depending on the behavior of the elementary divisors, we can distinguish three cases, namely: to each root $\lambda_j(\tau)$ $(j=1, 2, \ldots, p)$ there may correspond:

a) k_j simple elementary divisors;

b) one elementary divisor of multiplicity k_j;

c) $r_j\,(1 < r_j < k_j)$ elementary divisors of multiplicity $s_{j1},\ s_{j2}, \ldots, s_{jr_j}, (s_{j1} + s_{j2} + \ldots + s_{jr_j} = k_j;\ j = 1, 2, \ldots, p)$.

Below we will consider each of these cases separately. In addition, for greater generality, we will investigate nonhomogeneous systems of the type (17.4); as in Sec. 17, we will consider the following two cases separately:

1. resonance—when the function $i\nu(\tau)$ for certain values $\tau \in [0, L]$ becomes equal to one of the roots of the characteristic equation (12.3), for example, the root $\lambda_1(\tau)$, but

$$i\nu(\tau) \neq \lambda_r(\tau), \quad r = 2, 3, \ldots, p, \tag{19.4}$$

for any $\tau \in [0, L]$;

2. nonresonance—when

$$i\nu(\tau) \neq \lambda_j(\tau), \quad j = 1, 2, \ldots, p, \tag{19.5}$$

for all $\tau \in [0, L]$.

20. The Case of Simple Elementary Divisors

Before turning to construction of the solution, we recall that in the given case [15] the canonical matrix for the matrix $A_0(\tau)$ will have a simple structure. In other words, we can find a nonsingular matrix $T(\tau)$ such that

$$W(\tau) = T^{-1}(\tau)\,A_0(\tau)\,T(\tau) = \begin{bmatrix} W_1(\tau) & & & 0 \\ & W_2(\tau) & & \\ & & \ddots & \\ 0 & & & W_p(\tau) \end{bmatrix}, \tag{20.1}$$

where $W_j(\tau)$ is a square matrix of order k_j, of the form

$$W_j(\tau) = \begin{bmatrix} \lambda_j(\tau) & & & 0 \\ & \lambda_j(\tau) & & \\ & & \ddots & \\ 0 & & & \lambda_j(\tau) \end{bmatrix}, \quad j = 1, 2, \ldots, p. \tag{20.2}$$

Then condition (15.3) is satisfied here even in the case of pure imaginary roots, since $W_0(\tau)+W_0^*(\tau)=0$. Consequently, in this case, Theorems III.1 and III.3, which allow asymptotic decomposition of system (17.1) into p isolated subsystems of the form

$$\frac{d\xi_j}{dt}=[W_j(\tau)+\varepsilon W_j(\tau,\varepsilon)]\,\xi_j{}^*, \qquad j=1,2,\ldots,p, \tag{20.3}$$*

are applicable to system (17.4). Here the $W_j(\tau,\varepsilon)$ are square matrices of order k_j, of the form

$$W_j(\tau,\varepsilon)=\sum_{s=0}^{m}\varepsilon^{s-1}W_{js}(\tau) \tag{20.4}$$

(m is any natural number).

In addition, we transform system (20.3) as follows:

$$\xi_j(t,\varepsilon)=\exp\left\{\int_0^t\lambda_j(\tau)\,dt\right\}q_j, \qquad j=1,2,\ldots,p. \tag{20.5}$$

Then, by (20.2), we obtain

$$\frac{dq_j}{dt}=\varepsilon W_j(\tau,\varepsilon)\,q_j, \qquad j=1,2,\ldots,p. \tag{20.6}$$

In system (20.6) we convert from differentiation with respect to t to differentiation with respect to $\tau=\varepsilon t$; we have

$$\frac{dq_j}{d\tau}=W_j(\tau,\varepsilon)\,q_j, \qquad j=1,2,\ldots,p. \tag{20.7}$$

In contrast to the original system (17.1), system (20.7) allows application of the method of successive approximations. Consequently, applying this method to system (20.7) we obtain, for the vector q_j, a solution in the form of a convergent series in powers of the parameter ε. Then, using (20.5), we obtain the required solution for the vector ξ_j, $j=1,\ldots,p$.

Note. The original system of differential equations (17.1) usually cannot be integrated by the method of successive

---

*For simplicity, we consider the nonresonance case.

approximations in the general case. In fact, let us transform system (17.1) from differentiation with respect to t to differentiation with respect to τ. We will have

$$\frac{dx}{dt} = \frac{1}{\varepsilon} A(\tau, \varepsilon) x + \frac{1}{\varepsilon} b(\tau,\varepsilon) e^{i\theta(t,\varepsilon)}. \tag{20.8}$$

From this it follows that as $\varepsilon \to 0$, the matrix $1/\varepsilon\ A(\tau, \varepsilon)$ and the vector $1/\varepsilon\ b(\tau,\varepsilon)$ tend to infinity.

21. A Formal Solution in the Presence of One Multiple Elementary Divisor

We now turn to construction of an asymptotic solution of a system of the form (17.1):

$$\frac{dx}{dt} = A(\tau, \varepsilon) x + \varepsilon b(\tau, \varepsilon) e^{i\theta(t,\varepsilon)} \tag{17.1'}$$

in the case when, to the root $\lambda_j(\tau)$ $(j=1, 2, \dots, p)$ there corresponds an elementary divisor of the same multiplicity as that of the root $\lambda_j(\tau)$ itself. Here, in obtaining the asymptotic solution, we apply the method developed in [104-106],[107-109],[110-112],[113-115].

We note that in this case the canonical form of the matrix $A_0(\tau)$ consists of Jordan blocks, i.e., is of the type (18.3).

Thus we can prove the following theorem.

Theorem IV.1. *If $A(\tau, \varepsilon)$, $b(\tau, \varepsilon)$, $\nu(\tau)$ have derivatives with respect to τ of all orders on $[0, L]$ and the matrix*

$$C(\tau) = T^{-1}(\tau)\, [A(\tau)\, T(\tau) - T'(\tau)] \tag{21.1}$$

is such that its elements standing at the intersection of the r_jth row and the $r_{j-1}+1$-st column ($r_j = k_1 + k_2 + \dots + k_j$, $j = 1, 2, \dots, p$) are nowhere equal to zero, i.e.,

$$\{c(\tau)\}_{r_j, r_{j-1}+1} \neq 0 \tag{21.2}$$

for all $\tau \in [0, L]$ and all $j = 1, 2, \dots, p$, then a formal particular solution of system (17.1) in the resonance case can be represented in the form

$$x(t, \varepsilon) = [U_1(\tau, \mu_1)\, h_1 + P(\tau, \mu_1)]\, e^{i\theta(t,\varepsilon)} + \sum_{k=2}^{p} U_k(\tau, \mu_k) h_k, \tag{21.3}$$

where the $U_j(\tau, \mu_j)$ $(j = 1,2, \dots, p)$, and $P(\tau, \mu_1)$ are n-dimensional vectors, the h_j are scalar functions defined by the linear differential equations

$$\frac{dh_1}{dt} = [\lambda_1(\tau, \mu_1) - i\nu(\tau)]\, h_1 + z(\tau, \mu_1), \tag{21.4}$$

$$\frac{dh_k}{dt} = \lambda_k(\tau, \mu_k)\, h_k, \quad k = 2, 3, \ldots, p, \tag{21.5}$$

and the formal expansions

$$\begin{aligned} U_j(\tau, \mu_j) &= \sum_{s=0}^{\infty} \mu_1^s U_{js}(\tau), & \lambda_j(\tau, \mu_j) &= \sum_{s=0}^{\infty} \mu_j^s \lambda_{js}(\tau), \\ P(\tau, \mu_1) &= \sum_{s=0}^{\infty} \mu_1^s P_s(\tau), & z(\tau, \mu_1) &= \sum_{s=0}^{\infty} \mu_1^s z_s(\tau), \end{aligned} \tag{21.6}$$

hold, where the $\mu_j\, (j = 1, 2, \ldots, p)$ *are parameters related to the parameter* ε *by the equations*

$$\mu_j = \sqrt[k_j]{\varepsilon}, \qquad j = 1, 2, \ldots, p. \tag{21.7}$$

Proof. The proof of this theorem, just like the proofs of previous theorems relating to the formal construction of a solution, consists of exhibiting an algorithm for determination of the coefficients of the formal series (21.6). As soon as the latter are properly defined, we can find the functions $h_j(t, \varepsilon)$ from the scalar equations (21.4) and (21.5); then, using (21.3), we can construct the required formal solution of system (17.1′).

To do this, we substitute the vector x, determined from Eqs. (21.3)-(21.5), into system (17.1′). We have

$$\begin{aligned} &\{\varepsilon U_1'(\tau, \mu_1) - [A(\tau, \varepsilon) - \lambda_1(\tau, \mu_1) E]\, U_1(\tau, \mu_1)\, h_1 e^{i\theta(t,\varepsilon)} + \\ &+ \sum_{k=2}^{p} \{\varepsilon U_k'(\tau, \mu_k) - [A(\tau, \varepsilon) - \lambda_k(\tau, \mu_k) E]\, U_k(\tau, \mu_k)\}\, h_k + \\ &+ \{U_1(\tau, \mu_1)\, z(\tau, \mu_1) + \varepsilon P'(\tau, \mu_1) - \\ &- [A(\tau, \varepsilon) - i\nu(\tau) E]\, P(\tau, \mu_1) - \varepsilon b(\tau, \varepsilon)\}\, e^{i\theta(t,\varepsilon)} = 0. \end{aligned} \tag{21.8}$$

Now, in identity (21.8), we require that the coefficients of the functions $h_1 e^{i\theta(t,\varepsilon)}$, $h_k\, (k = 2, 3, \ldots, p)$ and $e^{i\theta(t,\varepsilon)}$ be equal to zero; we obtain

$$[A(\tau, \varepsilon) - \lambda_j(\tau, \mu_j) E]\, U_j(\tau, \mu_j) = \varepsilon U_j'(\tau, \mu_j) \qquad (j = 1, 2, \ldots, p), \tag{21.9}$$

$$[A(\tau, \varepsilon) - i\nu(\tau) E]\, P(\tau, \mu_1) = U_1(\tau, \mu_1)\, z(\tau, \mu_1) + \varepsilon\, [P'(\tau, \mu_1) - b(\tau, \varepsilon)\,]. \tag{21.10}$$

Relationships (21.9) and (21.10) make possible determination of the coefficients of the formal series (21.6).

1. First, we make use of Eqs. (21.9) relating the unknown vectors $U_j(\tau, \mu_j)$ and the unknown functions $\lambda_j(\tau, \mu_j)$, $j = 1, \ldots, p$.

Now we will show how we can determine the vectors $U_j(\tau, \mu_j)$ and the functions $\lambda_j(\tau, \mu_j)$ $(j = 1, \ldots, p)$. by using relationship (21.9). In order not to complicate the formulas obtained below with numerous indices, we will restrict ourselves here to determination of the vectors $U_1(\tau, \mu_1)$ and the functions $\lambda_1(\tau, \mu_1)$.

Then, setting $j = 1$ in (21.9) and equating the coefficients of like powers of the parameter $\mu_1 = \sqrt[k_1]{\varepsilon}$, we obtain

$$[A_0(\tau) - \lambda_{10}(\tau) E] U_{10}(\tau) = 0, \tag{21.11}$$

$$[A_0(\tau) - \lambda_{10}(\tau) E] U_{1s}(\tau) = \sum_{k=0}^{s-1} U_{1k}(\tau) \lambda_{1s-k}(\tau) + H_{1s}(\tau) \qquad (s = 1, 2, \ldots), \tag{21.12}$$

where

$$H_{1s}(\tau) = U'_{1s-k_1}(\tau) - \sum_{k=1}^{\left[\frac{s}{k_1}\right]} A_k(\tau) U_{1,s-k_1k}(\tau)^*, \quad s = k_1, k_1 + 1, \ldots,$$
$$H_{1s}(\tau) \equiv 0 \qquad (s = 1, 2, \ldots, k_1 - 1), \tag{21.13}$$
$$\lambda_{10}(\tau) = \lambda_1(\tau).$$

(* - $[r]$, as usual, indicates the largest whole number less than r).

Henceforth, it will be convenient to transform the vectors $U_{1s}(\tau)$ $(s = 0, 1, \ldots)$ to the vectors

$$Q_{1s}(\tau) = T^{-1}(\tau) U_{1s}(\tau). \tag{21.14}$$

Then, multiplying the vector equations (21.11), (21.12) from the left by the matrix $T^{-1}(\tau)$ and taking into account (18.2) and (21.14), we have

$$[W_0(\tau) - \lambda_{10}(\tau) E] Q_{10}(\tau) = 0, \tag{21.15}$$

$$[W_0(\tau) - \lambda_{10}(\tau) E] Q_{1s}(\tau) = \sum_{k=0}^{s-1} Q_k(\tau) \lambda_{1s-k}(\tau) + \overline{H}_{1s}(\tau), \tag{21.16}$$

where

$$\overline{H}_{1s}(\tau) = T^{-1}(\tau) H_{1s}(\tau), \qquad s = 1, 2, \ldots . \tag{21.17}$$

Let us consider Eq. (21.15) first. By (18.3) it can be decomposed into p vector equations of the form

$$[W_{r0}(\tau) - \lambda_{10}(\tau) E_{k_r}] Q_{1r0}(\tau) = 0, \quad r = 1.2, \ldots, p, \tag{21.18}$$

where $Q_{1r0}(\tau)$ is a vector of dimension k_r $(r = 1, 2, \ldots, p)$, formed from the corresponding components of the vector $Q_{10}(\tau)$.

Since

$$\det [W_{r0}(\tau) - \lambda_{10}(\tau) E_{k_r}] \neq 0, \quad r = 2, 3, \ldots, p, \tag{21.19}$$

for any $\tau \in [0, L]$, then from (21.18) it follows that

$$Q_{1r0}(\tau) \equiv 0 \tag{21.20}$$

for all $r = 2, 3, \ldots, p$.

For $r = 1$, Eq. (21.18), by (18.7), is converted to the equation

$$I_1 Q_{110}(\tau) = 0, \tag{21.21}$$

where I_1 is of the form

$$I_1 = \begin{bmatrix} 0 & 1 & 0 & 0 & \ldots & 0 \\ 0 & 0 & 1 & 0 & \ldots & 0 \\ & \cdot & \cdot & \cdot & \cdot & \cdot \\ 0 & 0 & 0 & 0 & \ldots & 1 \\ 0 & 0 & 0 & 0 & \ldots & 0 \end{bmatrix}. \tag{21.22}$$

In Eq. (21.21) we pass to coordinate form and take into account the form of the matrix I_1; we obtain

$$\{q_{10}(\tau)\}_2 = \{q_{10}(\tau)\}_3 = \ldots = \{q_{10}(\tau)\}_{k_1} = 0. \tag{21.23}$$

The component $\{q_{10}(\tau)\}_1$ remains arbitrary. In order to obtain a nontrivial solution, we set

$$\{q_{10}(\tau)\} = 1. \tag{21.24}$$

Thus, we have determined vector $Q_{10}(\tau)$. On the basis of (21.20), (21.23), (21.24), it has the form

$$Q_{10}(\tau) = \begin{bmatrix} 1 \\ 0 \\ 0 \\ \cdot \\ \cdot \\ \cdot \\ 0 \end{bmatrix}. \tag{21.25}$$

Knowing the vector $Q_{10}(\tau)$, we can determine the vector $U_{10}(\tau)$ from relationship (21.14):

$$U_{10}(\tau) = T(\tau) Q_{10}(\tau), \tag{21.26}$$

i.e., $U_{10}(\tau)$ is the characteristic vector of the matrix $A_0(\tau)$ corresponding to the characterististic value $\lambda_{10}(\tau)$.

We now turn to determination of the vectors $Q_{1s}(\tau)$ and the functions $\lambda_{1s}(\tau)$ $(s = 1, 2, \ldots)$. For this we use the vector equation (21.16), which, by (18.3), just like Eq. (21.15), can be decomposed into p equations

$$[W_{r0}(\tau) - \lambda_{10}(\tau) E_{r_k}] Q_{1rs}(\tau) = \sum_{k=0}^{s-1} Q_{1kr}(\tau) \lambda_{1s-k}(\tau) + \overline{H}_{1rs}(\tau) \tag{21.27}$$
$$(r = 1, 2, \ldots, p, \quad s = 1, 2, \ldots),$$

in which $Q_{1rs}(\tau)$, $\overline{H}_{1rs}(\tau)$ are vectors of dimension k_r $(r = 1, 2, \ldots, p)$ formed from the components of the vectors $Q_{1s}(\tau)$, $\overline{H}_{1s}(\tau)$.

Since for all $r = 2, \ldots, p$ the determinant of system (21.27) is not equal to zero, then

$$Q_{1rs}(\tau) = [W_{r0}(\tau) - \lambda_{10}(\tau) E_{k_r}]^{-1} \left[\sum_{k=0}^{s-1} Q_{1k_r}(\tau) \lambda_{1s-k}(\tau) + \overline{H}_{1rs}(\tau) \right] \tag{21.28}$$
$$(r = 2, 3, \ldots, p; \ s = 1, 2, \ldots).$$

Thus, by (21.13),

$$Q_{1rs}(\tau) = 0, \quad r = 2, \ldots, p; \quad s = 1, 2, \ldots, k_1 - 1. \tag{21.29}$$

All the subsequent vectors $Q_{1rs}(\tau)$ $(r = 2, 3, \ldots, p; \ s = k_1, k_1 + 1, \ldots)$ can be determined from Eqs. (21.28); however, the right-hand sides of these equations contain the functions $\lambda_{11}(\tau)$, $\lambda_{12}(\tau), \ldots$, which are still to be determined.

For $r = 1$, on the basis of (18.4), Eq. (21.27) can be written in the following way:

$$I_1 Q_{11s}(\tau) = \sum_{k=0}^{s-1} Q_{11k}(\tau)\,\lambda_{1s-k}(\tau) + \overline{H}_{11s}(\tau) \qquad (s = 1, 2, \ldots). \quad (21.30)$$

From this, taking into account the form of the matrix I_1, we conclude that the first components of the vectors $Q_{11s}(\tau)$ $(s = 1, 2, \ldots)$ remain arbitrary. Therefore, we can set them equal to zero, i.e.,

$$\{q_{1s}(\tau)\}_1 = 0 \qquad (s = 1, 2, \ldots). \quad (21.31)$$

The remaining components of the vectors $Q_{11s}(\tau)$ $(s = 1, 2, \ldots)$ as well as all the components of the vectors $Q_{1rs}(\tau)$ $(r = 2, 3, \ldots, p;$ $s = 1, 2, \ldots)$, are again expressed by means of the unknown functions $\lambda_{1s}(\tau)$ $(s = 1, 2, \ldots)$, as follows from Eq. (21.30). Let us now determine these unknown functions.

Since the last row of the matrix I_1 consists of zeros, the last scalar equation in system (21.30) is of the form

$$\sum_{k=0}^{s-1} \{q_{1k}(\tau)\}_{k_1} \lambda_{1s-k}(\tau) + \{h_{1s}(\tau)\}_{k_1} = 0 \qquad (s = 1, 2, \ldots). \quad (21.32)$$

The obtained equation (21.32) makes possible determination of the unknown functions $\lambda_{11}(\tau)$, $\lambda_{12}(\tau), \ldots$. In fact, as we will show below, k_1 components of the vectors $Q_{1s}(\tau)$ $(s = 1, 2, \ldots)$ can be expressed in definite fashion by using the functions $\lambda_{1s}(\tau)$ $(s = 1, 2, \ldots)$. Therefore, substituting the obtained expressions for $\{q_{1k}(\tau)\}_{k_1}$, into Eq. (21.32), we can find the functions $\lambda_{1s}(\tau)$ $(s = 1, 2, \ldots)$.

Let us verify the above-mentioned relationships. In order to do this, we set $s = 1$ in Eq. (21.30); we have

$$I_1 Q_{111}(\tau) = Q_{110}(\tau)\lambda_{11}(\tau). \quad (21.33)$$

Converting here to coordinate form and taking into account the form of the matrix I_1 and the vector $Q_{110}(\tau)$, as well as (21.13), we obtain

$$\begin{gathered} \{q_{11}(\tau)\}_2 = \lambda_{11}(\tau), \\ \{q_{11}(\tau)\}_3 = \ldots = \{q_{11}(\tau)\}_{k_1} = 0. \end{gathered} \quad (21.34)$$

Let $s = 2$. Then Eq. (21.30) can be written as:

$$I_1 Q_{112}(\tau) = Q_{110}(\tau)\lambda_{12}(\tau) + Q_{111}(\tau)\lambda_{11}(\tau). \tag{21.35}$$

From which

$$\begin{gathered}\{q_{12}(\tau)\}_2 = \lambda_{12}(\tau),\\ \{q_{12}(\tau)\}_3 = \{q_{11}(\tau)\}_2\lambda_{11}(\tau) = [\lambda_{11}(\tau)]^2,\\ \{q_{12}(\tau)\}_4 = \ldots = \{q_{12}(\tau)\}_{k_1} = 0.\end{gathered} \tag{21.36}$$

For $s = 3$ from Eq. (21.30) we obtain

$$\begin{gathered}\{q_{13}(\tau)\}_2 = \lambda_{13}(\tau),\\ \{q_{13}(\tau)\}_3 = 2\lambda_{11}(\tau)\lambda_{12}(\tau),\\ \{q_{14}(\tau)\}_4 = [\lambda_{11}(\tau)]^3,\\ \{q_{13}(\tau)\}_5 = \ldots = \{q_{13}(\tau)\}_{k_1} = 0.\end{gathered} \tag{21.37}$$

Thus, we see that the k_1th components of the vectors $Q_{110}(\tau)$, $Q_{111}(\tau)$, $Q_{112}(\tau)$, and $Q_{113}(\tau)$ are equal to zero. If we set $s = 4, \ldots, k_1 - 2$, in Eq. (21.30), it is not difficult to show that the k_1th components of the vectors $Q_{114}(\tau), \ldots, Q_{11k_1-2}(\tau)$ are also equal to zero, i.e.,

$$\{q_{1s}(\tau)\}_{k_1} = 0, \qquad 0 \leqslant s \leqslant k_1 - 2. \tag{21.38}$$

As for the k_1th components to the vector Q_{11k_1-1}, it is equal to

$$\{q_{1k_1-1}(\tau)\}_{k_1} = [\lambda_{11}(\tau)]^{k_1-1}. \tag{21.39}$$

Then, setting $s = k_1$ in the scalar equation (21.32) [for $1 \leqslant s \leqslant k_1 - 1$ the above equation becomes an identity, by (21.13) and (21.38)], we obtain

$$\{q_{1k_1-1}(\tau)\}_{k_1}\lambda_{11}(\tau) + \{\bar{h}_{1k_1}(\tau)\}_{k_1} = 0. \tag{21.40}$$

From this, taking into account Eq. (21.39), we find

$$\lambda_{11}(\tau) = \sqrt[k_1]{-\{h_{1k_1}(\tau)\}_{k_1}}\ . \tag{21.41}$$

Since, by (21.13) and (21.17),

$$\begin{aligned}-\{h_{1k_1}(\tau)\}_{k_1} &= \{T^{-1}(\tau)[A_1(\tau)U_0(\tau) - U_0'(\tau)]\}_{k_1} = \{C(\tau)Q_0(\tau)\}_{k_1} =\\ &= \{c(\tau)\}_{k_1,1},\end{aligned} \tag{21.42}$$

then finally

$$\lambda_{11}(\tau) = \sqrt[k_1]{\{c(\tau)\}_{k_1,1}}. \tag{21.43}$$

Thus, the function $\lambda_{11}(\tau)$ is determined. Then, by Eqs. (21.31) and (21.34), we obtain the vector

$$Q_{11}(\tau) = \begin{bmatrix} 0 \\ \lambda_{11}(\tau) \\ 0 \\ \cdot \\ \cdot \\ \cdot \\ 0 \end{bmatrix}$$

In order to determine the function $\lambda_{12}(\tau)$, we set $s = k_1 + 1$ in Eq. (21.32). We then have

$$\{q_{1k_1-1}(\tau)\}_{k_1}\lambda_{12}(\tau) + \{q_{1k_1}(\tau)\}_{k_1}\lambda_{11}(\tau) + \{\bar{h}_{1k_1+1}(\tau)\}_{k_1} = 0. \tag{21.44}$$

On the basis of (21.13), the vector $\bar{H}_{1k_1+1}(\tau)$ contains within itself the vector $Q_{11}(\tau)$, which we have already found. Therefore, the component $\{\bar{h}_{1k_1+1}(\tau)\}_{k_1}$, in Eq. (21.44) is known.

As for the component $\{q_{1k_1}(\tau)\}_{k_1}$, from Eq. (21.30) we find

$$\{q_{1k_1}(\tau)\}_{k_1} = \{q_{1k_1-1}(\tau)\}_{k_1-1}\lambda_{11}(\tau) + \{q_{1k_1-2}(\tau)\}_{k_1-1}\lambda_{12}(\tau) + \{\bar{h}_{1k_1}(\tau)\}_{k_1-1}. \tag{21.45}$$

Since $\{q_{12}(\tau)\}_2 = \lambda_{12}(\tau)$, then, applying the recurrent formula

$$\{q_{1k_1-1}(\tau)\}_{k_1-1} = \{q_{1k_1-2}(\tau)\}_{k_1-2}\lambda_{11}(\tau) + \{q_{1k_1-3}(\tau)\}_{k_1-2}\lambda_{12}(\tau) \tag{21.46}$$

and taking into account that

$$\{q_{1k_1-3}(\tau)\}_{k_1-2} = [\lambda_{11}(\tau)]^{k_1-3}, \tag{21.47}$$

from Eq. (21.45) we have

$$\{q_{1k_1}(\tau)\}_{k_1} = (k_1 - 1)[\lambda_{11}(\tau)]^{k_1-2}\lambda_{12}(\tau) + \{\bar{h}_{1k_1}(\tau)\}_{k_1-1}. \tag{21.48}$$

Then, substituting the value of $\{q_{1k_1}(\tau)\}_{k_1}$ into Eq. (21.44) and solving it with respect to $\lambda_{12}(\tau)$, we obtain

$$\lambda_{12}(\tau) = -\frac{\{\bar{h}_{1k_1+1}(\tau)\}_{k_1} + \lambda_{11}(\tau)\{\bar{h}_{1k_1}(\tau)\}_{k_1-1}}{k_1[\lambda_{11}(\tau)]^{k_1-1}}. \tag{21.49}$$

We should note that the denominator on the right-hand side of the last expression, in accordance with the conditions of the theorem and (21.43), is not equal to zero for any $\tau \in [0, L]$.

Thus, having determined the function $\lambda_{12}(\tau)$, we have at the same time determined the vector $Q_{112}(\tau)$, since

$$Q_{112}(\tau) = \begin{bmatrix} 0 \\ \dfrac{\lambda_{12}(\tau)}{[\lambda_{11}(\tau)]^2} \\ 0 \\ \cdot \\ \cdot \\ \cdot \\ 0 \end{bmatrix}. \qquad (21.50)$$

In a similar manner, we can find all the subsequent functions $\lambda_{13}(\tau)$, $\lambda_{14}(\tau)$, ..., and, therefore, the vectors $Q_{113}(\tau)$, $Q_{114}(\tau)$, ... To do this, we must set $s = k_1 + 2, k_1 + 3, \ldots$, respectively, in Eq. (21.32), and, using the original vector equation (21.30), find the relationship between the k_1th components of the vectors $Q_{11k_1+1}(\tau)$, $Q_{11k_1+2}(\tau)$, ... and the scalar functions $\lambda_{11}(\tau)$, $\lambda_{12}(\tau)$, ...

However, such an approach to determination of the unknown functions $\lambda_{11}(\tau)$, $\lambda_{12}(\tau)$, ... can be rather cumbersome, since, each time, we must find the relationship between the corresponding components and the above-mentioned functions. Establishment of these relationships, with increase in s, can often lead to a very painstaking investigation.

Therefore, the following question arises: is it possible, beginning from Eqs. (21.30), to obtain a new scalar equation which would be equivalent to Eq. (21.32), and which would consist of only the unknown functions $\lambda_{11}(\tau), \lambda_{12}(\tau), \ldots$?

It appears that such an equation can be obtained by using the nilpotent property of the matrix I_1; this property means that

$$I_1^m = 0, \qquad m \geqslant k_1. \qquad (21.51)$$

In fact,

$$I_1^2 = \begin{bmatrix} 0 & 0 & 1 & 0 & \ldots & 0 \\ 0 & 0 & 0 & 1 & \ldots & 0 \\ \cdot & \cdot & \cdot & \cdot & \cdot\;\cdot\;\cdot & \cdot \\ 0 & 0 & 0 & 0 & & 1 \\ 0 & 0 & 0 & 0 & & 0 \\ 0 & 0 & 0 & 0 & & 0 \end{bmatrix}, \ldots, \qquad (21.52)$$

$$I_1^j = \begin{bmatrix} 0 & 0 & \dots & 1 & 0 & \dots & 0 \\ 0 & 0 & \dots & 0 & 1 & \dots & 0 \\ \dots & & & & & & \dots \\ 0 & 0 & \dots & 0 & 0 & \dots & 1 \\ 0 & 0 & \dots & & & \dots & 0 \\ \dots & & & & & & \dots \\ 0 & 0 & \dots & & & \dots & 0 \end{bmatrix} \Bigg\} k_1 - j, \tag{21.52}$$

from which it follows that relationship (21.51) holds.

It is not difficult to see that the matrix I_1, in addition to property (21.51), has another property which is very important to us, namely: in multiplication of the vector equation (21.30) from the left by the matrix I_1, all of its scalar equations rise one place in height. In particular, the last equation in system (21.30), i.e., Eq. (21.32) becomes the next-to-last one. Therefore, multiplying Eq. (21.30) from the left by the matrix I_1 $k_1 - 1$ times, we obtain a new vector equation

$$I_1^{k_1} Q_{11s}(\tau) = I_1^{k_1-1} \sum_{i=0}^{s-1} Q_{11i}(\tau)\lambda_{1s-i}(\tau) + I_1^{k_1-1} H_{11s}(\tau) \qquad (s = 1, 2, \dots), \tag{21.53}$$

in which Eq. (21.32) will occupy the first place.

Equation (21.53), by (21.51), is transformed to

$$I_1^{k_1-1} \sum_{i=0}^{s-1} Q_{11i}(\tau)\lambda_{1s-i}(\tau) + I_1^{k_1-1}\overline{H}_{11s}(\tau) = 0. \tag{21.54}$$

We carry out certain transformations on the left-hand side of the above equation by using the original system of equations (21.30). To do this, we write Eq. (21.54) in the following way:

$$I_1^{k_1-2} \sum_{i=0}^{s-1} I_1 Q_{11i}(\tau)\lambda_{1s-i}(\tau) + I_1^{k_1-1}\overline{H}_{11s}(\tau) = 0. \tag{21.55}$$

Since the vector $I_1 Q_{110}(\tau)$ is equal to the zero vector by (21.21), and the vector $I_1 Q_{11j}(\tau)$ $(j = 1, 2, \dots)$ is equal to

$$I_1 Q_{11j}(\tau) = \sum_{j_0=0}^{j} Q_{11j_0}(\tau)\lambda_{1j-j_0}(\tau) + \overline{H}_{11j}(\tau), \quad j = 1, 2, \dots, \tag{21.56}$$

by (21.30), then Eq. (21.55) can be written in the form

$$I_1^{k-2}\sum_{i=1}^{s-1}\sum_{i_0=0}^{i-1}[Q_{11i_0}(\tau)\lambda_{1i-i_0}(\tau)+\overline{H}_{11i}(\tau)]\lambda_{1s-i}(\tau)+I^{k_1-1}\overline{H}_{11s}(\tau)=0,$$

or

$$I_1^{k_1-2}\sum_{i=1}^{s-1}\sum_{i_0=0}^{i-1}Q_{11i_0}(\tau)\lambda_{1i-i_0}(\tau)\lambda_{1s-i}(\tau)+I_1^{k_1-2}\sum_{i=k_1}^{s-1}\overline{H}_{11i}(\tau)\lambda_{1s-i}(\tau)+ \tag{21.57}$$
$$+I_1^{k_1-1}\overline{H}_{11s}(\tau)=0$$
$$(s=1,2,\ldots).$$

If $k_1>2$, then, by applying to Eq. (21.57) the same transformation that we applied to Eq. (21.54), we obtain

$$I_1^{k_1-3}\sum_{i=2}^{s-1}\sum_{i_1=1}^{i-1}\sum_{i_0=0}^{i_1-1}Q_{11i_0}(\tau)\lambda_{1i_1-i_0}(\tau)\lambda_{1i-i_1}(\tau)\lambda_{1s-i}(\tau)+$$
$$+I_1^{k_1-3}\sum_{i=k+1}^{s-1}\sum_{i_1=k}^{i-1}\overline{H}_{11i_1}\lambda_{1i-i_1}(\tau)\lambda_{1s-i}(\tau)+I_1^{k_1-2}\sum_{i=k}^{s-1}\overline{H}_{11i}\lambda_{1s-i}(\tau)+$$
$$+I_1^{k_1-1}\overline{H}_{11s}(\tau)=0. \tag{21.58}$$

Continuing this process $k-3$ more times, we finally obtain

$$\sum_{i_{k_1-1}=k_1-1}^{s-1}\;\sum_{i_{k_1-2}=k_1-2}^{i_{k_1-1}-1}\cdots\sum_{i_0=0}^{i_1-1}Q_{11i_0}(\tau)\lambda_{1i_1-i_0}(\tau)\lambda_{1i_2-i_1}(\tau)\ldots\lambda_{1s-i_{k_1-1}}(\tau)+ \tag{21.59}$$
$$+F_{11s}(\tau)=0\qquad(s=1,2,\ldots),$$

where

$$F_{11s}(\tau)=I_1^{k_1-1}\overline{H}_{11s}(\tau)+I_1^{k_1-2}\sum_{i_1=k_1}^{s-1}\overline{H}_{11i_1}\lambda_{1s-i_1}(\tau)+$$
$$+I_1^{k_1-3}\sum_{i_2=k_1+1}^{s-1}\sum_{i_1=k_1}^{i_2-1}\overline{H}_{11i_1}(\tau)\lambda_{1i_2-i_1}(\tau)\lambda_{1s-i_2}(\tau)+\ldots+$$
$$+\sum_{i_{k_1-1}=2k_1-2}^{s-1}\;\sum_{i_{k_1-2}=2k_1-3}^{i_{k_1-1}-1}\cdots\sum_{i_1=k_1}^{i_2-1}\overline{H}_{11i_1}(\tau)\lambda_{1i_2-i_1}(\tau)\ldots\lambda_{1s-i_{k_1-1}}(\tau)$$
$$(s=1,2,\ldots). \tag{21.60}$$

The obtained equation (21.59) is an equation from which without much difficulty, we can determine the unknown functions $\lambda_{11}(\tau)$, $\lambda_{12}(\tau)$, ... Here we should note that since Eq. (21.59) is obtained from Eq. (21.30) by means of multiplication of the latter by the singular matrix $I_1^{k_1-1}$, Eq. (21.59) cannot be considered equivalent to Eq. (21.30). Thus, in the subsequent discussion, we will consider only the first scalar equation in the vector equation (21.59), since, according to previous considerations, the first scalar equation is identical to (21.32).

Thus, we set $s = k$ in Eq. (21.59). (It is easy to see that for $1 \leqslant s \leqslant k_1 - 1$, we have an identity.) We will have

$$Q_{110}(\tau)\,[\lambda_{11}(\tau)]^{k_1} + F_{11k}(\tau) = 0. \tag{21.61}$$

From which, by (21.25), we obtain

$$\lambda_{11}(\tau) = \sqrt[k_1]{-\{f_{1k_1}(\tau)\}}\ . \tag{21.62}$$

Since, according to (21.60),

$$F_{11k_1}(\tau) = I_1^{k_1-1}\overline{H}_{11k_1}(\tau) = \begin{bmatrix} \{h_{1k_1}(\tau)\}_{k_1} \\ 0 \\ \cdot \\ \cdot \\ \cdot \\ 0 \end{bmatrix}, \tag{21.63}$$

then, taking account of (21.42), we obtain

$$\lambda_{11}(\tau) = \sqrt[k_1]{\{c(\tau)\}_{k_1 1}}. \tag{21.64}$$

Thus, the function $\lambda_{11}(\tau)$ determined from Eq. (21.59) coincides with the function $\lambda_{11}(\tau)$ determined from Eq. (21.32).

Now we set $s = k_1 + 1$ in Eq. (21.59); we have

$$k_1\,[\lambda_{11}(\tau)]^{k_1-1}\,\lambda_{12}Q_{110}(\tau) + [\lambda_{11}(\tau)]^{k_1}Q_{111}(\tau) + F_{11k_1+1}(\tau) = 0. \tag{21.65}$$

Now, taking the first scalar equation, we find

$$\lambda_{12}(\tau) = -\frac{\{f_{1k_1+1}(\tau)\}_1}{k_1\,[\lambda_{11}(\tau)]^{k_1-1}}\,. \tag{21.66}$$

The component $\{f_{1k_1+1}(\tau)\}_1$ is a function which we already know, since the vector $F_{11k_1+1}(\tau)$ is equal to

$$F_{11k_1+1}(\tau) = I_1^{k_1-1}\overline{H}_{11k_1+1}(\tau) + I_1^{k_2-2}\overline{H}_{11k_1}(\tau)\,\lambda_{11}(\tau). \tag{21.67}$$

Thus, we have found the function $\lambda_{12}(\tau)$. Then, from (21.30), we can find the vector $Q_{112}(\tau)$ without any special difficulties.

In the same way, we can determine all the subsequent functions $\lambda_{13}(\tau)$, $\lambda_{14}(\tau)$, ... In particular, setting $s=k_1+m-1$ in Eq. (21.59) (m is any natural number) and considering that the functions $\lambda_{11}(\tau), \ldots, \lambda_{1m-1}(\tau)$ are already known, we find

$$\lambda_{1m}(\tau) = -\frac{\{\widetilde{f}_{1k_1+m-1}(\tau)\}_1}{k_1[\lambda_{11}(\tau)]^{k_1-1}}, \tag{21.68}$$

where $\{\widetilde{f}_{1k_1+m-1}(\tau)\}_1$ is the first component of the vector

$$\begin{aligned}\widetilde{F}_{11k_1+m-1}(\tau) &= I_1^{k_1-1}\overline{H}_{11k_1+m-1}(\tau) + I_1^{k_1-2}\sum_{j_1=k_1}^{k_1+m-2}\overline{H}_{11j_1}(\tau)\lambda_{1m+k_1-1-j_1}(\tau) + \\ &+ I_1^{k_1-3}\sum_{j_2=k_1+1}^{k_1+m-2}\sum_{j_1=k_1}^{j_2-1}\overline{H}_{11j_1}\lambda_{1j_2-j_1}(\tau)\lambda_{1k_1+m-1-j_2}(\tau) + \ldots + \\ &+ \sum_{j_{k_1-1}=2k_1-2}^{k_1+m-2}\ \sum_{j_{k_1-2}=2k_1-3}^{j_{k_1-1}-1}\cdots\sum_{j_1=k_1}^{j_2-1}\overline{H}_{11j_1}(\tau)\lambda_{1j_2-j_1}(\tau)\ldots\lambda_{1k_1+m-1-j_{k_1-1}}(\tau) + \\ &+ Q_{110}(\tau)\sum_{h=1}^{k_1-1}\ \sum_{j_{k_1-h}=k_1-h+1}^{k_1+m-2-h}\ \sum_{j_{k_1-h-1}=k_1-h-1}^{j_{k_1-h}-1}\cdots\sum_{j_1=1}^{j_2-1}\lambda_{1j_1}(\tau)\lambda_{1j_2-j_1}(\tau)\ldots \\ &\ldots\lambda_{1k_1+m-h-j_{k_1-h}}(\tau)(\lambda_{11}(\tau))^{h-1}.\end{aligned} \tag{21.69}$$

As already noted above, knowing the functions $\lambda_{1s}(\tau)$, $s=1,2,\ldots$, we can easily determine the unknown vectors $Q_{11s}(\tau)$, $s=1,2,\ldots$ from the system of equations (21.30). In particular, using the systems of equations (21.33), (21.35), which are obtained from system (21.30) for $s=1, 2$, respectively, we obtain

$$Q_{111}(\tau) = \begin{bmatrix} 0 \\ \lambda_{11}(\tau) \\ 0 \\ \cdot \\ \cdot \\ \cdot \\ 0 \end{bmatrix}, \quad Q_{112}(\tau) = \begin{bmatrix} 0 \\ \lambda_{12}(\tau) \\ \lambda_{11}^2(\tau) \\ 0 \\ \cdot \\ \cdot \\ \cdot \\ 0 \end{bmatrix}. \tag{21.70}$$

Having determined $Q_{1s}(\tau)$, we can, on the basis of Eq. (21.14), obtain the vectors

$$U_{1s}(\tau) = T(\tau)Q_{1s}(\tau) \qquad (s=0,1,\ldots).$$

The method presented here for determination of the vectors $U_{1s}(\tau)$ and the functions $\lambda_{1s+1}(\tau)$ $(s=0, 1, \ldots)$ can also be applied to the determination of the vectors $U_{js}(\tau)$ and the functions $\lambda_{js+1}(\tau)$ $(j=2, 3, \ldots, p)$ which occur in the solution. In fact, the vectors

$$Q_{js}(\tau) = T^{-1}(\tau) U_{js}(\tau) \qquad (j=2, 3, \ldots, p) \tag{21.71}$$

can be determined from the formulas obtained for the vectors $Q_{1s}(\tau)$, provided, in the latter, we change the function $\lambda_{1s+1}(\tau)$ to the function $\lambda_{js+1}(\tau)$

$$(j=2, 3, \ldots, p; \qquad s=0, 1, 2, \ldots).$$

2. In order to complete the proof of the theorem, we must still exhibit a method for determining the coefficients of the vector $P(\tau, \mu_1)$ and the function $z(\tau, \mu_1)$. For this we use relationship (21.10). Equating the coefficients of like powers of the parameter $\mu_1 = \sqrt[k_1]{\varepsilon}$, we obtain

$$[A_0(\tau) - i\nu(\tau) E] P_s(\tau) = \sum_{j_0=0}^{s-1} U_{1j_0}(\tau) z_{s-j_0}(\tau) + \Pi_s(\tau) \qquad (s=0, 1, 2, \ldots), \tag{21.72}$$

where

$$\Pi_s(\tau) = P'_{s-k_1}(\tau) - b_{s-k_1}(\tau) - \sum_{i=1}^{\left[\frac{s}{k_1}\right]} A_i(\tau) P_{s-k_1-i}(\tau). \tag{21.73}$$

Setting

$$R_s(\tau) = T^{-1}(\tau) P_s(\tau), \tag{21.74}$$

Eq. (21.72), on the basis of (18.2) and (21.14), can be represented in the following way:

$$[W_0(\tau) - i\nu(\tau) E] R_s(\tau) = \sum_{j_0=0}^{s-1} Q_{1j_0}(\tau) z_{s-j_0}(\tau) + \overline{\Pi}_s(\tau), \tag{21.75}$$

where

$$\overline{\Pi}_s(\tau) = T^{-1}(\tau) \Pi_s(\tau) \qquad (s=0, 1, \ldots). \tag{21.76}$$

The system (21.75), because of (18.3), can be decomposed into p subsystems of the form

$$[W_{j0}(\tau) - i\nu(\tau)E]\,R_{js}(\tau) = \sum_{j_0=0}^{s-1} Q_{11j_0}(\tau)\,z_{s-j_0}(\tau) + \overline{\Pi}_{sj}(\tau), \qquad (j = 1, 2, \ldots, p; \quad s = 0, 1, \ldots). \tag{21.77}$$

Since

$$\det[W_{j0}(\tau) - i\nu(\tau)E] \neq 0 \tag{21.78}$$

for all $\tau \in [0, L]$ and $j = 2, 3, \ldots, p$, then from the subsystems (21.77) it follows that

$$R_{js}(\tau) = [W_{j0}(\tau) - i\nu(\tau)E]^{-1}\left[\sum_{j_0=0}^{s-1} Q_{11j_0}(\tau)\,z_{s-j_0}(\tau) + \overline{\Pi}_{sj}(\tau)\right] \qquad (j = 2, 3, \ldots, p; \quad s = 0, 1, 2, \ldots). \tag{21.79}$$

Therefore, it remains for us to consider the equation

$$[W_{10}(\tau) - i\nu(\tau)E]\,R_{1s}(\tau) = \sum_{j_0=0}^{s-1} Q_{11j_0}(\tau)\,z_{s-j_0}(\tau) + \overline{\Pi}_{1s}(\tau) \qquad (s = 0, 1, 2, \ldots). \tag{21.80}$$

In the resonance case the function $i\nu(\tau)$ becomes equal to the function $\lambda_{10}(\tau)$ at certain points of the interval [0, L]. Consequently, for these values of

$$W_{10}(\tau) - i\nu(\tau)E = I_1. \tag{21.81}$$

Then Eq. (21.80) can be written in the form

$$I_1 R_{1s}(\tau) = \sum_{j_0=0}^{s-1} Q_{11j_0}(\tau)\,z_{s-j_0}(\tau) + \overline{\Pi}_{1s}(\tau). \tag{21.82}$$

In the obtained equation (21.82) the first components of the vectors $R_{1s}(\tau)$ $(s = 0, 1, 2, \ldots)$ remain arbitrary. Let us set them equal to zero:

$$\{r_{1s}(\tau)\}_1 = 0 \qquad (s = 0, 1, 2, \ldots). \tag{21.83}$$

To determine the remaining components of the vector $R_{1s}(\tau)$, we convert to coordinate form in Eq. (21.82). We will have

$$\{r_{1s}(\tau)\}_l = \sum_{j_0=0}^{s-1} \{q_{1j_0}(\tau)\}_{l-1} z_{s-j_0}(\tau) + \{p_{1s}(\tau)\}_{l-1}, \quad (2 \leqslant l \leqslant k_1), \tag{21.84}$$

$$\sum_{j_0=0}^{s-1} \{q_{1j_0}(\tau)\}_{k_1} z_{s-j_0}(\tau) + \{p_{1s}(\tau)\}_{k_1} = 0 \quad (s = 0, 1, 2, \ldots). \tag{21.85}$$

The obtained equation (21.85) makes possible determination of the unknown functions $z_s(\tau)$, $s = 0, 1, \ldots$, and, knowing the latter, we can find the components of the vector $R_{1s}(\tau)$ from Eq. (21.84). In fact, Eq. (21.85), by (21.38), can be written in the form

$$\sum_{j_0=k_1-1}^{s-1} \{q_{1j_0}(\tau)\}_{k_1} z_{s-j_0}(\tau) + \{p_{1s}(\tau)\}_{k_1} = 0. \tag{21.86}$$

This equation, by (21.73) and (21.76), becomes an identity for all $0 \leqslant s \leqslant k_1 - 2$. For $s = k_1 - 1$, we obtain

$$[\lambda_{11}(\tau)]^{k_1-1} z_0(\tau) = 0. \tag{21.87}$$

Since $\lambda_{11}(\tau)$, by virtue of its construction, is never zero on the interval $[0, L]$, then from (21.87) it follows that

$$z_0(\tau) = 0. \tag{21.88}$$

Now setting $s = k_1$ in Eq. (21.86), we have

$$[\lambda_{11}(\tau)]^{k_1-1} z_1(\tau) + \{p_{1k_1}(\tau)\}_{k_1} = 0. \tag{21.89}$$

Hence

$$z_1(\tau) = -\frac{\{p_{1k_1}(\tau)\}_{k_1}}{[\lambda_{11}(\tau)]^{k_1-1}}. \tag{21.90}$$

Considering the functions $z_0(\tau)$, $z_1(\tau)$, $\ldots$, $z_{m-1}(\tau)$ to be already determined (m is any natural number), we can, on the basis of Eq. (21.86), find the function $z_m(\tau)$ as well. In fact, setting $s = k_1 + m - 1$ in Eq. (21.86), we obtain

$$[\lambda_{11}(\tau)]^{k_1-1} z_m(\tau) + \sum_{j_0=k_1}^{k_1+m-2} \{q_{1j_0}(\tau)\}_{k_1} z_{s-j_0}(\tau) + \{p_{1k_1+m-1}(\tau)\}_{k_1} = 0, \quad (21.91)$$

or

$$z_m(\tau) = -\frac{\sum_{j_0=k_1}^{k_1+m-2} \{q_{1j_0}(\tau)\}_{k_1} z_{s-j_0}(\tau) + \{p_{1k_1+m-1}(\tau)\}_{k_1}}{[\lambda_{11}(\tau)]^{k_1-1}}. \quad (21.92)$$

Thus, our algorithm allows us to find the functions $z_m(\tau)$ for all natural numbers m. Knowing these, we can determine the components of the vectors $R_{1s}(\tau)$ $(s = 0, 1, \ldots)$ from relationship (21.84). Indeed, setting $s = 0$ in them, we obtain

$$\{r_{10}(\tau)\}_l = \{q_{10}(\tau)\}_{l-1} z_0(\tau) = 0. \quad (21.93)$$

From this, on the basis of (21.88), we find

$$\{r_{10}(\tau)\}_l = 0, \quad 2 \leqslant l \leqslant k_1. \quad (21.94)$$

For $s = 1$, from (21.84), we have

$$\{r_{11}(\tau)\}_l = \{q_{10}(\tau)\}_{l-1} z_1(\tau), \quad (21.95)$$

or, taking into account the form of the vector $Q_{10}(\tau)$,

$$\begin{gathered} \{r_{11}(\tau)\}_2 = z_1(\tau), \\ \{r_{11}(\tau)\}_3 = \ldots = \{r_{11}(\tau)\}_{k_1} = 0. \end{gathered} \quad (21.96)$$

In a similar manner, we can determine all the subsequent vectors $R_{12}(\tau)$, $R_{13}(\tau), \ldots$. Knowing them, from (21.74) we can find the vectors

$$R_s(\tau) = T(\tau) R_s(\tau) \qquad (s = 0, 1, \ldots). \quad (21.97)$$

Thus, by exhibiting a method of determining the coefficients of the formal series (21.6) we have proved Theorem IV.1.

Note 1. The theorem which we have just proved allows us to obtain not only a formal particular solution of the system (17.1′), but also the formal general solution of that system. Indeed, the function $\lambda_{11}(\tau)$ [and, as can be shown, all the subsequent functions $\lambda_{1s}(\tau)$, $(s = 2, \ldots)$, as well] has k_1 different values by virtue of (21.43). Consequently, for the characteristic root

$\lambda_{10}(\tau)$, on the basis of (21.4), we can obtain k_1 different linearly independent particular solutions. Then, for the characteristic value $\lambda_{j0}(\tau)$ $(j = 1, \ldots, p)$, we obtain k_j linearly independent formal particular solutions. But since $\sum_{j=1}^{p} k_j = n$, then, on the basis of the above, we obtain n linearly independent particular solutions. This means that we can construct a formal general solution for system (17.1′).

Note 2. A theorem analogous to Theorem IV.1 holds in the nonresonance case as well.

Theorem IV.2. *If the conditions of Theorem IV.1 are satisfied, then the formal general solution in the nonresonance case can be represented in the form*

$$x(t, \varepsilon) = \sum_{j=1}^{p} U_j(\tau, \mu_j)\tilde{h}_j(t, \varepsilon) + \tilde{P}(\tau, \varepsilon)e^{i\theta(t,\varepsilon)}, \tag{21.98}$$

$$\frac{d\tilde{h}_j}{dt} = \lambda_j(\tau, \mu_j)\tilde{h}_j, \qquad j = 1, 2, \ldots, p, \tag{21.99}$$

where $U_j(\tau, \mu_j)$, $\lambda_j(\tau, \mu_j)$ *are the same as in Theorem IV.1, and* $\tilde{P}(\tau, \varepsilon)$ *is an* n*-dimensional vector admitting the expansion*

$$\tilde{P}(\tau, \varepsilon) = \sum_{s=0}^{\infty} \varepsilon^s \tilde{P}_s(\tau). \tag{21.100}$$

Proof. The proof of the above theorem reduces to finding the coefficients of the vector $\tilde{P}(\tau, \varepsilon)$. Repeating the same considerations used in the proof of Theorem III. 3, we obtain

$$\tilde{P}_s(\tau) = [A_0(\tau) - i\nu(\tau)E]^{-1}\Phi_s(\tau), \qquad s = 0, 1, 2, \ldots, \tag{21.101}$$

where $\Phi_s(\tau)$ are determined from Eq. (17.26′), in which we must change $H_s(\tau)$ to $\Phi_s(\tau)$.

22. An Example

As an example we consider the fourth-order equation

$$\frac{d^4y}{dt^4} + \varepsilon p_1(\tau, \varepsilon)\frac{d^3y}{dt^3} + 2p_2(\tau, \varepsilon)\frac{d^2y}{dt^2} + \varepsilon p_3(\tau, \varepsilon)\frac{dy}{dt} + p_4(\tau, \varepsilon)y = \varepsilon b_1(\tau, \varepsilon)e^{i\theta(t,\varepsilon)}, \tag{22.1}$$

where $p_i(\tau, \varepsilon)$ $(i = 1, 2, 3, 4)$, and $b_1(\tau, \varepsilon)$ are real functions, sufficiently differentiable with respect to $\tau = \varepsilon t$, which admit the representation

$$p_i(\tau, \varepsilon) = \sum_{s=0}^{\infty} \varepsilon^s p_{is}(\tau), \quad b_1(\tau, \varepsilon) = \sum_{s=0}^{\infty} \varepsilon^s b_{s1}(\tau), \quad i = 1, 2, 3, 4, \tag{22.2}$$

where ε is a small real parameter.

By using the change of variables

$$y = x_1, \quad \frac{dy}{dt} = x_2, \quad \frac{d^2y}{dt^2} = x_3, \quad \frac{d^3y}{dt^3} = x_4 \tag{22.3}$$

we can reduce Eq. (22.1) to an equivalent system of equations

$$\frac{dx_1}{dt} = x_2, \quad \frac{dx_2}{dt} = x_3, \quad \frac{dx_3}{dt} = x_4,$$

$$\frac{dx_4}{dt} = -[p_4(\tau, \varepsilon)x_1 + \varepsilon p_3(\tau, \varepsilon)x_2 + 2p_2(\tau, \varepsilon)x_3 + \varepsilon p_1(\tau, \varepsilon)x_4] + \varepsilon b_1(\tau, \varepsilon)e^{i\theta(t, \varepsilon)}. \tag{22.4}$$

We introduce the vectors

$$x = \begin{bmatrix} x_1 \\ x_2 \\ x_3 \\ x_4 \end{bmatrix}, \quad b(\tau, \varepsilon) = \begin{bmatrix} 0 \\ 0 \\ 0 \\ b_1(\tau, \varepsilon) \end{bmatrix} \tag{22.5}$$

and the matrix

$$A(\tau, \varepsilon) = \begin{bmatrix} 0 & 1 & 0 & 0 \\ 0 & 0 & 1 & 0 \\ 0 & 0 & 0 & 1 \\ -p_4(\tau, \varepsilon) & -\varepsilon p_3(\tau, \varepsilon) & -2p_2(\tau, \varepsilon) & -\varepsilon p_1(\tau, \varepsilon) \end{bmatrix}. \tag{22.6}$$

Then system (22.4) can be written in the form (17.1′).

We will henceforth assume that, on the interval $[0, L]$, the realtionship

$$p_{40}(\tau) \equiv [p_{20}(\tau)]^2, \quad p_{20}(\tau) > 0 \tag{22.7}$$

holds. Therefore, the roots of the characteristic equation (12.3) will be

$$\begin{aligned} \lambda_{10}(\tau) &\equiv \lambda_{30}(\tau) = i\sqrt{p_{20}(\tau)}, \\ \lambda_{20}(\tau) &\equiv \lambda_{40}(\tau) = -i\sqrt{p_{20}(\tau)}, \end{aligned} \tag{22.8}$$

i.e., the matrix $A_0(\tau)$ has identically multiple characteristic values of the interval $[0, L]$. We will assume that the corresponding elementary divisors also have the same multiplicity.

Then, as the transforming matrix $T(\tau)$ which reduces the matrix $A_0(\tau)$ to Jordan form, we can take the matrix

$$\begin{bmatrix} 1 & 1 & 1 & 1 \\ \lambda_{10}(\tau) & 1+\lambda_{10}(\tau) & \lambda_{20}(\tau) & 1+\lambda_{20}(\tau) \\ \lambda_{10}^2(\tau) & \lambda_{10}(\tau)[2+\lambda_{10}(\tau)] & \lambda_{20}^2(\tau) & \lambda_{20}(\tau)[2+\lambda_{20}(\tau)] \\ \lambda_{10}^3(\tau) & \lambda_{10}^2(\tau)[3+\lambda_{10}(\tau)] & \lambda_{20}^3(\tau) & \lambda_{20}^2(\tau)[3+\lambda_{20}(\tau)] \end{bmatrix}. \tag{22.9}$$

The inverse matrix of $T(\tau)$ is the form

$$T^{-1}(\tau) = \frac{1}{4}\begin{bmatrix} 2+\lambda_{10}(\tau) & \dfrac{\lambda_{10}(\tau)+3}{\lambda_{10}(\tau)} & -\dfrac{1}{\lambda_{10}(\tau)} & -\dfrac{1+\lambda_{10}(\tau)}{\lambda_{10}^3(\tau)} \\ -\lambda_{10}(\tau) & -1 & \dfrac{1}{\lambda_{10}(\tau)} & \dfrac{1}{\lambda_{10}^2(\tau)} \\ 2+\lambda_{20}(\tau) & \dfrac{\lambda_{20}(\tau)+3}{\lambda_{20}(\tau)} & -\dfrac{1}{\lambda_{20}(\tau)} & -\dfrac{1+\lambda_{20}(\tau)}{\lambda_{20}^3(\tau)} \\ -\lambda_{20}(\tau) & -1 & \dfrac{1}{\lambda_{20}(\tau)} & \dfrac{1}{\lambda_{20}^2(\tau)} \end{bmatrix}. \tag{22.10}$$

In this case, the canonical matrix $W_0(\tau)$ is of the form:

$$W_0(\tau) = \begin{bmatrix} i\sqrt{p_{20}(\tau)} & 1 & 0 & 0 \\ 0 & i\sqrt{p_{20}(\tau)} & 0 & 0 \\ 0 & 0 & -i\sqrt{p_{20}(\tau)} & 1 \\ 0 & 0 & 0 & -i\sqrt{p_{20}(\tau)} \end{bmatrix}. \tag{22.11}$$

The functions $\{c(\tau)\}_{r_j, r_{j-1}+1}$ $(j = 1, 2;\ r_j = k_1 + k_2)$, which in this case become the functions $\{c(\tau)\}_{21}$, $\{c(\tau)\}_{41}$, have the form

$$\{c(\tau)\}_{21} =$$

$$= \frac{2p_{21}(\tau)\lambda_{10}^2(\tau) + p_{10}(\tau)\lambda_{10}^3(\tau) + 2\lambda_{10}^2(\tau)\lambda_{10}'(\tau) - p_{41}(\tau) - p_{31}(\tau)\lambda_{10}(\tau)}{4\lambda_{10}^2(\tau)},$$

$$\{c(\tau)\}_{41} = \tag{22.12}$$

$$= \frac{2p_{21}(\tau)\lambda_{20}^2(\tau) + p_{10}(\tau)\lambda_{20}^3(\tau) + 2\lambda_{20}^2(\tau)\lambda_{20}'(\tau) - p_{41}(\tau) - p_{31}(\tau)\lambda_{20}(\tau)}{4\lambda_{20}^2(\tau)},$$

respectively.

Consequently, if the functions $\{c(\tau)\}_{21}$, $\{c(\tau)\}_{41}$ are not equal to zero anywhere on the interval $[0, L]$, then to obtain the formal solution of the system we can apply Theorems IV.1 and IV.2. In particular, in accordance with Theorem IV.1, the formal solution of system (22.4), in the first approximation, can be represented as follows:

$$x(t, \varepsilon) = \{[U_{10}(\tau) + \sqrt{\varepsilon}U_{11}(\tau)]\,[c_1 e^{\int_0^t (\lambda_{10}(\tau) - i\nu(\tau) + \sqrt{\varepsilon}\lambda_{11}(\tau))dt} +$$

$$+ \sqrt{\varepsilon}\int_0^t z_1(\tau_1)\, e^{\int_{t_1}^t (\lambda_{10}(\tau) - i\nu(\tau) + \sqrt{\varepsilon}\lambda_{11}(\tau))dt} dt_1] + \sqrt{\varepsilon}p_1(\tau)\}\, e^{i\theta(t,\varepsilon)} + \tag{22.13}$$

$$+ c_2 e^{\int_0^t [\lambda_{20}(\tau) + \sqrt{\varepsilon}\lambda_{21}(\tau)]dt} [U_{20}(\tau) + \sqrt{\varepsilon}U_{21}(\tau)],$$

where

$$\lambda_{11}(\tau) = +\sqrt{\{c(\tau)\}_{21}},$$

$$\lambda_{21}(\tau) = +\sqrt{\{c(\tau)\}_{41}},$$

$$U_{j0}(\tau) = \begin{bmatrix} 1 \\ \lambda_{j0}(\tau) \\ \lambda_{j0}^2(\tau) \\ \lambda_{j0}^3(\tau) \end{bmatrix}, \qquad j = 1, 2,$$

$$U_{j1}(\tau) = \begin{bmatrix} 1 \\ 1 + \lambda_{j0}(\tau) \\ \lambda_{j0}(\tau)\,[2 + \lambda_{j0}(\tau)] \\ \lambda_{j0}^2(\tau)\,[3 + \lambda_{j0}(\tau)] \end{bmatrix} \lambda_{j1}(\tau), \quad j = 1,2, \tag{22.14}$$

$$P_1(\tau) = \begin{bmatrix} 1 \\ 1+\lambda_{10}(\tau) \\ \lambda_{10}(\tau)\,[2+\lambda_{10}(\tau)] \\ \lambda_{10}^2(\tau)\,[3+\lambda_{10}(\tau)] \end{bmatrix} z_1(\tau),$$

where

$$z_1(\tau) = \frac{1}{4\lambda_{10}^3(\tau)}, \tag{22.15}$$

c_1, c_2 are constants of integration.

Having obtained the solution to system (22.4), it is not difficult, using (22.3), to write out the solution of Eq. (22.1) in the resonance case.

Similarly, by using Theorem IV.2, we can obtain the solution of Eq. (22.1) in the nonresonance case.

23. The Asymptotic Nature of the Solution

In this section we will show that the formal solutions constructed in Sec. 21, for certain given conditions, are of an asymptotic nature in the sense that the vector $x^{(m)}(t, \varepsilon)$, formed from the vector $x(t, \varepsilon)$ by cutting off the formal series at the mth terms, differs in norm from the exact solution of system (17.1′) by an arbitrarily small amount for fixed m and for sufficiently small values of the parameter ε.

In proving this, we will henceforth consider in detail only the resonance case. The nonresonance case can be investigated similarly.

Thus, we consider the vector

$$x^{(m)} = [U_1^{(m)}(\tau, \mu_1)\, h_1^{(m)} + P^{(m)}(\tau, \mu_1)]\, e^{i\theta(t,\varepsilon)} + \sum_{k=2}^{p} U_k^{(m)}(\tau, \mu_k)\, h_k^{(m)}, \tag{23.1}$$

$$\frac{dh_1^{(m)}}{dt} = [\lambda^{(m)}(\tau, \mu_1) - i\nu(\tau)]\, h_1^{(m)} + z^{(m)}(\tau, \mu_1), \tag{23.2}$$

$$\frac{dh_k^{(m)}}{dt} = \lambda_k^{(m)}(\tau, \mu_k)\, h_k^{(m)} \qquad (k = 2, 3, \ldots, p), \tag{23.3}$$

where

$$U_j^{(m)}(\tau, \mu_j) = \sum_{s=0}^{m} \mu_j^s U_{js}(\tau), \quad \lambda_j^{(m)}(\tau, \mu_j) = \sum_{s=0}^{m} \mu_j^s \lambda_{js}(\tau),$$

$$P^{(m)}(\tau, \mu_1) = \sum_{s=0}^{m} \mu_1^s P_s(\tau), \quad z^{(m)}(\tau, \mu_1) = \sum_{s=0}^{m} \mu_1^s z_s(\tau). \tag{23.4}$$

Then we can prove the following lemma.

Lemma IV.1. *If the conditions of Theorem IV.1 are satisfied and for* $\tau \in [0, L]$

$$\mathrm{Re}\left(\sum_{s=0}^{k_j-1} \mu_j^s \lambda_{js}(\tau)\right) \leqslant 0 \tag{23.5}$$

for all $j = 1, 2, \ldots, p$, *then*

$$\frac{dx^{(m)}}{dt} = A(\tau, \varepsilon)\, x^{(m)} + b(\tau, \varepsilon)\, e^{i\theta(t,\varepsilon)} + \mu_1^{m+2-k_1} R_m^*(\tau, \mu_1), \tag{23.6}$$

where $R_m^*(\tau, \mu_1)$ *is a vector which is holomorphic with respect to the parameter* $\mu_1 = \sqrt[k_1]{\varepsilon}$ *in a neighborhood of the point* $\varepsilon = 0$.

To prove the lemma we substitute the vector $x^{(m)}$ into the following expression:

$$\frac{dx^{(m)}}{dt} - A(\tau, \varepsilon)\, x^{(m)} - \varepsilon b(\tau, \varepsilon)\, e^{i\theta(t,\varepsilon)}.$$

We will have

$$\frac{dx^{(m)}}{dt} - A(\tau, \varepsilon)\, x^{(m)} - \varepsilon b(\tau, \varepsilon)\, e^{i\theta(t,\varepsilon)} =$$

$$= \Big\{\varepsilon \frac{dU_1^{(m)}(\tau, \mu_1)}{d\tau} h_1^{(m)} + U_1^{(m)}(\tau, \mu_1)\,[(\lambda_1^{(m)}(\tau, \mu_1) - i\nu(\tau))\, h_1^{(m)} +$$

$$+ z^{(m)}(\tau, \mu_1)] + \varepsilon \frac{dP^{(m)}(\tau,\mu_1)}{d\tau} +$$

$$+ i\nu(\tau)\,[U_1^{(m)}(\tau, \mu_1)\, h_1^{(m)} + P^{(m)}(\tau, \mu_1)]\Big\}\, e^{i\theta(t,\varepsilon)} +$$

$$+\sum_{k=2}^{p}\left[\varepsilon\frac{dU_k^{(m)}}{d\tau}h_k^{(m)}+U_k^{(m)}(\tau,\ \mu_k)\lambda_k^{(m)}(\tau,\ \mu_k)h_k^{(m)}\right]-$$
$$-A(\tau,\ \varepsilon)\{[U_1^{(m)}(\tau,\ \mu_1)h_1^{(m)}+P^{(m)}(\tau,\ \mu_1)]e^{i\theta(t,\varepsilon)}+$$
$$+\sum_{k=2}^{p}U_k^{(m)}(\tau,\ \mu_k)h_k^{(m)}\}-\varepsilon b(\tau,\ \varepsilon)e^{i\theta(t,\varepsilon)}$$

or

$$\frac{dx^{(m)}}{dt}=A(\tau,\ \varepsilon)x^{(m)}+\varepsilon b(\tau,\ \varepsilon)e^{i\theta(t,\varepsilon)}+[U_1^{(m)}(\tau,\ \mu_1)\lambda_1^{(m)}(\tau,\ \mu_1)+$$
$$+\varepsilon\frac{dU_1^{(m)}}{d\tau}-A(\tau,\ \varepsilon)U_1^{(m)}(\tau,\ \mu_1)]h_1^{(m)}e^{i\theta(t,\varepsilon)}+$$
$$+\sum_{k=2}^{p}[U_k^{(m)}(\tau,\ \mu_k)\lambda_k^{(m)}(\tau,\ \mu_k)+\varepsilon\frac{dU_k^{(m)}}{d\tau}-$$
$$-A(\tau,\ \varepsilon)U_k^{(m)}(\tau,\ \mu_k)]h_k^{(m)}+$$
$$+\{U_1^{(m)}(\tau,\ \mu_1)z^{(m)}(\tau,\ \mu_1)+\varepsilon\frac{dP^{(m)}}{d\tau}-$$
$$-[A(\tau,\ \varepsilon)-i\nu(\tau)E]P^{(m)}(\tau,\ \mu_1)-\varepsilon b(\tau,\ \varepsilon)\}e^{i\theta(t,\varepsilon)}. \qquad (23.7)$$

The vectors standing in front of the functions $h_1^{(m)}e^{i\theta(t,\varepsilon)}$, $h_k^{(m)}$ ($k = 2, 3,\ldots, p$) and $e^{i\theta(t,\varepsilon)}$ on the right-hand side of Eq. (23.7) are, by Theorem IV.1, of the order of μ_1^{m+1}, μ_k^{m+1} ($k=2,\ldots, p$) and μ_1^{m+1}, respectively. Therefore,

$$\frac{dx^{(m)}}{dt}=A(\tau,\ \varepsilon)x^{(m)}+b(\tau,\ \varepsilon)e^{i\theta(t,\varepsilon)}+\mu_1^{m+1}R_{1m}(\tau,\ \mu_1)h_1^{(m)}+$$
$$+\sum_{k=2}^{p}\mu_k^{m+1}R_{km}(\tau,\ \mu_k)h_k^{(m)}+\mu_1^{m+1}F_m(\tau,\ \mu_1), \qquad (23.8)$$

where the vectors $R_{jm}(\tau,\ \mu_j)$, $F_m(\tau,\ \mu_1)$ are bounded in a neighborhood of the point $\mu_j = 0$ ($j = 1,\ 2,\ldots,\ p$).

Integrating Eqs. (23.2), (23.3), and taking into account (23.5), we obtain

$$|h_1^{(m)}|\leqslant\frac{N_1}{\mu_1^{k_1-1}},\quad |h_k^{(m)}|\leqslant N_k,\ \ k=2,\ 3,\ldots,\ p, \qquad (23.9)$$

where the N_j are constants which are independent of the parameters $\mu_j (j = 1,2,\ldots, p)$ which vary in the interval $0 < \mu_j \leqslant \mu_{j0}$.

Then the system of differential equations (23.8) can be written in the form

$$\frac{dx^{(m)}}{dt} = A(\tau, \varepsilon)\, x^{(m)} + b(\tau, \varepsilon)\, e^{i\theta(t,\varepsilon)} + \mu_1^{m+2-k_1}\overline{R}_{1m}(\tau, \mu_1) + \\ + \sum_{k=2}^{p} \mu_k^{m+1}\,\overline{R}_{km}(\tau, \mu_k) + \mu_1^{m+1}F_m(\tau, \mu_1), \tag{23.10}$$

where the $\overline{R}_{jm}(\tau, \mu_j)$ are vectors which are bounded in a neighborhood of $\mu_j = 0$ $(j = 1, 2,\ldots, p)$.

Let the roots of Eq. (12.3) be numbered in such a way that

$$k_1 \geqslant k_2 \geqslant \ldots \geqslant k_p. \tag{23.11}$$

Then

$$\mu_1 \geqslant \mu_2 \geqslant \ldots \geqslant \mu_p. \tag{23.12}$$

Consequently,

$$\mu_1^{m+2-k_1}\overline{R}_{1m} + \sum_{k=2}^{p} \mu_k^{m+1}\,\overline{R}_{km}(\tau, \mu_k) + \mu_1^{m+1}F_m(\tau, \mu_1) = O(\mu_1^{m+2-k_1}). \tag{23.13}$$

From this it follows that relationship (23.6) holds.

Theorem IV.3. *If the conditions of Lemma IV.1 are satisfied and the* $t = 0$

$$x = x^{(m)}, \tag{23.14}$$

then for any $L > 0$ *and* $0 < \mu_j \leqslant \mu_{j0}$ $(j = 1, 2,\ldots, p)$ *we can find a constant C, independent of* ε, *such that*

$$\| x - x^{(m)} \| \leqslant \mu_1^{m+2-2k_1} C. \tag{23.15}$$

To prove the above theorem we represent the exact solution of system (17.1′) as follows:

$$x = [U_1^{(m)}(\tau, \mu_1)\, q_1 + P^{(m)}(\tau, \mu_1)]\, e^{i\theta(t,\varepsilon)} + \sum_{k=2}^{p} U_k^{(m)}(\tau, \mu_k)\, q_k. \tag{23.16}$$

Then the vector

$$y = x - x^{(m)} = \sum_{j=1}^{p} U_j^{(m)}(\tau, \mu_j)\eta_j, \tag{23.17}$$

where

$$\eta_1 = (q_1 - h_1^{(m)}) e^{i\theta(t,\varepsilon)}, \quad \eta_k = q_k - h_k^{(m)} \qquad (k = 2, 3, \ldots, p), \tag{23.18}$$

will satisfy the system

$$\frac{dy}{dt} = A(\tau, \varepsilon) y - \mu_1^{m+2-k_1} R_m^*(\tau, \mu_1). \tag{23.19}$$

The obtained system (23.19), by (23.17), can be represented in the following way:

$$\sum_{j=1}^{p} U_j^{(m)}(\tau, \mu_j)\left[\frac{d\eta_j}{dt} - \lambda_j^{(m)}(\tau, \mu_j)\eta_j\right] =$$

$$= \sum_{j=1}^{p}\left[A(\tau, \varepsilon) U_j^{(m)}(\tau, \mu_j) - \right.$$

$$\left. - U_j^{(m)}(\tau, \mu_j)\lambda_j^{(m)}(\tau, \mu_j) - \varepsilon \frac{dU_j^{(m)}}{d\tau}(\tau, \mu_j)\right]\eta_j -$$

$$- \mu_1^{m+2-k_1} R_m^*(\tau, \mu_1)$$

or

$$\sum_{j=1}^{p} U_j^{(m)}(\tau, \mu_j)\left[\frac{d\eta_j}{dt} - \lambda_j^{(m)}(\tau, \mu_j)\eta_j\right] =$$
$$= \sum_{j=1}^{p} \mu_j^{m+1} R_{jm}(\tau, \mu_j)\eta_j - \mu_1^{m+2-k_1} R_m^*(\tau, \mu_1). \tag{23.20}$$

We will consider (23.20) as an algebraic system with respect to the scalar quantities $d\eta_j/dt - \lambda_j^{(m)}(\tau, \mu_j)\eta_j$ $(j = 1, 2, \ldots, p)$. It is not difficult to show, on the basis of the construction of the vectors $U_j^{(m)}(\tau, \mu_j)$, that for $0 < \mu_j \leqslant \mu_{j0}$ the rank of the above system is equal to p.

$$U_j^{(m)}(\tau, \mu_j) = U_{j0}(\tau) + \sum_{=1}^{m} \mu_j^s U_{js}(\tau) \to U_{j0}(\tau) \text{ as } \mu_j \to 0.$$

Therefore the system is solvable and

$$\frac{d\eta_j}{dt} = \lambda_j^{(m)}(\tau, \mu_j)\eta_j + \sum_{i=1}^{p} \mu_i^{m+1}\alpha_{ji}(\tau, \mu_i)\eta_i + \mu_1^{m+2-k_1}\beta_j(\tau, \mu_1) \tag{23.21}$$

$$(j = 1, 2, \ldots, p),$$

where $\alpha_{ji}(\tau, \mu_i)$, $\beta_j(\tau, \mu_1)$ are functions which are bounded in a neighborhood of the point $\mu_i = 0$ $(i = 1, 2, \ldots, p)$.

Then, integrating system (23.21), and taking into account that $\eta_j = 0$ when $t = 0$, we find

$$\eta_j = \mu_1^{m+2-k_1}\int_0^t \beta_j(\tau_1, \mu_1)e^{\int_{t_1}^{t}\lambda_j^{(m)}(\tau,\mu_j)dt} dt_1 + \\ + \int_0^t \sum_{i=1}^{p} \mu_i^{m+1}\alpha_{ji}(\tau_1, \mu_i)\eta_i e^{\int_{t_1}^{t}\lambda_j^{(m)}(\tau,\mu_j)dt} dt_1. \tag{23.22}$$

Assuming that $m \geqslant k_j - 1$, from Eq. (23.22) we obtain, by (23.5), the following estimate:

$$|\eta_j| \leqslant \mu_1^{m+2-k_1}\beta_j^* N_j^* t + N_j^* \int_0^t \sum_{i=1}^{p} \alpha_{ji}^* \mu_i^{m+1} |\eta_i| dt, \tag{23.23}$$

where

$$\beta_j^* = \max|\beta_j(\tau, \mu_1)|, \quad \alpha_{ji}^* = \max|\alpha_{ji}(\tau, \mu_i)|,$$

$$N_j^* = \max e^{\int_{t_1}^{t}\lambda_j^{(m)}(\tau,\mu_j)dt}, \quad \tau \in [0, L], \ 0 < \mu_j \leqslant \mu_{j0} \quad (i, j = 1, 2, \ldots, p). \tag{23.24}$$

Adopting the notation

$$\max_i \alpha_{ji}^* = \alpha_j^* \tag{23.25}$$

and taking into account (23.12), from inequality (23.23), we have

$$|\eta_j| \leqslant \mu_1^{m+2-k_1}\beta_j^* N_j^* t + \alpha^* N^* \mu_1^{m+1} \int_0^t \sum_{i=1}^{p} |\eta_i| \, dt \quad (j = 1, 2, \ldots, p). \tag{23.26}$$

We introduce into consideration the function

$$\omega = \sum_{i=1}^{p} |\eta_i|. \tag{23.27}$$

Then, adding the obtained inequalities (23.26), we have

$$\omega \leqslant \mu_1^{m+1} N_1 \int_0^t \omega dt + \mu_1^{m+2-k_1} N_2 t, \tag{23.28}$$

where

$$N_1 = \sum_{j=1}^{p} \beta_j^* N_j^*, \quad N_2 = \sum_{j=1}^{p} \alpha_j N_j^*. \tag{23.29}$$

Applying Lemma I.1 from Chap. 1 to inequality (23.28), we obtain

$$\omega \leqslant \mu_1^{m+2-2k_1} C_{1m}, \tag{23.30}$$

where

$$C_{1m} = N_2 L e^{\mu_{10}^{m+1-k_1} N_1 L}. \tag{23.31}$$

Then from Eq. (23.27) and inequality (23.30) it follows that

$$|\eta_j| \leqslant C_{1m} \mu_1^{m+2-2k_1} \quad (j = 1, 2, \ldots, p). \tag{23.32}$$

Taking the norm of Eq. (23.17) we obtain

$$\| x - x^{(m)} \| \leqslant \sum_{j=1}^{p} \| U_j^{(m)}(\tau, \mu_j) \| \, |\eta_j|. \tag{23.33}$$

Since the vectors $U_j^{(m)}(\tau, \mu_j)$ $(j = 1, 2, \ldots, p)$ are differentiable with respect to τ on $[0, L]$, then for all

$$\tau \in [0, L] \text{ и } 0 < \mu_j \leqslant \mu_{j0} \; (j = 1, 2, \ldots, p),$$
$$\| U_j^{(m)}(\tau, \mu_j) \| \leqslant M, \tag{23.34}$$

where M is a constant which is independent of ε.

Consequently, relationships (23.30), (23.33), (23.34) prove inequality (23.15), in which

$$C = pMC_{1m}. \tag{23.35}$$

The theorem is proved.

We note that the obtained estimate (23.15) does indicate the asymptotic nature of the solution $x^{(m)}$. In fact, from inequality (23.15) it follows that for all $m > 2k_1 - 2x^{(m)} \to x$ as $\mu_1 \to 0$.

Note. By applying the method explained in this section, we can obtain an estimate similar to (23.15) for the nonresonance case. In that case the estimate will be even better, namely: if the conditions of Theorem IV.3 are satisfied in the nonresonance case, then we find that

$$\| x - x^{(m)} \| \leqslant \mu_1^{m+1-k_1} C, \tag{23.36}$$

where C is a constant which is independent of ε. From inequality (23.36) it follows that for all $m > k_1 - 1$, $x_m \to x$ as $\mu_1 \to 0$.

24. Asymptotic Solution in the Presence of Several Multiple Elementary Divisors

In Sec. 21 we described in detail the process of constructing a formal solution of system (17.1′) in the case when the multiplicity of the elementary divisors coincided with the multiplicity of the corresponding roots of the characteristic equation (12.3).

In this section we will present the basic results obtained in [111] for the more general case when several multiple elementary divisors correspond to some root of the characteristic equation.

Thus, to the root $\lambda_j(\tau)$ $(j = 1, 2, \ldots, p)$ let there correspond $r_j (1 < r_j < k_j)$ elementary divisors, each of which has the multiplicity $s_{j1}, s_{j2}, \ldots, s_{jr_j}$ $(s_{j1} + s_{j2} + \ldots + s_{jr_j} = k_j;\; j = 1, 2, \ldots, p)$, respectively. In this case, from linear algebra it follows that for the matrix $A_0(\tau)$ we can find a nonsingular matrix $T(\tau)$ such that

$$W_0(\tau) = T^{-1}(\tau) A_0(\tau) T(\tau) = \begin{bmatrix} W_{k1}(\tau) & & & 0 \\ & W_{k2}(\tau) & & \\ & & \ddots & \\ 0 & & & W_{kp}(\tau) \end{bmatrix}, \tag{24.1}$$

where

$$W_{kj}(\tau) = \begin{bmatrix} W_{sj_1}(\tau) & & & \\ & W_{sj_2}(\tau) & & \\ & & \ddots & \\ & & & W_{s_jr_j}(\tau) \end{bmatrix}, \tag{24.2}$$

$$W_{sjn_j} = \begin{bmatrix} \lambda_{j_0}(\tau) & 1 & 0 \ldots 0 \\ 0 & \lambda_{j_0}(\tau) & 1 \; 0 \ldots 0 \\ \cdot & \cdot & \cdot \; \cdot \; \cdot \; \cdot \; \cdot \\ 0 & 0 & 0 \; 0 \ldots \lambda_{j_0}(\tau) \end{bmatrix}$$

$$(n_j = 1, 2, \ldots, r_j, \; j = 1, 2, \ldots, p).$$

Then we can prove the following theorem for the resonance case.

Theorem IV.4. *If $A(\tau, \varepsilon)$, $b(\tau, \varepsilon)$, $\nu(\tau)$ have derivatives of all orders with respect to τ, and for all $\tau \in [0, L]$, the m_{jn_j}-component of the vector*

$$C_j(\tau) = T^{-1}(\tau) \left[A(\tau) T_{m_{jn_{j-1}}+1}(\tau) - T'_{m_{jn_{j-1}}+1}(\tau)\right], \tag{24.3}$$

where $T_{m_{jn_{j-1}}+1}(\tau)$ is the column of the matrix $T(\tau)$ with the *index number $m_{jn_{j-1}} + 1$*

$$(m_{jn_j} = k_1 + k_2 + \ldots + k_{j-1} + s_{j1} + s_{j2} + \ldots + s_{jn_j}; \quad n_j = 1, 2, \ldots, r_j;$$
$$j = 1, 2, \ldots, p)$$

satisfies the relationship

$$\{c_j(\tau)\}_{m_{jn_j}} \neq 0, \tag{24.4)*}$$

then a particular formal solution of the system (17.1′) can be represented in the form

$$x = \sum_{n_1=1}^{r_1} [U_{1n_1}(\tau, \mu_{1n_1}) h_{1n_1} + P_{n_1}(\tau, \mu_{1n_1})] e^{i\theta(t,\varepsilon)} +$$

$$+ \sum_{k=2}^{p} \sum_{n_k=1}^{r_k} U_{kn_k}(\tau, \mu_{kn_k}) h_{kn_k}, \tag{24.5}$$

$$\frac{dh_{1n_1}}{dt} = [\lambda_{1n_1}(\tau, \mu_{1n_1}) - i\nu(\tau)] h_{1n_1} + zn_1(\tau, \mu_{1n_1}) \tag{24.6}$$

$$(n_1 = 1, 2, \ldots, r_1),$$

$$\frac{dh_{kn_k}}{dt} = \lambda_{kn_k}(\tau, \mu_{kn_k}) h_{kn_k} \qquad (n_k = 1, 2, \ldots, r_k, \tag{24.7}$$

$$k = 2, 3, \ldots, p),$$

where the $U_{jn_j}(\tau, \mu_{jn_j})$, $P_{n_1}(\tau, \mu_{1n_1})$ *are n-dimensional vectors;* h_{jn_j}, $z_{n_1}(\tau, \mu_{1n_1})$ *are scalar functions admitting the formal expansions*

$$U_{jn_j}(\tau, \mu_{jn_j}) = \sum_{s=0}^{\infty} \mu_{jn_j}^s U_{jn_js}(\tau),$$

$$\lambda_{jn_j}(\tau, \mu_{jn_j}) = \sum_{s=1}^{\infty} \mu_{jn_j}^s \lambda_{jn_js}(\tau) + \lambda_{j_0}(\tau), \tag{24.8}$$

$$P_{n_1}(\tau, \mu_{1n_1}) = \sum_{s=0}^{\infty} \mu_{1n_1}^s P_{n_1s}(\tau), \quad z_{n_1}(\tau, \mu_{1n_1}) = \sum_{s=0}^{\infty} \mu_{1n_1}^s z_{n_1s}(\tau)$$

$$(n_j = 1, 2, \ldots, r_j; \qquad j = 1, 2, \ldots, p),$$

where the μ_{jn_j} *are parameters, related to the parameter* ε *by the relationships*

$$\mu_{jn_j} = \sqrt[s_{jn_j}]{\varepsilon} \; (n_j = 1, 2, \ldots, r_j, \; j = 1, 2, \ldots, p). \tag{24.9}$$

---

*We assume that on the interval [0, L] the "conditional" equations—those which do not contain unknowns—are also satisfied [76, p. 83].

For the proof of the above theorem we refer the reader to [111].

In the nonresonance case we have the following theorem.

Theorem IV.5. *If the conditions of Theorem IV.4 are satisfied, then the formal general solution of system (17.1′) in the non-resonance case can be represented in the form*

$$x = \sum_{j=1}^{p} \sum_{n_j=1}^{r_j} U_{jn_j}(\tau, \mu_{jn_j}) \widetilde{h}_{jn_j} + \widetilde{\Phi}(\tau, \varepsilon) e^{i\theta(t,\varepsilon)}, \tag{24.10}$$

$$\frac{d\widetilde{h}_{jn_j}}{dt} = \lambda_{jn_j}(\tau, \mu_{jn_j}) \widetilde{h}_{jn_j}. \quad (n_j = 1, 2, \ldots, r_j, \ j = 1, 2, \ldots, p), \tag{24.11}$$

where $U_{jn_j}(\tau, \mu_{jn_j}), \lambda_{jn_j}(\tau, \mu_{jn_j})$ *are the same as in Theorem IV.4, and* $\widetilde{\Phi}(\tau, \varepsilon)$ *is an n-dimensional vector admitting the formal expansion*

$$\widetilde{\Phi}(\tau, \varepsilon) = \sum_{s=1}^{\infty} \varepsilon^s \widetilde{P}_s(\tau). \tag{24.12}$$

The asymptotic nature of solution (24.5) is proved by the following theorem.

Theorem IV.6. *If the conditions of Theorem IV.4 are satisfied and*

$$x|_{t=0} = x^{(m)}|_{t=0}; \ \operatorname{Re}(\lambda_{j_0}(\tau) + \sum_{s=1}^{s_{jn_j}-1} \mu_{jn_j}^s \lambda_{jn_js}) \leqslant 0, \tag{24.13}$$

where $x^{(m)}$ *is the vector determined from relationships (24.5) - (24.7) in which the series (24.8) have been cut off at the mth terms, then for any* $L > 0$ *and* $0 < \mu_{jn_j} \leqslant \bar{\mu}_{jn_j}$ *we can find constants* C_{jn_j}*, independent of the parameter* ε*, such that*

$$\| x - x^{(m)} \| \leqslant \sum_{j=1}^{p} \sum_{n_j=1}^{r_j} \mu_{jn_j}^{m+2-2s_{jn_j}} C_{jn_j}. \tag{24.14}$$

In the nonresonance case we can obtain the estimate

$$\| x - x^{(m)} \| \leqslant \sum_{j=1}^{p} \sum_{n_j=1}^{r_j} \mu_{jn_j}^{m+1-s_{jn_j}} C_{jn_j}. \tag{24.15}$$

The proofs of inequalities (24.14), (24.15) are carried out in the same way as the proof of inequality (23.15).

25. Construction of an Asymptotic Solution in the Case of Other Sufficient Conditions

In constructing an asymptotic solution of system (17.1) in the presence of multiple elementary divisors we required, for example, in the case when one elementary divisor of multiplicity k_j corresponded to the root $\lambda_i(\tau)$, that the coefficients of the system be infinitely differential with respect to τ, and, in addition, that condition (21.2) be satisfied.

In this section we will exhibit an algorithm for construction of an asymptotic solution of system (17.1′) in the case when condition (21.2) is not satisfied on the interval $[0, L]$, i.e.,

$$\{c(\tau)\}_{r_j r_{j-1}+1} \equiv 0 \tag{25.1}$$

for all $j=1, 2,\dots, p$ $(r_j = k_1 + k_2 + \dots + k_j)$.

However, in order to satisfy condition (25.1), as is shown in [113-114], we must require of the matrix $C(\tau) = T^{-1}(\tau)[A_1(\tau)T(\tau) - T'(\tau)]$ that

$$\alpha_j(\tau) = \{c(\tau)\}_{r_j, r_{j-1}+2} + \{c(\tau)\}_{r_j-1,\ r_{j-1}+1} \neq 0 \tag{25.2}$$

for any $\tau \in [0, L]$ and all $j = 1, 2,\dots, p$.

In addition, we will assume that all the numbers $k_j (j = 1, 2,\dots,p)$ denoting the multiplicity of the corresponding roots of the characteristic equation satisfy the condition

$$k_j > 2 \ (j = 1, 2,\dots, p). \tag{25.3}$$

If among the numbers k_j $(j = 1, 2, \dots p)$ there appear any which are equal to two, then the algorithm presented below for construction of an asymptotic solution to system (17.1′) cannot be effective, since it leads us to the problem of finding a solution to the Ricatti equation. We will consider this case, which we call "singular," at the end of Sec. 25 (see the note following Theorem IV.9).

Thus, assuming condition (25.3) is satisfied, we can prove the following theorem.

Theorem IV.7. *If* $A(\tau, \varepsilon)$, $b(\tau,\varepsilon)$, $\nu(\tau)$ *have derivatives with respect to* τ *of all orders on the interval [0, L], and the corresponding elements of the matrix* $C(\tau) = T^{-1}(\tau)\,[A_1(\tau)T(\tau) - T'(\tau)]$

satisfy conditions (25.1) and (25.2), then a formal particular solution of system (17.1′) in the resonance case can be represented in the form

$$x = [U_1(\tau, \mu_1)h_1 + P(\tau, \varepsilon)]\, e^{i\theta(t,\varepsilon)} + \sum_{k=2}^{p} U_k(\tau, \mu_k)h_k, \tag{25.4}$$

$$\frac{dh_1}{dt} = [\lambda_1(\tau, \mu_1) - i\nu(\tau)]\, h_1 + z(\tau, \varepsilon), \tag{25.5}$$

$$\frac{dh_k}{dt} = \lambda_k(\tau, \mu_k)h_k, \quad k = 2, 3, \ldots, p, \tag{25.6}$$

where $U_j(\tau, \mu_j)\,(j = 1, 2, \ldots, p)$, $P(\tau, \varepsilon)$ *are n-dimensional vectors;* $\lambda_j(\tau, \mu_j)$, $z(\tau, \varepsilon)$ *are scalar functions admitting formal expansion in powers of the parameter*

$$\mu_j = \sqrt[k_j-1]{\varepsilon} \quad (j = 1, 2, \ldots, p), \tag{25.7}$$

[*this parameter differs from (21.7)*]; *i.e.*,

$$\begin{gathered} U_j(\tau, \mu_j) = \sum_{s=0}^{\infty} \mu_j^s U_{js}(\tau), \quad \lambda_j(\tau, \mu_j) = \sum_{s=0}^{\infty} \mu_j^s \lambda_{js}(\tau), \\ P(\tau, \varepsilon) = \sum_{s=0}^{\infty} \varepsilon^s P_s(\tau), \quad z(\tau, \varepsilon) = \sum_{s=0}^{\infty} \varepsilon^s z_s(\tau). \end{gathered} \tag{25.8}$$

Proof. If the vector x determined by Eqs. (25.4)-(25.6) is a formal solution of the system, then it must satisfy that system. Therefore, substituting x into system (17.1) we obtain an identity. In this identity, we require that the coefficients of the h_j and the free terms be equal. As a result we obtain

$$[A(\tau, \varepsilon) - \lambda_j(\tau, \mu_j)E]\, U_j(\tau, \mu_j) = \varepsilon U_j'(\tau, \mu_j), \tag{25.9}$$

$$[A(\tau, \varepsilon) - i\nu(\tau)E]\, P(\tau, \varepsilon) = U_1(\tau, \mu_1)z(\tau, \varepsilon) + \varepsilon(P'(\tau, \varepsilon) - b(\tau, \varepsilon)). \tag{25.10}$$

1. To determine the coefficients of the vector $U_j(\tau, \mu_j)$ and the function $\lambda_j(\tau, \mu_j)$ we use Eq. (25.9). Equating coefficients of like powers of the parameter μ_j, we obtain

$$[A_0(\tau) - \lambda_{j_0}(\tau)E]\, U_{j_0}(\tau) = 0, \tag{25.11}$$

$$[A_0(\tau) - \lambda_{j_0}(\tau) E] U_{js}(\tau) = \sum_{i_0=1}^{s-1} U_{ji_0}(\tau)\lambda_{js-i_0}(\tau) + H_{js}(\tau),$$

$$(s = 1, 2, \ldots; \qquad j = 1, 2, \ldots, p), \tag{25.12}$$

where

$$H_{js}(\tau) = U'_{js+1-k_j}(\tau) - \sum_{k=1}^{\left[\frac{s}{k_j-1}\right]} A_k(\tau) U_{js-k(k_j-1)}(\tau) \tag{25.13}$$

$$(j = 1, 2, \ldots, p).$$

In what follows we will need the vector

$$Q_{js}(\tau) = T^{-1}(\tau) U_{js}(\tau) \; (s = 0, 1, \ldots; \qquad j = 1, 2, \ldots, p) \tag{25.14}$$

and the vector of dimension k_i $(i = 1, \ldots, p)$

$$Q_{jis}(\tau) = \begin{bmatrix} \{q_{js}\}_{r_{i-1}+1} \\ \{q_{js}\}_{r_{i-1}+2} \\ \cdot \\ \cdot \\ \cdot \\ \{q_{js}\}_{r_i} \end{bmatrix} \begin{matrix} (r_i = k_1 + k_2 + \ldots + k_i; \\ i = 1, 2, \ldots, p), \end{matrix} \tag{25.15}$$

formed from the corresponding components of the vector $Q_{js}(\tau)$.

Then, on the basis of (20.1), Eq. (25.11) can be written in the form

$$[W_i(\tau) - \lambda_{j_0}(\tau) E] Q_{ji_0}(\tau) = 0 \; (i, j = 1, 2, \ldots, p). \tag{25.16}$$

Since

$$\det [W_i(\tau) - \lambda_{j_0}(\tau) E] \neq 0, \; i \neq j, \tag{25.17}$$

for all $\tau \in [0, L]$, then from Eq. (25.16) it follows that

$$Q_{ji_0}(\tau) = 0 \; (i \neq j; \quad i, j = 1, 2, \ldots, p). \tag{25.18}$$

For $i = j$ Eq. (25.16) is converted to the form

$$I_j Q_{jj_0}(\tau) = 0 \; (j = 1, 2, \ldots, p), \tag{25.19}$$

where

$$I_j = \begin{bmatrix} 0 & 1 & 0 & 0 & \dots & 0 \\ 0 & 0 & 1 & 0 & \dots & 0 \\ \cdot & \cdot & \cdot & \cdot & \cdot\cdot\cdot & \cdot \\ 0 & 0 & 0 & 0 & \dots & 1 \\ 0 & 0 & 0 & 0 & \dots & 0 \end{bmatrix}. \tag{25.20}$$

From this we find

$$\{q_{j_0}(\tau)\}_{r_{j-1}+n_j} = 0 \ (n_j = 2,\ 3, \dots,\ k_j; \qquad j = 1, \dots,\ p). \tag{25.21}$$

Since the component $\{q_{j_0}(\tau)\}_{r_{j-1}+1}$ is arbitrary we can set it equal to

$$\{q_{j_0}(\tau)\}_{r_{j-1}+1} = 1 \ (j = 1,\ 2, \dots,\ p). \tag{25.22}$$

Thus, the vector $Q_{j_0}(\tau)$ is determined. Then, from formula (25.14) we can find the vector $U_{j_0}(\tau)\,(j = 1,\ 2, \dots,\ p)$.

To determine the vector $U_{js}(\tau)$ and the function $\lambda_{js}(\tau)$ we use Eq. (25.12), which can be written in the following way:

$$[W_i(\tau) - \lambda_{j_0}(\tau)E]\,Q_{jis}(\tau) = \sum_{k=0}^{s-1} Q_{jik}(\tau)\,\lambda_{js-k}(\tau) + \overline{H}_{jis}(\tau)$$

$$(j,\ i = 1,\ 2, \dots,\ p; \qquad s = 1,\ 2, \dots), \tag{25.23}$$

where

$$\overline{H}_{js}(\tau) = T^{-1}(\tau)\,H_{js}(\tau). \tag{25.24}$$

Then, taking into account relationship (25.17), we have

$$Q_{jis}(\tau) = [W_i(\tau) - \lambda_{j0}(\tau)E]^{-1}\left[\sum_{k=0}^{s-1} Q_{jis}(\tau)\lambda_{js-k}(\tau) + \widetilde{H}_{jis}(\tau)\right]$$

$$(i \neq j; \qquad i,\ j = 1,\ 2, \dots,\ p; \qquad s = 1,\ 2, \dots). \tag{25.25}$$

We note that since

$$\overline{H}_{ji}(\tau) \equiv 0 \ \text{ for } 1 \leqslant s \leqslant k_j - 2,$$

then

$$Q_{jis}(\tau) \equiv 0, \quad 1 \leqslant s \leqslant k_j - 2; \qquad i \neq j. \tag{25.26}$$

We now must investigate Eq. (25.23) for $j = i$. In the given case it is converted to the form

$$I_j Q_{jjs}(\tau) = \sum_{k=0}^{s-1} Q_{jjk}(\tau)\lambda_{js-k}(\tau) + \overline{H}_{jjs}(\tau)$$
$$(s = 1, 2, \ldots; \qquad j = 1, 2, \ldots, p). \tag{25.27}$$

In Eq. (25.27) the first components of the vectors $Q_{jjs}(\tau)$ remain arbitrary. For simplicity, we set

$$\{q_{js}(\tau)\}_{r_{j-1}+1} = 0 \quad (r_j = k_1 + k_2 + \ldots + k_j, \ j = 1, 2, \ldots, p,$$
$$s = 1, 2, \ldots). \tag{25.28}$$

The remaining components of the vectors $Q_{jjs}(\tau)$ contain the unknown functions $\lambda_{js}(\tau)$; in order to determine these we use the last equation in system (25.27):

$$\sum_{k=0}^{s-1} \{q_{jk}(\tau)\}_{r_j} \lambda_{js-k}(\tau) + \{\overline{h}_{js}(\tau)\}_{r_j} = 0 \ (s = 1, 2, \ldots; \ j = 1, 2, \ldots, p). \tag{25.29}$$

In investigating Eq. (25.29) we proceed in the same way as we did with Eq. (21.32), i.e., instead of Eq. (25.29) we will consider an equivalent equation. This equivalent equation will be the first scalar equation in a new system obtained from system (25.27) by multiplying the latter from the left by the matrix I_j $(k_j - 1)$ times. As a result we will have

$$\sum_{i_{k_j-1}=k_j-1}^{s-1} \ \sum_{i_{k_j-2}=k_j-2}^{i_{k_j-1}-1} \cdots \sum_{i_0=0}^{i_1-1} Q_{jji_0}(\tau)\lambda_{ji_1-i_0}(\tau)\lambda_{ji_2-i_1}(\tau)\ldots\lambda_{js-i_{k_j-1}} +$$
$$+ F_{jjs}(\tau) = 0 \ (s = 1, 2, \ldots), \tag{25.30}$$

where

$$F_{jjs}(\tau) = \sum_{i_{k_j-1}=2k_j-2}^{s-1} \ \sum_{i_{k_j-2}=2k_j-3}^{i_{k_j-1}-1} \cdots \sum_{i_1=k_j-1}^{i_2-1} \overline{H}_{jji_1}(\tau)\lambda_{ji_2-i_1}(\tau)\ldots\lambda_{js-i_{k_j-1}}(\tau) + \tag{25.31}$$

$$+\sum_{i_{k_j-1}=2k_j-3}^{s-1}\ \sum_{i_{k_j-2}=2k_j-4}^{i_{k_j-1}-1}\ \cdots\ \sum_{i_2=k_j-1}^{i_3-1} I_j\overline{H}_{jji_2}(\tau)\,\lambda_{ji_3-i_2}(\tau)\ldots\lambda_{js-i_{k_j-1}}(\tau)+\ldots+$$

$$+\sum_{i_{k_j-1}=k_j-1}^{s-1} I_j^{k_j-2}\,\overline{H}_{jji_{k_j-1}}(\tau)\,\lambda_{js-i_{k_j-1}}(\tau)+I_j^{k_j-1}\overline{H}_{jjs}(\tau)$$

$$(s=1,\ 2,\ldots,\ j=1,\ 2,\ldots,\ p).$$

Setting $s=k_j-1$ in Eq. (25.30) [for $1\leqslant s\leqslant k_j-2$, the equation is an identity by (25.13)], we have

$$F_{jjk_j-1}(\tau)=0 \tag{25.32}$$

or, taking into account (25.31), we have

$$I_j^{k_j-1}H_{jjk_j-1}(\tau)=0,\ j=1,\ 2,\ldots,\ p, \tag{25.33}$$

where

$$\overline{H}_{jjk_j-1}(\tau)=C_j(\tau)\,Q_{j0}(\tau), \tag{25.34}$$

$C_j(\tau)$ is a rectangular $(k_j\times n)$-matrix formed from the corresponding elements of the matrix $C(\tau)$.

By (25.1), Eq. (25.33) becomes an identity.

Now let $s=k_j$. Then Eq. (25.30) becomes the equation

$$Q_{jj_0}(\tau)\,[\lambda_{j_1}(\tau)]^{k_j}+F_{jjk_j}(\tau)=0, \tag{25.35}$$

in which

$$F_{jjk_j}(\tau)=I_j^{k_j-2}\overline{H}_{jjk_j-1}(\tau)\lambda_{j_1}(\tau)+I_j^{k_j-1}\,(Q'_{jj_1}(\tau)+C_j(\tau)\,Q_{j_1}(\tau)). \tag{25.36}$$

The vector $Q_{j_1}(\tau)$, as follows from formulas (25.26) and (25.27), has its components equal to zero, except the components

$$\{q_{j_1}(\tau)\}_{r_{j-1}+2}=\lambda_{j_1}(\tau)\ \ (j=1,\ 2,\ldots,\ p). \tag{25.37}$$

Then, by condition (25.3), from Eq. (25.35) we obtain

$$[\lambda_{j_1}(\tau)]^{k_j}+\alpha_j(\tau)\,\lambda_{j_1}(\tau)=0\ \ (j=1,\ 2,\ldots,\ p) \tag{25.38}$$

(for $k_j=2$ the first equation in system (23.35) becomes the Ricatti equation).

From this

$$\lambda_{j_1}^{(1)}(\tau)=0,\ \lambda_{j_1}^{(2)}(\tau)=\sqrt[k_j-1]{-\alpha_j(\tau)},\ j=1,\ 2,\ldots,p. \tag{25.39}$$

For $s=k_j+1$, from Eq. (25.30) we have

$$k_j[\lambda_{j_1}(\tau)]^{k_j-1}\lambda_{j_2}(\tau)Q_{jj_0}(\tau)+[\lambda_{j_1}(\tau)]^{k_j}Q_{jj_1}(\tau)+F_{jjk_j+1}(\tau)=0$$
$$(j=1,\ 2,\ldots,p), \tag{25.40}$$

where

$$F_{jjk_j+1}(\tau)=I_j^{k_j-1}(Q'_{jj_2}(\tau)+C_j(\tau)Q_{j_2}(\tau))+I_j^{k_j-2}\overline{H}_{jjk_j-1}(\tau)\lambda_{j_2}(\tau)+$$
$$+I_j^{k_j-3}\overline{H}_{jjk_j}(\tau)\lambda_{j_1}(\tau)\ (j=1,\ 2,\ldots,p). \tag{25.41}$$

Taking the first equation from system (25.40) and recalling that

$$\{q_{j2}(\tau)\}_{r_{j-1}+2}=\lambda_{j2}(\tau), \tag{25.42}$$

we obtain

$$\lambda_{j2}(\tau)[k_j(\lambda_{j1}(\tau))^{k_j-1}+\alpha_j(\tau)]+\beta_{j2}(\tau)=0, \tag{25.43}$$

where

$$\beta_{j2}(\tau)=\sum_{i=1}^{n}{}^{*}\{C(\tau)\}_{r_j,i}\{q_{ji}(\tau)\}_2+\{c(\tau)\}_{r_j-3,\ r_{j-1}-2}(\lambda_{j_1}(\tau))^2 \tag{25.44}$$

[in the summation $\sum^*$ the term corresponding to $i=r_{j-1}+2$ is omitted; the components of the vector $Q_{j2}(\tau)$ occurring in the sum $\sum^*$ are expressed by using the already-known function $\lambda_{j1}(\tau)$]. Then from formula (23.43) we find

$$\lambda_{j2}(\tau)=-\frac{\beta_{j2}(\tau)}{k_j\lambda_{j1}(\tau)+\alpha_j(\tau)}\quad (j=1,2,\ldots,p). \tag{25.45}$$

All the subsequent functions $\lambda_{js}(\tau)$ $(s=3,4,\ldots)$ can be determined in the same way. Thus, for example, setting $s=k_j+m-1$ in (23.30) (m is any natural number), we have

$$\lambda_{jm}(\tau) = -\frac{\beta_{jm}(\tau)}{k_j(\lambda_{j1})^{k_j-1} + \alpha_j} \quad (j = 1,\ 2, \ldots, p), \tag{25.46}$$

where

$$\beta_{jm}(\tau) = \sum_{i=1}^{n}{}^{*} \{c(\tau)\}_{r_j, i} \{q_{jm}(\tau)\}_i + \{c(\tau)\}_{r_j, r_{j-1}+2} \{\overline{h}_{jm}(\tau)\}_{r_{j-1}+1} + \\ + \gamma_{jm}(\tau), \ j = 1,\ 2, \ldots, p, \tag{25.47}$$

$\gamma_{jm}(\tau)$ is the first component of the vector $F_{jjm}(\tau)$:

$$F_{jjm}(\tau) = I_j^{k_j-1} [Q'_{jjm}(\tau) - \sum_{k=2}^{\left(\frac{k_j+m-1}{k_j-1}\right)} c_{jk}(\tau) Q_{jk_j+m-1-k(k_j-1)}(\tau) + \\ + \sum_{i_{k_j-1}=k_j}^{k_j+m-2} I_j^{k_j-2} \overline{H}_{jji_{k_j-1}}(\tau) \lambda_{jm+k_j-1-i_{k_j-1}}(\tau) + \ldots + \\ \sum_{i_{k_j-1}=2k_j-2}^{k_j+m-2} \sum_{i_{k_j-2}=2k_j-3}^{i_{k_j-1}-1} \ldots \sum_{i_1=k_j-1}^{i_2-1} \overline{H}_{jji_1}(\tau) \lambda_{ji_2-i_1}(\tau) \ldots \lambda_{jk_j+m-1-i_{k_j-1}}(\tau), \\ (j = 1,\ 2, \ldots, p), \tag{25.48}$$

where $C_{jk}(\tau)$ is a rectangular $(k_j \times n)$-matrix formed from the elements of the matrix $T^{-1}(\tau) A_k(\tau) T(\tau)$ $(k = 2,\ 3, \ldots, [k_j + m - 1/k_j - 1])$.

We should note that, by (25.2) and (25.39), the denominator in the formulas (25.45) and (25.46) is not equal to zero for any $\tau \in [0, L]$.

Thus, the method presented above allows us to determine the functions $\lambda_{j1}(\tau), \ldots, \lambda_{jm}(\tau)$ $(j = 1, 2, \ldots, p)$ for any natural m. Knowing the latter, from (25.27) it is very easy to determine the vectors $Q_{jj1}(\tau)$, $Q_{jj2}(\tau), \ldots, Q_{jjm}(\tau)$.

2. Let us find the coefficients of the vector $P(\tau, \varepsilon)$ and the function $z(\tau, \varepsilon)$.

To do this we isolate in relationship (25.10) the coefficients of the powers ε^s; we obtain

$$[A_0(\tau) - i\nu(\tau) E] P_s(\tau) = \sum_{k=0}^{s} U_{1k(k_1-1)}(\tau) z_{s-k}(\tau) + \\ + P'_{s-1}(\tau) - b_{s-1}(\tau) - \sum_{k=1}^{s} A_k(\tau) P_{s-k}(\tau) \ (s = 0,\ 1, \ldots). \tag{25.49}$$

We introduce into consideration the vector

$$R_s(\tau) = T^{-1}(\tau) P_s(\tau) \quad (s = 0, 1, 2, \ldots). \tag{25.50}$$

Then, for $s=0$, Eq. (25.49) can be written in the form

$$[W_0(\tau) - iv(\tau)E]\, R_0(\tau) = Q_{10}(\tau) z_0(\tau),$$

or

$$[W_{j0}(\tau) - iv(\tau)E]\, R_{j0}(\tau) = Q_{1j0}(\tau) z_0(\tau) \quad (j = 1, 2, \ldots, p). \tag{25.51}$$

From this, by (19.4), we have

$$R_{j0}(\tau) = 0 \quad (j = 2, 3, \ldots, p). \tag{25.52}$$

For $j=1$ the function $iv(\tau)$ becomes equal to $\lambda_{10}(\tau)$. Therefore from Eq. (25.51) it follows that

$$\{r_0(\tau)\}_2 = z_0(\tau), \quad \{r_0(\tau)\}_{r_1} = 0, \quad 3 \leqslant r_1 \leqslant k_1. \tag{25.53}$$

The first components of the vectors $R_s(\tau)\ (s = 1, 2, \ldots)$ are arbitrary; we set them equal to zero.

Let $s=1$. We have

$$\begin{gathered}[W_0(\tau) - iv(\tau)E]\, R_1(\tau) = Q_{10}(\tau) z_1(\tau) + Q_{1k_1-1}(\tau) z_0(\tau) + \\ + c(\tau) R_0(\tau) + R_0'(\tau) + G_0(\tau),\end{gathered} \tag{25.54}$$

where

$$G_0(\tau) = -T^{-1}(\tau) b_0(\tau). \tag{25.55}$$

Equation (25.54), in accordance with (18.3), can be written in the form

$$\begin{gathered}[W_{j0}(\tau) - iv(\tau)E]\, R_{j1}(\tau) = Q_{1j0}(\tau) z_1(\tau) + Q_{1jk_1-1}(\tau) z_0(\tau) + \\ + c_j(\tau) R_0(\tau) + R_{j0}'(\tau) + G_{j0}(\tau) \quad (j = 1, 2, \ldots, p)\end{gathered} \tag{25.56}$$

from which

$$\begin{gathered}R_{j1}(\tau) = [W_{j0}(\tau) - iv(\tau)E]^{-1} [Q_{1jk_1-1}(\tau) z_0(\tau) + \\ + c_j(\tau) R_0(\tau) + G_{j0}(\tau)] \quad (j = 2, 3, \ldots, p).\end{gathered} \tag{25.57}$$

For $j = 1$, Eq. (25.56) can be written as follows:

$$\{r_1(\tau)\}_2 = z_1(\tau) + \{c(\tau)\}_{12}\{r_0(\tau)\}_2 + \{g_0(\tau)\}_1,$$
$$\{r_1(\tau)\}_l = \{q_{1k_1-1}(\tau)\}_{l-1} z_0(\tau) + \{c(\tau)\}_{l-1,2}\{r_0(\tau)\}_2 + \{g_0(\tau)\}_l \quad (3 \leqslant l \leqslant k_1), \tag{25.58}$$

$$\{q_{1k_1-1}(\tau)\}_k z_0(\tau) + \{c(\tau)\}_{k_12}\{r_0(\tau)\}_2 + \{g_0(\tau)\}_{k_1} = 0. \tag{25.59}$$

Then from Eq. (25.59) we find

$$z_0(\tau) = -\frac{\{g_0(\tau)\}_{k_1}}{\alpha_1(\tau)}. \tag{25.60}$$

This method can also be applied in determining all the subsequent coefficients of $R_s(\tau)$, $Z_s(\tau)$ $(s = 1, 2, \ldots)$. For example, let us find $R_m(\tau)$, $Z_m(\tau)$, considering $R_0(\tau)$, $R_1(\tau), \ldots, R_{m-1}(\tau)$, $Z_0(\tau)$, $Z_1(\tau), \ldots, Z_{m-1}(\tau)$ to be already known. To do this we set $s = m$ in Eq. (25.49). We will have

$$[W(\tau) - i\nu(\tau)E]R_m(\tau) = Q_{10}(\tau)Z_m(\tau) + G_{m-1}(\tau), \tag{25.61}$$

where

$$G_{m-1}(\tau) = T^{-1}(\tau)\left[\sum_{i=1}^{m}(U_{1i(k_1-1)}(\tau)Z_{m-i}(\tau) - A_i(\tau)P_{m-i}(\tau)) + P'_{m-1}(\tau) - b_{m-1}(\tau)\right]. \tag{25.62}$$

From Eq. (25.61) we find

$$R_{jm}(\tau) = [W_{j0}(\tau) - i\nu(\tau)E]^{-1} G_{jm-1}(\tau) \quad (j = 2, 3, \ldots, p), \tag{25.63}$$
$$\{r_m(\tau)\}_2 = Z_m(\tau) + \{g_{m-1}(\tau)\}_1,$$

$$\{r_m\}_l = \{g_{m-1}(\tau)\}_{l-1} \quad (3 \leqslant l \leqslant k_1),$$
$$\{g_{m-1}(\tau)\}_{k_1} = 0. \tag{25.64}$$

The latter equation determines the function $z_{m-1}(\tau)$.

Now we set $s = m + 1$ in Eq. (25.49) and repeat the same considerations that were used in finding the function $z_0(\tau)$; we obtain

$$z_m(\tau) = \frac{\{g_m(\tau)\}_{k_1} + \sum_{i=3}^{n}\{c(\tau)\}_{k_1i}\{r_m(\tau)\}_i + \{c(\tau)\}_{k_12}\{g_{m-1}(\tau)\}_2}{\alpha_1(\tau)}, \tag{25.65}$$

where $\{g_m(\tau)\}_{k_1}$ is the k_1th component of the vector

$$G_m(\tau) = \sum_{i=2}^{m+1}(Q_{1i(k_1-1)}(\tau)\, z_{m+1-i}(\tau) - T^{-1}(\tau)\, A_i(\tau)\, P_{m+1-i}(\tau)) - \\ - T^{-1}(\tau)\,(b_m(\tau) - P'_m(\tau)). \tag{25.66}$$

Thus, by exhibiting a method of determining the coefficients of the formal series (25.8) we have proved the given theorem.

1′. We note that the theorem which we have proved allows us to obtain not only a particular solution of system (17.1′), but the general solution as well. In fact, by (25.39), the functions $\lambda_{j1}(\tau)$ [and, as can be shown, all the subsequent functions $\lambda_{js}(\tau)$, $s = 2, 3, \ldots$] have k_j different values. Consequently, for the differential equations (25.5), (25.6) we can construct k_j $\left(\sum_{j=1}^{p} k_j = n,\ j = 1, 2, \ldots, p\right)$ linearly independent particular solutions, which means that we can construct the general solution. Substituting this general solution for h_j $(j = 1, 2, \ldots, p)$ into the particular solution (25.4) we obtain the formal general solution of system (17.1′).

2′. A similar algorithm for construction of the formal solution to system (17.1′) can be proposed in the nonresonance case; namely, we can prove the following theorem.

Theorem IV.8. *If the conditions of Theorem IV.7 are satisfied, the formal general solution of system (17.1′) in the nonresonance case can be represented in the form*

$$x = \sum_{j=1}^{p} U_j(\tau, \mu_j)\, \widetilde{h}_j + \widetilde{P}(\tau, \varepsilon)\, e^{i\theta(t,\varepsilon)}, \tag{25.67}$$

$$\frac{d\widetilde{h}_j}{dt} = \lambda_j(\tau, \mu_j)\, \widetilde{h}_j \qquad (j = 1, 2, \ldots, p), \tag{25.68}$$

where

$$U_j(\tau, \mu_j), \qquad \lambda_j(\tau, \mu_j) \qquad (j = 1, 2, \ldots, p)$$

are the same as in Theorem IV.7, and $\widetilde{P}(\tau, \varepsilon)$ *is an* n*-dimensional vector admitting the formal expansion*

$$\widetilde{P}(\tau, \varepsilon) = \sum_{s=1}^{\infty} \varepsilon^s \widetilde{P}_s(\tau). \tag{25.69}$$

Proof. As in paragraph 1 of this section, we can exhibit a method of determining the vectors $U_j(\tau, \mu_j)$ and the functions $\lambda_j(\tau, \mu_j)$ $(j = 1, 2, \ldots, p)$; thus, to prove the theorem, it remains only to show a way of determining the coefficients of the vector $\widetilde{P}(\tau, \varepsilon)$.

Substituting the vector x defined by Eqs. (26.67), (25.68) into the system, we obtain an identity. Equating the coefficients of the $\widetilde{h}_j$ and of the free terms, we obtain relationship (25.9) and the equation

$$[A(\tau, \varepsilon) - i\nu(\tau) E]\widetilde{P}(\tau, \varepsilon) = \varepsilon(\widetilde{P}'(\tau, \varepsilon) - b(\tau, \varepsilon)). \tag{25.70}$$

Now, isolating the coefficients of the powers ε^s $(s = 1, 2, \ldots)$, we have

$$[A_0(\tau) - i\nu(\tau) E]\widetilde{P}_s(\tau) = \Phi_s(\tau), \tag{25.71}$$

where

$$\Phi_s(\tau) = \widetilde{P}'_{s-1}(\tau) - b_{s-1}(\tau) - \sum_{i=1}^{s} A_i(\tau)\widetilde{P}_{s-1}(\tau) \tag{25.72}$$

(according to the expansion (25.69), $\widetilde{P}_0(\tau) = 0$).

Since

$$\det[A_0(\tau) - i\nu(\tau) E] \neq 0 \tag{25.73}$$

for any $\tau \in [0, L]$, then from Eq. (25.71) we find

$$\widetilde{P}_s(\tau) = [A_0(\tau) - i\nu(\tau) E]^{-1}\Phi_s(\tau) \qquad (s = 1, 2, \ldots). \tag{25.74}$$

3. By applying the method presented in Sec. 23, we could prove that the formal solutions (25.4) and (25.67) constructed here are of an asymptotic nature; namely, the following theorem is true.

Theorem IV.9. *If the conditions of Theorem IV.7 are satisfied for all* $\tau \in [0, L]$

$$\operatorname{Re}\left(\sum_{s=0}^{k_j-2} \mu_j^s \lambda_{js}(\tau)\right) \leqslant 0, \tag{25.75}$$

then for any $L>0$ and $0<\varepsilon\leqslant\varepsilon_0$ we can find a constant C, independent of ε, such that

$$\| x - x^{(m)} \| \leqslant \mu_1^{m+2-2k_1} C \tag{25.76}$$

(we assume that $x|_{t=0} = x^{(m)}|_{t=0}$ and $k_1 \geqslant k_2 \geqslant \ldots \geqslant k_p$).

In the nonresonance case we can obtain the estimate.

$$\| x - x^{(m)} \| \lesssim \mu_1^{m+2-k_1} C. \tag{25.77}$$

Note. The algorithm which we have proposed for construction of an asymptotic solution to system (17.1′) cannot be effective in the presence of double roots of the characteristic equation, since we then obtain the Ricatti equation. Therefore, in the above case, it is convenient to apply the method presented below.

Using the method of Sec. 13, system (17.1′) can be asymptotically decomposed into p subsystems of orders k_j ($j=1, 2, \ldots, p$). For example, let $k_1 = 2$. Then the corresponding "decomposed" system (for simplicity, we consider the nonresonance case) is of the form

$$\frac{d\xi}{dt} = W(\tau, \varepsilon)\,\xi, \tag{25.78}$$

in which ξ is a two-dimensional vector: $\xi = \begin{bmatrix} \xi_1 \\ \xi_2 \end{bmatrix}$, and $W(\tau, \varepsilon)$ is a square matrix of order two

$$W(\tau, \varepsilon) = \sum_{s=0}^{m} \varepsilon^s W_s(\tau), \tag{25.79}$$

where

$$W_0(\tau) = \begin{bmatrix} \lambda_{10}(\tau) & 1 \\ 0 & \lambda_{10}(\tau) \end{bmatrix}, \qquad W_1(\tau) = \begin{bmatrix} \{C(\tau)\}_{11} & \{C(\tau)\}_{12} \\ 0 & \{C(\tau)\}_{22} \end{bmatrix}, \tag{25.80}$$

(by (25.1) $\{C(\tau)\}_{21} = 0$).

To system (25.78) we apply the transformation

$$\xi_1 = q_1, \qquad \xi_2 = \varepsilon q_2. \tag{25.81}$$

Then system (25.78) becomes

$$\frac{dq}{dt} = [\lambda_{10}(\tau) E + \varepsilon \widetilde{W}(\tau, \varepsilon)]\, q, \tag{25.82}$$

where

$$\widetilde{W}(\tau, \varepsilon) = \begin{bmatrix} \{W(\tau, \varepsilon)\}_{11} & 1 + \varepsilon \{W(\tau, \varepsilon)\}_{12} \\ \{W(\tau, \varepsilon)\}_{21} & \{W(\tau, \varepsilon)\}_{22} \end{bmatrix}, \tag{25.83}$$

q is a two-dimensional vector; $q = \begin{bmatrix} q_1 \\ q_2 \end{bmatrix}$.

Applying to system (25.82) the exponential transformation

$$q = \exp\left\{\int_0^t \lambda_{10}(\tau)\, dt\right\} v, \tag{25.84}$$

we obtain

$$\frac{dv}{dt} = \varepsilon \widetilde{W}(\tau, \varepsilon) v,$$

or

$$\frac{dv}{d\tau} = \widetilde{W}(\tau, \varepsilon) v. \tag{25.85}$$

The obtained system (25.85), in contrast to system (17.4), is of rank zero (see [76], p. 80).

Therefore, we can apply the method of successive approximations to this system. Consequently, for the vector v, which means for ξ as well, we can obtain a solution in the form of a convergent series in powers of ε.

26. Differential Equations with a Small Parameter in the Highest Derivatives

As already mentioned in the introduction, the asymptotic method which we have applied to differential equations with slowly varying coefficients can also be applied to differential equations in which, as a multiplier of the highest derivatives, we have a small parameter. Such equations have been investigated in detail in [78-80], [16-17], [9-12]. It seems that in this case the characteristic equation has the peculiarity that its multiple root is the number zero.

Thus, differential equations with small parameters in the highest derivatives can serve as example of the type of differential equation which we have been considering in Secs. 20–25 of this chapter.

Hence, we consider the differential equation

$$\sum_{i=0}^{k} \alpha_i(\tau)\frac{d^i y}{d\tau^i} + \sum_{r=1}^{l} \varepsilon^r \alpha_{k+r}(\tau)\frac{d^{k+r} y}{d\tau^{k+r}} = \varepsilon b(\tau) e^{i\theta(\tau)}, \tag{26.1}$$

in which the $\alpha_h(\tau)$ $(h = 1, 2, \ldots, k+l)$ are sufficiently differentiable functions on the interval $0 \leqslant \tau \leqslant L$, $(\alpha_{k+l}(\tau) \neq 0,\ \tau \in [0, L])$, ε is a small parameter.

Equation (26.1) can be considered a special case of the system of linear differential equations

$$E_1 \frac{dx}{d\tau} = A(\tau)x + E_1 B(\tau) e^{i\theta(\tau)}, \tag{26.2}$$

where x, $B(\tau)$ are n-dimensional vectors; $A(\tau)$ is a real square matrix of order n; E_1 is a diagonal matrix of the form:

$$E_1 = \begin{bmatrix} 1 & & & & & & & 0 \\ & 1 & & & & & & \\ & & \ddots & & & & & \\ & & & 1 & & & & \\ & & & & \varepsilon & & & \\ & & & & & \ddots & & \\ 0 & & & & & & & \varepsilon \end{bmatrix} \begin{matrix} \left.\vphantom{\begin{matrix}1\\1\\1\\1\end{matrix}}\right\} k \\ \left.\vphantom{\begin{matrix}1\\1\\1\end{matrix}}\right\} n-k \end{matrix} . \tag{26.3}$$

In fact, setting

$$\begin{gathered} y = x_1, \quad \frac{dy}{d\tau} = x_2, \ldots, \frac{d^k y}{d\tau^k} = x_{k+1}, \\ \varepsilon \frac{d^{k+1} y}{d\tau^{k+1}} = x_{k+2}, \ldots, \varepsilon^{l-1} \frac{d^{k+l-1} y}{d\tau^{k+l-1}} = x_{k+l}, \end{gathered} \tag{26.4}$$

we reduce Eq. (26.1) to system (26.2) in which

$$A(\tau) = \begin{bmatrix} 0 & 1 & 0 & \ldots & 0 \\ 0 & 0 & 1 & \ldots & 0 \\ \ldots & \ldots & \ldots & \ldots & \ldots \\ -a_0(\tau) & -a_1(\tau) & -a_2(\tau) & \ldots & -a_{k+l-1}(\tau) \end{bmatrix}, \tag{26.5}$$

$$B(\tau)=\begin{bmatrix}0\\0\\ \cdot\\ \cdot\\ \cdot\\ \varepsilon\dfrac{b(\tau)}{\alpha_{k+l}(\tau)}\end{bmatrix}$$

where

$$a_i(\tau)=\frac{\alpha_i(\tau)}{\alpha_{k+l}(\tau)}\quad(i=0,\ 1,\ 2,\ldots,k+l-1). \tag{26.6}$$

Therefore, instead of Eq. (26.1), we will henceforth consider system (26.2), which is equivalent to it. By using the substitution

$$\tau=\varepsilon t \tag{26.7}$$

as in [95, 96], we transform the above system to the system

$$\frac{dx}{dt}=[A_0(\tau)+\varepsilon A_1(\tau)]\,x+\varepsilon B(\tau)\,e^{i\theta(t,\varepsilon)}, \tag{26.8}$$

where

$$A_0(\tau)=\begin{bmatrix}0 & 0 & \ldots & 0\\ 0 & 0 & \ldots & 0\\ \cdot & \cdot & \cdot & \cdot\\ 0 & 0 & \ldots & 0\\ a_{k+1,1}(\tau) & a_{k+1,2}(\tau) & \ldots & a_{k+1,n}(\tau)\\ \cdot & \cdot & \cdot & \cdot\\ a_{n1}(\tau) & a_{n2}(\tau) & & a_{nn}(\tau)\end{bmatrix},$$

$$A_1(\tau)=\begin{bmatrix}a_{11}(\tau) & a_{12}(\tau) & \ldots & a_{1n}(\tau)\\ \cdot & \cdot & \cdot & \cdot\\ a_{k1}(\tau) & a_{k2}(\tau) & \ldots & a_{kn}(\tau)\\ 0 & 0 & \ldots & 0\\ \cdot & \cdot & \cdot & \cdot\\ 0 & 0 & \ldots & 0\end{bmatrix}, \tag{26.9}$$

$a_{ij}(\tau)$ $(i,\ j=1,\ 2,\ldots,n)$ are elements of the matrix $A(\tau)$.

The obtained system of linear differential equations (26.8) is a special case of system (17.1′), which we considered in the previous sections. Here, from the form of the matrix $A_0(\tau)$ it follows that its characteristic equation (12.3) will have the k-tuple root zero. Therefore, in constructing an asymptotic solution for system (26.8), we can use the method presented in Secs. 20-25.

We will not construct the asymptotic solution for system (26.8) in the general case; rather, we will illustrate the ideas used in the method on the following example, which was considered in [35].

27. Finding the Characteristic Values of a Boundary-Value Problem for a Fourth-Order Differential Equation Consisting of Two Self-Adjoint Expressions

We will seek the characteristic values of the boundary-value problem consisting of the equation

$$\frac{d^4u}{dy^4} + \frac{d}{dy}\left[a(y)\frac{du}{dy}\right] + b(y)u = -\lambda\left[\frac{d^2u}{dy^2} + C(y)u\right] \tag{27.1}$$

and the boundary conditions

$$\begin{gathered} u(0) = 0, \quad u(T) = 0, \\ \sin\alpha \frac{du}{dy}\bigg|_{y=0} + \cos\alpha \frac{d^2u}{dy^2}\bigg|_{y=0} = 0, \\ \sin\beta \frac{du}{dy}\bigg|_{y=T} + \cos\beta \frac{d^2u}{dy^2}\bigg|_{y=T} = 0. \end{gathered} \tag{27.2}$$

We use the substitution

$$\begin{gathered} u = \varepsilon x_1, \qquad \frac{du}{dy} = \varepsilon x_3, \qquad \frac{d^2u}{dy^2} = x_4, \\ \varepsilon\frac{d^2u}{dy^2} + \varepsilon a(y)\frac{du}{dy} = x_2 - x_3, \qquad \varepsilon = \frac{1}{\sqrt{\lambda}}, \end{gathered} \tag{27.3}$$

and arrive at the system

$$\begin{gathered} \frac{dx_1}{dy} = x_3, \\ \frac{dx_2}{dy} = -[c(y) + \varepsilon^2 b(y)]\,x_1, \end{gathered} \tag{27.4}$$

$$\varepsilon \frac{dx_3}{dy} = x_4,$$

$$\varepsilon \frac{dx_4}{dy} = x_2 - [1 + \varepsilon^2 a(y)]x_3.$$

By the change of variables

$$y = \varepsilon t = \tau$$

we reduce the obtained system (27.4) to the form

$$\frac{dx}{dt} = [A_0(\tau) + \varepsilon A_1(\tau, \varepsilon)]\, x, \tag{27.5}$$

where

$$A_0(\tau) = \begin{bmatrix} 0 & 0 & 0 & 0 \\ 0 & 0 & 0 & 0 \\ 0 & 0 & 0 & 1 \\ 0 & 1 & -1 & 0 \end{bmatrix},$$

$$A_1(\tau) = \begin{bmatrix} 0 & 0 & 1 & 0 \\ -[c(\tau) + \varepsilon^2 b(\tau)] & 0 & 0 & 0 \\ 0 & 0 & 0 & 0 \\ 0 & 0 & -\varepsilon a(\tau) & 0 \end{bmatrix}.$$

Then the roots of characteristic equation (12.3) are as follows:

$$\lambda_{10}(\tau) = \lambda_{20}(\tau) = 0, \qquad \lambda_{30}(\tau) = i, \qquad \lambda_{40}(\tau) = -i.$$

Using the asymptotic method presented above, we will seek a solution of the problem (27.1), (27.2) in the form of an expansion in powers of ε.

The form of this expansion, as follows from Secs. 20-25, essentially depends upon whether the elementary divisors corresponding to the multiple root $\lambda_{10} = 0$ are multiple or simple. (In the first case the expansion will be in fractional powers of ε, in the second case it will be in integral powers.) As is well known, the elementary divisors are simple if and only if the rank of the matrix $A_0(\tau) - \lambda E$ is equal to $n - k$, where n is the dimension of the matrix and k is the multiplicity of the root λ_{10}. In this case, as is easy to see, the elementary divisors are simple. Therefore, the canonical form of the matrix $A_0(\tau)$:

$$W(\tau) = T^{-1}(\tau)\, A_0(\tau)\, T(\tau)$$

is of the form

$$W(\tau) = \begin{bmatrix} W_1(\tau) & 0 \\ 0 & W_2(\tau) \end{bmatrix},$$

where

$$W_1(\tau) = \begin{bmatrix} 0 & 0 \\ 0 & 0 \end{bmatrix}, \qquad W_2(\tau) = \begin{bmatrix} i & 0 \\ 0 & -i \end{bmatrix}.$$

Here the matrices $T(\tau)$ and $T^{-1}(\tau)$ are as follows:

$$T(\tau) = \begin{bmatrix} 1 & 0 & 0 & 0 \\ 1 & 1 & 0 & 0 \\ 1 & 1 & 1 & 1 \\ 0 & 0 & i & -i \end{bmatrix}, \qquad T^{-1}(\tau) = \frac{1}{2}\begin{bmatrix} 2 & 0 & 0 & 0 \\ -2 & 2 & 0 & 0 \\ 0 & -1 & 1 & -i \\ 0 & -1 & 1 & i \end{bmatrix}.$$

Since the elementary divisors are simple, we seek a solution to Eq. (27.1) in the form

$$x = U_1(\tau, \varepsilon) h_1 + U_2(\tau, \varepsilon) h_2, \tag{27.6}$$

where $U_1(\tau, \varepsilon)$ and $U_2(\tau, \varepsilon)$ are (4×2)-matrices; h_1 and h_2 are two-dimensional vectors, defined by the equations

$$\frac{dh_k}{dt} = \mathfrak{A}_k(\tau, \varepsilon) h_k \qquad (k = 1, 2). \tag{27.7}$$

Here we assume that $\mathfrak{A}_k(\tau, \varepsilon)$ and $U_k(\tau, \varepsilon)$ can be represented as formal series in powers of ε

$$\begin{aligned} \mathfrak{A}_k(\tau, \varepsilon) &= \sum_{s=0}^{\infty} \varepsilon^s \mathfrak{A}_{ks}(\tau), \\ U_k(\tau, \varepsilon) &= \sum_{s=0}^{\infty} \varepsilon^s \mathfrak{A}_{ks}(\tau). \end{aligned} \tag{27.8}$$

Substituting (27.6) into system (27.5) and taking into account Eq. (27.7), we have

$$\sum_{k=1}^{2} [\varepsilon U_k'(\tau, \varepsilon) + U_k(\tau, \varepsilon) \mathfrak{A}_k(\tau, \varepsilon)] h_k = \sum_{k=1}^{2} [A_0(\tau) + \varepsilon A_1(\tau, \varepsilon)] U_k(\tau, \varepsilon) h_k.$$

Equating the coefficients of h_1 and h_2 on both sides of the equation, we obtain

$$\varepsilon U_k'(\tau, \varepsilon) + U_k(\tau, \varepsilon)\mathfrak{A}_k(\tau, \varepsilon) = [A_0(\tau) + \varepsilon A_1(\tau, \varepsilon)]\, U_k(\tau, \varepsilon) \quad (k = 1,\ 2).$$

It is easy to see that we obtain the following formulas for finding

$$U_{ks}(\tau) \quad \text{and} \quad \mathfrak{A}_{ks}(\tau) \qquad (k = 1,\ 2;\ s = 0,\ 1,\ 2, \ldots).$$

I. $U_{k0}(\tau)\mathfrak{A}_{k0}(\tau) = A_0(\tau) U_{k0}(\tau)$
or

$$Q_{k0}(\tau)\mathfrak{A}_{k0}(\tau) = W(\tau) Q_{k0}(\tau) \qquad (k = 1,\ 2), \tag{27.9}$$

where

$$Q_{k0}(\tau) = T^{-1}(\tau) U_{k0}(\tau) \qquad (k = 1,\ 2). \tag{27.10}$$

Each of Eqs. (27.9) decomposes into two independent equations

$$\begin{aligned} \tilde{Q}_{k0}\mathfrak{A}_{k0}(\tau) &= W_1(\tau)\tilde{Q}_{k0}(\tau), \\ \tilde{\tilde{Q}}_{k0}\mathfrak{A}_{k0}(\tau) &= W_2(\tau)\tilde{\tilde{Q}}_{k0}(\tau), \end{aligned} \qquad Q_{k0} = \begin{bmatrix} \tilde{Q}_{k0}(\tau) \\ \tilde{\tilde{Q}}_{k0}(\tau) \end{bmatrix}.$$

The matrices $\tilde{Q}_{10}(\tau)$, $\tilde{\tilde{Q}}_{20}(\tau)$ are at our disposal; we choose them such that

$$\tilde{Q}_{10}(\tau) = E, \qquad \tilde{\tilde{Q}}_{20} = E.$$

Then

$$\mathfrak{A}_{k0}(\tau) = W_k(\tau) \qquad (k = 1,\ 2),$$

i.e.,

$$\mathfrak{A}_{10}(\tau) = \begin{bmatrix} 0 & 0 \\ 0 & 0 \end{bmatrix}, \qquad \mathfrak{A}_{20}(\tau) = \begin{bmatrix} i & 0 \\ 0 & -i \end{bmatrix}, \tag{27.11}$$

and

$$\tilde{\tilde{Q}}_{10}(\tau) = \tilde{Q}_{20}(\tau) = 0.$$

From Eqs. (27.10) we have

$$U_{10}(\tau) = \begin{bmatrix} 1 & 0 \\ 1 & 1 \\ 1 & 1 \\ 0 & 0 \end{bmatrix}, \qquad U_{20}(\tau) = \begin{bmatrix} 0 & 0 \\ 0 & 0 \\ 1 & 1 \\ i & -i \end{bmatrix}. \tag{27.12}$$

II. We determine $\mathfrak{A}_{11}(\tau)$, $\mathfrak{A}_{21}(\tau)$ and $U_{11}(\tau)$, $U_{21}(\tau)$ from the equation

$$U_{k1}(\tau)\mathfrak{A}_{k0}(\tau) - A_0(\tau)U_{k1}(\tau) = A_{10}(\tau)U_{k0}(\tau) - U_{k0}(\tau)\mathfrak{A}_{k1}(\tau),$$

which can be written in the form

$$Q_{k1}(\tau)W_k(\tau) - W(\tau)Q_{k1}(\tau) = D_{k1}(\tau) - Q_{k0}(\tau)\mathfrak{A}_{k1}(\tau), \tag{27.13}$$

where

$$Q_{k1}(\tau) = T^{-1}(\tau)U_{k1}(\tau), \qquad D_{k1}(\tau) = T^{-1}(\tau)A_{10}(\tau)U_{k0}(\tau) \quad (k = 1,\ 2). \tag{27.14}$$

Due to the construction of matrix $W(\tau)$, Eq. (27.13) can be decomposed into the following:

$$\tilde{Q}_{k1}(\tau)W_k(\tau) - W_1(\tau)Q_{k1}(\tau) = \tilde{D}_{k1}(\tau) - \tilde{Q}_{k0}(\tau)\mathfrak{A}_{k1}(\tau), \tag{27.15}$$

$$\tilde{\tilde{Q}}_{k1}(\tau)W_k(\tau) - W_2(\tau)\tilde{\tilde{Q}}_{k1}(\tau) = \tilde{\tilde{D}}_{k1}(\tau) - \tilde{\tilde{Q}}_{k0}(\tau)\mathfrak{A}_{k1}(\tau) \quad (k = 1,\ 2).$$

Then

$$D_{11}(\tau) = \begin{bmatrix} 1 & 1 \\ -1 - c(\tau) & -1 - c(\tau) \\ \frac{1}{2}c(\tau) & \frac{1}{2}c(\tau) \\ \frac{1}{2}c(\tau) & \frac{1}{2}c(\tau) \end{bmatrix} \equiv \begin{bmatrix} \tilde{D}_{11} \\ \tilde{\tilde{D}}_{11} \end{bmatrix},$$

$$D_{21}(\tau) = \begin{bmatrix} 1 & 1 \\ -1 & -1 \\ 0 & 0 \\ 0 & 0 \end{bmatrix} \equiv \begin{bmatrix} \tilde{D}_{21} \\ \tilde{\tilde{D}}_{21} \end{bmatrix}.$$

From the first equation in (27.15) for $k=1$, we have

$$\mathfrak{A}_{11}(\tau)=\widetilde{D}_{11}(\tau)=\begin{bmatrix} 1 & 1 \\ -1-c(\tau) & -1-c(\tau)\end{bmatrix},$$

and $Q_{11}(\tau)$ is an arbitrary matrix. We set it equal to zero. We choose the matrix $\widetilde{\widetilde{Q}}_{21}(\tau)$ such that

$$\{Q_{21}(\tau)\}_{s_2p_2}=\begin{cases} 0 \quad \text{for } s_2=p_2, \\ \dfrac{\{D_{21}\}_{s_2p_2}}{\lambda_{p_20}(\tau)-\lambda_{s_20}(\tau)}, \quad s_2\neq p_2, \quad s_2,\ p_2=3,\ 4.\end{cases}$$

Consequently, taking into account the form of the matrix D_{21}, we have

$$\widetilde{\widetilde{Q}}_{21}(\tau)=0.$$

Then

$$\{\mathfrak{A}_{21}(\tau)\}_{s_2p_2}=\begin{cases}\{D_{21}\}_{s_2p_2} & s_2=p_2, \\ 0 & s_2\neq p_2,\ s_2,\ p_2=3,\ 4\end{cases}$$

and

$$\mathfrak{A}_{21}(\tau)=0. \tag{27.16}$$

From the first equation in (27.13) for $k=2$ and the second for $k=1$, we obtain

$$\widetilde{Q}_{21}(\tau)=i\begin{bmatrix}-1 & 1 \\ 1 & 1\end{bmatrix}, \qquad \widetilde{\widetilde{Q}}_{11}(\tau)=\frac{i}{2}c(\tau)\begin{bmatrix}1 & 1 \\ -1 & 1\end{bmatrix}.$$

Consequently,

$$U_{11}(\tau)=\begin{bmatrix}0 & 0 \\ 0 & 0 \\ 0 & 0 \\ -c(\tau) & -c(\tau)\end{bmatrix} \qquad U_{21}(\tau)=\begin{bmatrix}-i & i \\ 0 & 0 \\ 0 & 0 \\ 0 & 0\end{bmatrix}. \tag{27.17}$$

III. We can show that

$$\mathfrak{A}_{12}(\tau) = \begin{bmatrix} 0 & 0 \\ 0 & 0 \end{bmatrix}, \qquad \mathfrak{A}_{22}(\tau) = \begin{bmatrix} \frac{i}{2} a(\tau) & 0 \\ 0 & -\frac{i}{2} a(\tau) \end{bmatrix}, \tag{27.18}$$

$$U_{12}(\tau) = \begin{bmatrix} 0 & 0 \\ 0 & 0 \\ -[a(\tau) + c'(\tau)] & -[a(\tau) + c'(\tau)] \\ 0 & 0 \end{bmatrix}, \tag{27.19}$$

$$U_{22}(\tau) = \begin{bmatrix} 0 & 0 \\ 0 & 0 \\ -\frac{1}{4} a(\tau) & -\frac{1}{4} a(\tau) \\ \frac{i}{4} a(\tau) & -\frac{i}{4} a(\tau) \end{bmatrix}.$$

Taking into account the approximations which we have found for the matrices $\mathfrak{A}_k(\tau)$, $U_k(\tau)$, we obtain

$$x = \begin{bmatrix} 1 & 0 \\ 1 & 1 \\ 1 - \varepsilon^2[a(\tau) + \varepsilon c'(\tau)] & 1 - \varepsilon^2[a(\tau) + \varepsilon c'(\tau)] \\ -\varepsilon c(\tau) & -\varepsilon c(\tau) \end{bmatrix} h_1 +$$

$$+ \begin{bmatrix} -\varepsilon i & \varepsilon i \\ 0 & 0 \\ 1 - \frac{\varepsilon^2 a(\tau)}{4} & 1 - \frac{\varepsilon^2 a}{4} \\ i\left(1 + \frac{\varepsilon^2 a}{4}\right) & -i\left(1 + \frac{\varepsilon^2 a}{4}\right) \end{bmatrix} h_2, \tag{27.20}$$

h_1 and h_2 are determined by the systems

$$\frac{dh_1}{dt} = \varepsilon \begin{bmatrix} 1 & 1 \\ -1 - c(\tau) & -1 - c(\tau) \end{bmatrix} h_1, \tag{27.21}$$

$$\frac{dh_2}{dt} = \begin{bmatrix} i\left[1+\varepsilon^2\frac{a(\tau)}{4}\right] & 0 \\ 0 & -i\left[1+\varepsilon^2\frac{a(\tau)}{4}\right] \end{bmatrix} h_2. \tag{27.22}$$

We transform system (27.21) slightly, denoting

$$P(\tau) = \begin{bmatrix} 1 & 1 \\ -1-c(\tau) & -1-c(\tau) \end{bmatrix}.$$

Then Eq. (27.21) takes the form

$$\frac{dh_1}{d\tau} = P(\tau)\, h_1. \tag{27.23}$$

We will seek a transformation matrix $Q(\tau)$

$$h_1 = Q(\tau)\, z_1, \tag{27.24}$$

such that the matrix

$$R(\tau) = Q^{-1}(\tau)\, P(\tau)\, Q(\tau) - Q^{-1}(\tau)\, Q'(\tau)$$

has the form

$$R(\tau) = \begin{bmatrix} r_{11}(\tau) & 0 \\ r_{21}(\tau) & r_{22}(\tau) \end{bmatrix}.$$

Then Eq. (27.23) becomes the equation

$$\frac{dz}{dt} = R(\tau)\, z. \tag{27.25}$$

The matrix $Q(\tau)$ is of the form

$$Q(\tau) = \begin{bmatrix} 1 & y \\ 0 & 1 \end{bmatrix}.$$

Since the relationship

$$a(\tau)(p_{11} - p_{22}) + a^2(\tau)\, p_{21} - p_{12} = 0$$

is satisfied for $a = -1$, then $y = \text{const}$ (see [23]).

Therefore, for $y = -1$ we have

$$Q(\tau) = \begin{bmatrix} 1 & -1 \\ 0 & 1 \end{bmatrix}, \qquad R(\tau) = \begin{bmatrix} -c(\tau) & 0 \\ -1-c(\tau) & 0 \end{bmatrix}.$$

From system (27.25) we obtain

$$z_1 = c_1 e^{-\int\limits_0^{\tau} c(\tau)d\tau},$$

$$z_2 = -c_1 \int\limits_0^{\tau} [1 + c(\tau)]\, e^{-\int\limits_0^{\tau} c(\tau)d\tau} d\tau + c_2.$$

Taking account of (27.24), we have

$$\begin{aligned} h_{11} &= c_1 \left[e^{-\int\limits_0^{\tau} c(\tau)d\tau} + \int\limits_0^{\tau} [1 + c(\tau)]\, e^{-\int\limits_0^{\tau} c(\tau)d\tau} \right] - c_2, \\ h_{12} &= -c_1 \int\limits_0^{\tau} [1 + c(\tau)]\, e^{-\int\limits_0^{\tau} c(\tau)d\tau} d\tau + c_2. \end{aligned} \tag{27.26}$$

System (27.25) has the solution

$$\begin{aligned} h_{21} &= c_3 \exp\left\{ i \left[\frac{1}{\varepsilon}\tau + \frac{1}{2}\varepsilon \int\limits_0^{\tau} a(\tau)\, d\tau \right] \right\}, \\ h_{22} &= c_4 \exp\left\{ -i \left[\frac{1}{\varepsilon}\tau + \frac{1}{2}\varepsilon \int\limits_0^{\tau} a(\tau) d\tau \right] \right\}. \end{aligned} \tag{27.27}$$

Thus, the vector x is of the form

$$x = \begin{bmatrix} c_1 \left[e^{-\int\limits_0^{\tau} c(\tau)d\tau} + \int\limits_0^{\tau} (1 + c(\tau))\, e^{-\int\limits_2^{\tau} c(\tau)d\tau} d\tau \right] - c_2 - c_3 \varepsilon i e^{ik_1} + c_4 \varepsilon i e^{-ik_1} \\ c_1 \exp\left\{ -\int\limits_0^{\tau} c(\tau)\, d\tau \right\} \end{bmatrix}$$

$$\begin{bmatrix} c_1\{1-\varepsilon^2[a(\tau)+c'(\tau)]\}e^{-\int\limits_0^{\tau} c(\tau)d\tau} + c_3\left[1-\varepsilon^2\frac{a(\tau)}{4}\right]e^{ik_1}+c_4\left[1-\varepsilon^2\frac{a(\tau)}{4}\right]e^{-ik_1} \\ -c_1\varepsilon c(\tau)e^{-\int\limits_0^{\tau} c(\tau)d\tau} + c_3 i\left(1+\varepsilon^2\frac{a(\tau)}{4}\right)e^{ik_1} - c_4 i\left(1-\varepsilon^2\frac{a(\tau)}{4}\right)e^{-ik} \end{bmatrix}, \tag{27.28}$$

where

$$k_1 = \frac{\tau}{\varepsilon} + \varepsilon\frac{1}{2}\int\limits_0^{\tau} a(\tau)\,d\tau,$$

c_1, c_2, c_3 and c_4 are arbitrary constants.

From the boundary conditions (27.2), taking account of the substitution (27.3), we obtain the following system for finding the constants c_1, c_2, c_3 and c_4:

$$c_1 - c_2 - c_3\varepsilon i + c_4\varepsilon i = 0,$$

$$c_1\left[e^{-\int\limits_0^{T} c(\tau)d\tau} + \int\limits_0^{T}(1+c(\tau))e^{-\int\limits_0^{\tau} c(\tau)d\tau}d\tau\right] - c_2 - c_3\varepsilon i e^{ik_2} + c_4\varepsilon i e^{-ik_2} = 0,$$

$$c_1\varepsilon\{[1-\varepsilon^2(a(0)+c'(0))]\sin\alpha - c(0)\cos\alpha\} +$$
$$+ c_3\left\{\left[1-\frac{1}{4}\varepsilon^2 a(0)\right]\sin\alpha + i\left[1+\frac{1}{4}\varepsilon^2 a(0)\right]\cos\alpha\right\} +$$
$$+ c_4\left\{\left[1-\frac{1}{4}\varepsilon^2 a(0)\right]\sin\alpha - i\left[1+\frac{1}{4}\varepsilon^2 a(0)\right]\cos\alpha\right\} = 0, \tag{27.29}$$

$$c_1\varepsilon\{[1-\varepsilon^2(a(T)+c'(T))]\sin\beta - c(T)\cos\beta\}e^{-\int\limits_0^{T} c(\tau)d\tau} +$$
$$+ c_3\left\{\left[1-\frac{1}{4}\varepsilon^2 a(T)\right]\sin\beta + i\left[1+\frac{1}{4}\varepsilon^2 a(T)\right]\cos\beta\right\}e^{ik_2} +$$
$$+ c_4\left\{\left[1-\frac{1}{4}\varepsilon^2 a(T)\right]\sin\beta - i\left[1+\frac{1}{4}\varepsilon^2 a(T)\cos\beta\right]\right\}e^{-ik_2} = 0,$$

$$k_2 = \frac{T}{\varepsilon} + \frac{\varepsilon}{2}\int\limits_0^{T} a(\tau)\,d\tau.$$

From the first two equations in (27.29) we have

$$c_1 = \frac{i\varepsilon\,[c_4(1-e^{-ik_2}) - c_3(1-e^{ik_2})]}{K}, \tag{27.30}$$

where

$$K = e^{-\int_0^T c(\tau)d\tau} + \int_0^T [1+c(\tau)]e^{-\int_0^\tau c(\tau)d\tau}\,d\tau - 1.$$

Substituting the value of c_1 into the remaining two equations, we obtain equations for finding c_3 and c_4:

$$\begin{gathered}
c_3\Big\{-i\varepsilon^2\,[1-\varepsilon^2(a(0)+c'(0))\sin\alpha - c(0)\cos\alpha](1-e^{ik_2}) + \\
+ K\Big[\varepsilon\sin\alpha\Big(1-\frac{1}{4}\varepsilon^2 a(0)\Big) + i\cos\alpha\Big(1+\frac{1}{4}\varepsilon^2 a(0)\Big]\Big\} + \\
+ c_4\{i\varepsilon^2\,[(1-\varepsilon^2(a(0)+c'(0)))\sin\alpha - c(0)\cos\alpha]\,(1-e^{ik_2}) + \\
+ K\Big[\varepsilon\sin\alpha\Big(1-\frac{1}{4}\varepsilon^2 a(0)) - i\cos\alpha\Big(1+\frac{1}{4}\varepsilon^2 a(0)\Big)\Big]\Big\} = 0,
\end{gathered} \tag{27.31}$$

$$\begin{gathered}
c_3\Big\{-i\varepsilon^2\,[(1-\varepsilon^2(a(T)+c'(T)))\sin\beta - c(T)\cos\beta](1-e^{ik_2})\,e^{-\int_0^T c(\tau)d\tau} + \\
+ K\Big[\varepsilon\sin\beta\Big(1-\frac{1}{4}\varepsilon^2 a(T)\Big) + i\cos\beta\Big(1+\frac{1}{4}\varepsilon^2 a(T)\Big)\Big]e^{ik_2}\Big\} + \\
+ c_4\Big\{i\varepsilon^2\,[(1-\varepsilon^2(a(T)+c'(T)))\sin\beta - c(T)\cos\beta](1-e^{-ik_2})e^{-\int_0^T c(\tau)d\tau} + \\
+ K\Big[\varepsilon\sin\beta\Big(1-\frac{1}{4}\varepsilon^2 a(T)\Big) - i\cos\beta\Big(1+\frac{1}{4}\varepsilon^2 a(T)\Big)\Big]e^{-ik_2}\Big\} = 0.
\end{gathered}$$

In order for the system of equations (27.31) to have a non-trivial solution, the determinant of the system must be equal to zero, i.e., the relationship

$$\varepsilon^2\{[1-\varepsilon^2(a(0)+c'(0))]\sin\alpha - c(0)\cos\alpha\}\Big[\varepsilon\Big(\frac{1}{4}\varepsilon^2 a(T) - 1\Big)\times$$

$$\times \sin\beta \cos K_2 + \left(1 + \frac{1}{4}\varepsilon^2 a(T)\right) \cos\beta \sin K_2 +$$

$$+ \varepsilon\left(1 - \frac{1}{4}\varepsilon^2 a(T)\right)\sin\beta\Big] + \varepsilon^2\{[1 - \varepsilon^2(a(T) + c'(T))] \sin\beta - c(T)\cos\beta\} \times$$

$$\times \left\{\varepsilon\left[\varepsilon^2 \frac{a(0)}{4} - 1\right]\sin\alpha \cos K_2 - \left[1 + \frac{1}{4}\varepsilon^2 a(0)\right]\cos\alpha \sin K_2 +\right.$$

$$\left. + \varepsilon\left[1 - \frac{1}{4}\varepsilon^2 a(0)\right]\sin\alpha\right\} e^{-\int_0^T c(\tau)d\tau} + K\left\{\varepsilon^2\left[\frac{1}{4}\varepsilon^2 a(0) - 1\right] \times\right.$$

$$\times \left[1 - \frac{1}{4}\varepsilon^2 a(T)\right]\sin\alpha \sin\beta \sin K_2 - \left[1 + \frac{1}{4}\varepsilon^2 a(0)\right] \times \tag{27.32}$$

$$\times \left[1 + \frac{1}{4}\varepsilon^2 a(T)\right]\cos\alpha \cos\beta \sin K_2 - \varepsilon\left[1 - \frac{1}{4}\varepsilon^2 a(0)\right] \times$$

$$\times \left[1 + \frac{1}{4}\varepsilon^2 a(T)\right]\sin\alpha \cos\beta \cos K_2 + \varepsilon\left[1 + \frac{1}{4}\varepsilon^2 a(0)\right] \times$$

$$\left. \times \left[1 - \frac{1}{4}\varepsilon^2 a(T)\right]\cos\alpha \sin\beta \cos K_2\right\} = 0,$$

must be satisfied; we will use this relationship for determining the characteristic values of the boundary-value problem (27.1) - (27.2).

We consider the following cases:

1) $$\cos\alpha \neq 0, \qquad \cos\beta \neq 0.$$

From Eq. (27.32) we have

$$\sin K_2 = 0,$$

from which we obtain the following asymptotic formula:

$$\lambda_n \approx \frac{\pi^2 n^2}{T^2},$$

or, more simply,

$$\lambda_n \approx \frac{\pi^2 n^2}{T^2} - \frac{1}{T}\operatorname{tg}\alpha + \frac{1}{T}\operatorname{tg}\beta - \frac{1}{2T}\int_0^T a(\tau)\,d\tau;$$

2) $\cos\alpha \neq 0, \qquad \cos\beta = 0$

$$\lambda_n \approx \frac{(2n+1)^2}{4T^2}\pi^2 - \frac{1}{T}\operatorname{tg}\alpha - \frac{1}{2T}\int_0^T a(\tau)\,d\tau;$$

3) $\cos\alpha = 0, \quad \cos\beta \neq 0$

$$\lambda_n \approx \frac{(2n+1)^2}{4T^2}\pi^2 + \frac{1}{T}\operatorname{tg}\beta - \frac{1}{2T}\int_0^T a(\tau)\,d\tau;$$

4) $\cos\alpha = 0, \quad \cos\beta = 0$

$$\lambda_n \approx \frac{\pi^2 n^2}{T^2} \qquad (n = 1,\ 2, \ldots).$$

Chapter 5

ASYMPTOTIC SOLUTIONS OF DIFFERENTIAL EQUATIONS IN BANACH SPACE

28. Formulation of the Problem

In Chap. 3 we considered the question of asymptotic decomposition of a system of linear differential equations of order n into several independent systems of lower orders. The method which we described can be generalized to the case of differential equations in infinite-dimensional spaces (Hilbert, Banach), as was proved by Daletskiy and Kreyn in a number of papers [18-22].

In this chapter, we will present the basic results of these papers. However, we will not attempt to cover the most general case; for the convenience of the reader who is not too familiar with these questions, we will limit ourselves to a less general approach. The reader who is interested in the more general formulation of the problem can refer to [20, 22].

Thus, in the Banach space $\mathfrak{X}$ we will consider the differential equation

$$\frac{dx}{dt} = [A + \varepsilon B(\tau, \varepsilon)]\, x\,, \tag{28.1}$$

in which $x(t, \varepsilon)$ is the unknown function of the variable $t \in [0, L/\varepsilon]$ with values in the space $\mathfrak{X}$; A, $B(\tau, \varepsilon)$ are operators on the space $\mathfrak{X}$: A is unbounded, while B is bounded (the parameters τ, ε and $L > 0$ are of the same nature as previously).

We will call the vector-function $x(t, \varepsilon)$ a solution of Eq. (28.1) satisfying the given condition

$$x(t_0, \varepsilon) = x_0 \qquad (t_0 = 0), \tag{28.2}$$

where x_0 is some element in $\mathfrak{X}$, provided that $x(t, \varepsilon)$ has the following properties:

1. $x(t, \varepsilon)$ is strongly continuous and continuously differentiable on any closed interval contained in $[0, L/\varepsilon]$;

2. $x(t, \varepsilon)$, for any $t > 0$, belongs to the domain of definition $D(A)$ of the operator A and

$$\frac{dx}{dt} = [A + \varepsilon B(\tau, \varepsilon)]\, x;$$

3. $\lim_{t \to 0+} \| x(t, \varepsilon) - x_0 \| = 0$. (For the terminology and basic concepts of functional analysis see [102].)

Furthermore, we will assume that the unbounded operator A satisfies the conditions (S_1):

1. the domain of definition $D(A)$ of the operator A is dense in $\mathfrak{X}$;

2. A is closed and linear;

3. the resolvent of the operator A exists for all $\lambda > 0$, and satisfies the condition

$$\| R(\lambda; A) \| \equiv \| [A - \lambda I]^{-1} \| \leqslant \frac{1}{\lambda}, \qquad \lambda > 0.$$

The bounded linear operator $B(\tau, \varepsilon)$ is subject to the condition (S_2): the operator-valued function $B(\tau, \varepsilon)$ is not continuously differentiable with respect to $\tau \in [0, L]$ in the sense of the operator norm.

We will assume, in addition, that the spectrum $\sigma(A)$ of the operator A can be decomposed into $n + 1$ spectral sets

$$\sigma(A) = \bigcup_{0}^{n} \sigma_k, \tag{28.3}$$

where only the set σ_0 can contain the point at infinity, and the remaining σ_k $(k = 1, 2, \ldots, n)$ are bounded.

A nonempty set σ_k, which is a subset of the spectrum $\sigma(A)$, and which is at the same time both closed and open in $\sigma(A)$, is called a spectral set of the operator A (see [102]).

Furthermore, let Γ_k $(k = 1, 2, \ldots, n)$ be a closed smooth arc surrounding the bounded spectral set m and separating it from $\sigma(A) - \sigma_k$. By assumption, Γ_k lies in the resolvent set of the operator A and bounds some open set Δ_k which contains σ_k.

The orientation of Γ_k is defined in the ordinary way, i.e., when Γ_k is transversed in the positive direction the set Δ_k lies on the left.

We now introduce the projection operators for parallel projection P_k $(k = 1, 2, \ldots, n)$:

$$P_k = -\frac{1}{2\pi i}\int_{\Gamma_k} R(\lambda; A)\, d\lambda, \tag{28.4}$$

which, as is well known [102], have the following properties:

$$P_k^2 = P_k; \qquad P_jP_k = 0\ (j \neq k); \quad P_kD \subseteq D; \qquad P_kA \subseteq AP_k. \tag{28.5}$$

If we set

$$P_0 = I - \sum_{k=1}^{n} P_k, \tag{28.6}$$

then the properties enumerated above extend to the operator P_0 as well. (According to the theory of operator calculus for unbounded close operators [102], the projection P_0 can also be defined by using the formula

$$P_0 = I - \frac{1}{2\pi i}\int_{\Gamma_0} R(\lambda; A)\, d\lambda,$$

where Γ_0 is the envelope of the spectral set σ_0.)

In this chapter we will show that, in correspondence with the structure of the spectrum of the operator A, the differential equation (28.1) can be asymptotocally decomposed into $n + 1$ equations, as was done in Chap. 3.

Here, each of the decomposed equations will be a differential equation in a corresponding subspace $P_k[\mathfrak{X}]$, and, thus, is an equation of "lower order," so to speak, than the original one (28.1).

We will begin the discussion of this question by proving that the solution of Eq. (28.1) satisfying the condition (28.2), in the framework of assumptions (S_1) and (S_2), actually exists. This will be the subject of the next section.

29. Existence and Uniqueness of the Solution

In this section we will not concern ourselves with the asymptotic properties of the solution of Eq. (28.1), but only with its solvability. Therefore, we will rewrite (28.1) in the form

$$\frac{dx}{dt} = [A + B(t)]\,x, \qquad t \in \left[0, \frac{L}{\varepsilon}\right]. \tag{29.1}$$

The operators A and $B(t)$ are subject to the conditions (S_1) and (S_2), respectively. (For solvability of Eq. (29.1), condition (S_2) can be weakened by changing it to the requirement that the function $B(t)x$ be continuously differentiable with respect to t. Here and elsewhere in Sec. 29, we will understand continuity, differentiability, and convergence in the sense of the strong topology, unless otherwise noted.)

The existence and uniqueness of the solution to Eq. (29.1) for the given initial condition was studied by Phillips in [134]. However, in order to give a complete presentation, we will reproduce his results here.

We note first of all that if conditions (S_1) are fulfilled then there exists a bounded operator $T(t)$, $t \in [0, \infty]$, having the following properties:

$$\| T(t) \| \leqslant 1, \qquad T(t_1 + t_2) = T(t_1)\, T(t_2),$$

$T(t)$ is continuous with respect to t in the strong topology on $[0, \infty)$, $T(0) = I$. In addition, for any $x \in D$, the vector function $T(t)x$ is continuously differentiable and satisfies the equation

$$\frac{d\,[T(t)\,x]}{dt} = AT(t)\,x = T(t)\,Ax, \qquad x \in D. \tag{29.2}$$

In what follows, we will find the following lemma useful.

Lemma V.1. *If the function* $\varphi(t)$, *defined on* $[0, \infty)$ *and with values in the space* $\mathfrak{X}$, *is continuously differentiable, then the function*

$$g(t, s) = \int_s^t T(t-\sigma)\,\varphi(\sigma)\,d\sigma = \int_0^{t-s} T(\sigma)\,\varphi(t-\sigma)\,d\sigma$$
$$(0 \leqslant s < t < \infty) \tag{29.3}$$

is also continuously differentiable with respect to t; *thus, we have the following representation*:

$$\frac{dg}{dt} = T(t-s)\,\varphi(s) + \int_s^t T(t-\sigma)\,\varphi'(\sigma)\,d\sigma. \tag{29.4}$$

In addition, $\int_s^t T(t-\sigma)\varphi(\sigma)\,d\sigma \in D(A)$ *and the formula*

$$\frac{dg}{dt} = \varphi(t) + A\int_s^t T(t-\sigma)\varphi(\sigma)\,d\sigma \qquad (29.4')$$

also holds.

Proof. Since $\|T(t)\| \leqslant 1$, the element $T(t-\sigma)\varphi(\sigma)$ for $\sigma \in [0, t]$ is continuous with respect to σ, since the function $\varphi(\sigma)$ is continuous. Therefore, the integral

$$g(t, s) = \int_s^t T(t-\sigma)\varphi(\sigma)\,d\sigma \qquad (0 \leqslant s < t < \infty)$$

exists, and Eq. (29.3) is valid.

The function $g(t, s)$ is continuous with respect to t, which is easy to verify by using the following inequalities:

$$\|g(t+\Delta, s) - g(t, s)\| \leqslant \int_s^t \|T(\sigma)[\varphi(t+\Delta-\sigma) - \varphi(t-\sigma)]\|\,d\sigma +$$
$$+ \int_t^{t+\Delta} \|T(\sigma)\varphi(t+\Delta-\sigma)\|\,d\sigma \leqslant \int_s^t \|\varphi(t+\Delta-\sigma) - \varphi(t-\sigma)\|\,d\sigma +$$
$$+ \int_t^{t+\Delta} \|\varphi(t+\Delta-\sigma)\|\,d\sigma.$$

In fact, since $\varphi(t)$ is continuous with respect to $t \in [0, \infty)$, then, obviously, $\|g(t+\Delta, s) - g(t, s)\| \to 0$ as $\Delta \to 0$, i.e., the function $g(t, s)$ is continuous with respect to t.

Furthermore, on the strength of the assumptions of the lemma, the vector $T(\sigma)\varphi'(t-\sigma)$ is continuous with respect to σ for $\sigma \in [0, t]$; therefore, by the second part of Eq. (29.3), we can write

$$\frac{dg(t, s)}{dt} = T(t-s)\varphi(s) + \int_0^{t-s} T(\sigma)\varphi'(t-\sigma)\,d\sigma =$$
$$= T(t-s)\varphi(s) + \int_s^t T(t-\sigma)\varphi'(\sigma)\,d\sigma,$$

from which it is clear that the derivative $dg(t, s)/dt$ is also continuous with respect to t.

On the other hand, using the representation

$$g(t, s) = \int_s^t T(t-\sigma)\varphi(\sigma)d\sigma,$$

we consider the relationship

$$\frac{g(t+\Delta, s) - g(t, s)}{\Delta} = \frac{T(\Delta) - I}{\Delta}\int_s^t T(t-\sigma)\varphi(\sigma)\,d\sigma + \\ + \frac{1}{\Delta}\int_t^{t+\Delta} T(t+\Delta-\sigma)\varphi(\sigma)\,d\sigma \tag{29.5}$$

as $\Delta \to 0$.

Since $T(t+\Delta-\sigma)\varphi(\sigma)$ is a continuous function of its variable and $T(0) = I$, then

$$\frac{1}{\Delta}\int_t^{t+\Delta} T(t+\Delta-\sigma)\varphi(\sigma)\,d\sigma \to \varphi(t), \qquad \text{if} \quad \Delta \to 0.$$

Furthermore, by what was proved above, the function $g(t, s)$ is differentiable; i.e., the limit of relationship (29.5) as $\Delta \to 0$ exists, which means that $\int_s^t T(t-\sigma)\varphi(\sigma)\,d\sigma \in D(A)$ (here we use a known property of the operator $T(t)$ [102]:

$$\lim_{\eta\to 0}\frac{T(t+\eta) - I}{\eta}x = Ax).$$

Thus, we obtain the second equality (29.4′):

$$\frac{dg(t, s)}{dt} = \varphi(t) + A\int_s^t T(t-\sigma)\varphi(\sigma)\,d\sigma, \quad 0 \leqslant s < t < \infty.$$

In conclusion, we note that by (29.3) and the properties of the function $g(t, s)$ established above, it is easy to verify that the function $g(t, s)$ is also continuously differentiable with respect to the variable s, $0 \leqslant s < t < \infty$; i.e., $dg(t, s)/ds$ is continuous with respect to t.

Addition to Lemma V.1. If the function $\varphi(t)$ $[t \in [0, \infty)]$ given in Lemma V.1 is also a function of the real parameter s $(0 \leqslant s < t < \infty)$; i.e., $\varphi = \varphi(t, s)$, where the function $\varphi(t, s)$ is continuously differentiable with respect to the parameter s, and its derivative $d\varphi(t, s)/ds$ is also continuous with respect to t, then the function

$$g(t, s) = \int_s^t T(t - \sigma)\, \varphi(\sigma, s) d\sigma$$

will also have the same properties. Also

$$\frac{dg(t, s)}{ds} = -T(t - s)\, \varphi(s, s) + \int_s^t T(t - \sigma) \frac{d\varphi(\sigma, s)}{ds}\, d\sigma.$$

The proof of this assertion obviously follows from the results of Lemma V.1.

Let us now investigate the solvability of Eq. (29.1). The existence and uniqueness of the solution of Eq. (29.1) is established by the following theorem.

Theorem V.1. *Let the operator A satisfy conditions (S_1) and the operator $B(t)$ satisfy the conditions (S_2). [See the remark following Eq. (29.1)].*

Then there exists a unique bounded operator $V(t, t_0)$ $[0 \leqslant t_0 \leqslant t \leqslant L/\varepsilon]$ such that $V(t_0, t_0) = I$ and the function $x(t) = V(t, t_0)x_0$ $[x_0 \in D(A)]$ is a solution of Eq. (29.1) satisfying the condition

$$x(t_0) = x_0.$$

In addition, the operator-function $V(t,s)f$ for $f \in D(A)$, and the parameter s varying between the limits $0 \leqslant s \leqslant t \leqslant L/\varepsilon$, is continuously differentiable with respect to s and satisfies the equation

$$\frac{dV(t, s)}{ds} f = -V(t, s)\,[A + B(s)]\, f, \quad f \in D(A).$$

Proof. To construct the operator $V(t, t_0)$ we use the method of successive approximations and introduce the following notation:

$$V(t, t_0) = T(t - t_0),$$

$$V_n(t, t_0)x = T(t - t_0)x + \int_{t_0}^{t} T(t - s)B(s)V_{n-1}(s, t_0)xds$$

$$(x \in \mathfrak{X}, \quad n = 1, 2, \ldots). \tag{29.6}$$

Furthermore, if we set

$$\begin{aligned} W_0(t, t_0) &= V_0(t, t_0), \\ W_n(t, t_0)x &= [V_n(t, t_0) - V_{n-1}(t, t_0)]x = \\ &= \int_{t_0}^{t} T(t - s)B(s)W_{n-1}(s, t_0)xds, \end{aligned} \tag{29.7}$$

then the unknown operator $V(t, t_0)$ can be represented in the form

$$V(t, t_0) = \sum_{n=0}^{\infty} W_n(t, t_0). \tag{29.8}$$

Let us show that these constructions have meaning, and that the operator $V(t, t_0)$ really exists.

First of all, it is clear that for any $x \in \mathfrak{X}$, the vector-function $B(t)V_0(t, t_0)x \equiv B(t)T(t - t_0)x$ is continuous with respect to t, Consequently, by Lemma V.1, the function $W_1(t, t_0)x$ exists and also is continuous with respect to t. (Obviously, this is also true for the function $V_1(t, t_0)x$.) By induction we obtain an analogous assertion for any vector $W_n(t, t_0)x$, i.e., for any approximation $V_n(t, t_0)x$.

Since $\|W_0(t, t_0)\| \equiv \|T(t - t_0)\| \leqslant 1$ $(0 \leqslant t_0 \leqslant t)$, then obviously

$$\|W_n(t, t_0)\| \leqslant M^n \frac{(t - t_0)^n}{n!}, \tag{29.9}$$

where

$$M = \max_{0 \leqslant t \leqslant \frac{L}{\varepsilon}} [\|B(t)\|, \|B'(t)\|].$$

Consequently, the series (29.8) [or the sequence (29.6)] converges (in the sense of the operator norm) uniformly with respect to t (in each finite interval) to a bounded operator $V(t, t_0)$, continuous with respect to t in the strong topology on the interval $[t_0, \infty)$.

By (29.8) and (29.9), we have the estimate

$$\| V(t, t_0) \| \leqslant e^{M(t-t_0)}.$$

Since $V_n(t_0, t_0) = I$ for any n, then $V(t_0, t_0) = I$. Finally, passing to the limit in formulas (29.6) we obtain

$$V(t, t_0)x = T(t - t_0)x + \int_{t_0}^{t} T(t-s)B(s)V(s, t_0)x\,ds. \tag{29.10}$$

We now show that the function

$$x(t) = V(t, t_0)x_0 \quad (x_0 \in D(A)) \tag{29.11}$$

is a solution of Eq. (29.1).

First, we will establish the differentiability with respect to t of expression (29.11).

Obviously, the function $W_0(t, t_0)x = V_0(t, t_0)x_0$ for $x_0 \in D(A)$ is continuously differentiable with respect to t. Let us assume that this is also true for $W_n(t, t_0)x_0$. Then it is easy to verify that the element $B(t)W_n(t, t_0)x_0$ $(n = 0, 1, 2, \ldots)$ is also continuously differentiable with respect to t; consequently, by Lemma V.1, the function $W_{n+1}(t, t_0)x_0$ also has this property [see formula (29.7)].

On the basis of (29.4) and (29.7) we can write:

$$\frac{d}{dt} W_0(t, t_0)x_0 = T(t - t_0)Ax_0,$$

$$\frac{d}{dt} W_n(t, t_0)x_0 = T(t - t_0)B(t_0)W_{n-1}(t_0, t_0)x_0 + $$

$$+ \int_{t_0}^{t} T(t-s)B'(s)W_{n-1}(s, t_0)x_0\,ds +$$

$$+ \int_{t_0}^{t} T(t-s)B(s)\frac{dW(s, t_0)}{dt}x_0\,ds \qquad (n = 1, 2, \ldots).$$

This implies the estimates

$$\left\| \frac{d}{dt} W_0(t, t_0)x_0 \right\| \leqslant \| Ax_0 \|,$$

$$\left\| \frac{d}{dt} W_n(t, t_0)x_0 \right\| \leqslant M^n \frac{(t-t_0)^{n-1} + (t-t_0)^n}{(n-1)!}\alpha, \tag{29.12}$$

where

$$\alpha = \|Ax_0\| + \|x_0\| .$$

Thus, on the strength of inequalities (29.12) we can assert that the series

$$\sum_{n=0}^{\infty} \frac{d}{dt} W_n(t, t_0) x_0$$

converges uniformly with respect to t on any finite interval; consequently, the function

$$x(t) = V(t, t_0) x_0 = \sum_{n=0}^{\infty} W_n(t, t_0) x_0 \quad (x_0 \in D(A))$$

is differentiable with respect to t; in addition, by the properties of the expression $d/dt\ W_n(t, t_0) x_0$, the function $V(t, t_0) x_0$ is continuously differentiable with respect to t.

Since it is obvious here that the expression $B(t) V(t, t_0) x_0$ $(x_0 \in D(A))$ is also continuously differentiable, we can differentiate both sides of Eq. (29.10) with respect to t (by Lemma V.1). As a result we obtain

$$\begin{aligned} \frac{d}{dt}[V(t, t_0) x_0] &= AT(t - t_0) x_0 + B(t) V(t, t_0) x_0 + \\ &+ A \int_{t_0}^{t} T(t - s) B(s) V(s, t_0) x_0 ds = \\ &= [A + B(t)] V(t, t_0) x_0 \quad (x_0 \in D(A)). \end{aligned} \tag{29.13}$$

In this way we verify that the function

$$x(t) = V(t, t_0) x_0$$

satisfies Eq. (29.1) and the condition $x(t_0) = x_0$. We note, in addition, that from Eq. (29.13) it follows that the domain D is invariant under the operator $V(t, t_0)$:

$$V(t, t_0) D \subseteq D.$$

We will now prove the uniqueness of the constructed operator $V(t, t_0)$, satisfying the condition $V(t_0, t_0) = I$.

Suppose that there exists another operator $V_1(t, t_0)$ such that $V_1(t_0, t_0) = I$ and the function $x_1(t) = V_1(t, t_0)x_0$ also is a solution of Eq. (29.1). Then, obviously, Eq. (29.1) also has a solution of the form

$$y(t) = [V(t, t_0) - V_1(t, t_0)]\,x_0,$$

where $y(t)$ has all of the properties described above and, in addition:

$$y(t_0) = [V(t_0, t_0) - V_1(t_0, t_0)]\,x_0 = 0. \tag{29.14}$$

Let us investigate the constructed solution $y(t)$:

$$\frac{dy}{dt} = [A + B(t)]\,y. \tag{29.15}$$

To do this, we apply the operator $T(t-s)$ to both sides of Eq. (29.15) and integrate the result from t_0 to t:

$$\int_{t_0}^{t} T(t-s)\,y'(s)\,ds = \int_{t_0}^{t} T(t-s)\,Ay(s)\,ds + \int_{t_0}^{t} T(t-s)\,B(s)y(s)\,ds. \tag{29.16}$$

Since for $s \in [t_0, t]$ we have the equality

$$\frac{d}{ds}[T(t-s)\,y(s)] = -T(t-s)\,Ay(s) + T(t-s)\,y'(s),$$

then from Eq. (29.16) we find that

$$y(t) = \int_{t_0}^{t} T(t-s)\,B(s)\,y(s)\,ds. \tag{29.17}$$

On the basis of (29.14), $T(t-t_0)\,y(t_0) = 0,\ 0 \leqslant t_0 \leqslant t < \infty$.

We suppose that $\max\limits_{t_0 \leqslant s \leqslant t} \|y(s)\| = m_t$. Then, in accordance with (29.17), the inequality

$$m_t \leqslant Mm_t(t-t_0) \tag{29.18}$$

should hold for any $t \geqslant t_0$.

However, it is clear that for t close enough to t_0, $t_0 \leqslant t \leqslant t_1$, so that $M(t_1 - t_0) < 1$, inequality (29.18) is possible only under the condition $m_t = 0$. Thus, we reach the conclusion that the solution $y(t)$ which we have constructed must be identically equal to zero on the closed interval $[t_0, t_1]$.

If we now investigate, instead of expression (29.17), the equivalent relationship

$$y(t) = \int_{t_1}^{t} T(t - s) B(s) y(s) ds; \quad y(t) \equiv 0 \text{ for } t \in [t_0, t_1],$$

then by using the method applied above we can verify that $y(t) \equiv 0$ for any $t \geqslant t_0$, i.e., that the operators $V(t, t_0)$ and $V_1(t, t_0)$ are identical.

Thus, we have proved that Eq. (29.1) under the given initial condition

$$x(t_0) = x_0 \in D(A) \quad (t_0 \geqslant 0) \tag{29.19}$$

has a unique solution which can be represented in the form:

$$x(t) = V(t, t_0) x_0, \quad x_0 \in D(A).$$

We will now prove the second part of Theorem V.1, namely, the continuous differentiability of the function $V(t, s) x_0$ $(x_0 \in D(A))$ with respect to the parameter s $(0 \leqslant s \leqslant t < \infty)$.

Indeed, the function $V_0(t, s) x_0 = W_0(t, s) x_0 = T(t - s) x_0$ is continuously differentiable with respect to $s \in [0, t]$ for $x_0 \in D(A)$. In fact

$$\frac{dW_0(t, s)}{ds} x_0 = -T(t - s) Ax_0 = -W_0(t, s) Ax_0. \tag{29.20}$$

Consequently, by the addition to Lemma V.1, the derivative $dW_1(t, s)/ds\ x_0$ of the function $W_1(t, s)$ [see (29.7)] exists and is continuous with respect to t and s:

$$\frac{dW_1(t, s)}{ds} x_0 = -T(t - s) B(s)\, x_0 - \int_{s}^{t} T(t - \sigma) B(\sigma) W_0(\sigma, s) Ax_0 d\sigma =$$

$$= -W_0(t, s) B(s) x_0 - W_1(t, s) Ax_0.$$

By induction, we obtain

$$\frac{dW_n(t, s)}{ds} x_0 = -W_{n-1}(t, s) B(s) x_0 - W_n(t, s) Ax_0, \tag{29.21}$$

where $d/ds\, W_n(t, s) x_0$ is continuous in t and s $(0 \leqslant s \leqslant t < \infty)$.

From formulas (29.20) and (29.21) we obtain an estimate which is analogous to inequality (29.12):

$$\left\| \frac{dW_0(t, s)}{ds} x_0 \right\| \leqslant \| Ax_0 \| ,$$

$$\left\| \frac{dW_n(t, s)}{ds} x_0 \right\| \leqslant M^n \frac{(t-s)^{n-1} + (t-s)^n}{(n-1)!} \alpha \ (n = 1, 2, \ldots) .$$

By this estimate, we can assert that the function

$$x(t, s) = V(t, s) x_0 = \sum_{n=0}^{\infty} W_n(t, s) x_0 \ (x_0 \in D(A))$$

is continuously differentiable with respect to the parameter s, and the derivative $dV(t, s)/x_0\, ds$ is continuous in the variables t and s. For the derivative $dV(t,s)/x_0\, ds$ we have the estimate

$$\left\| \frac{dV(t, s)}{ds} x_0 \right\| \leqslant [1 + Me^{M(t-s)}(1 + t - s)] \alpha, \tag{29.22}$$

where

$$\alpha = \| Ax_0 \| + \| x_0 \| .$$

In addition, by (29.20) and (29.21) the relationship

$$\frac{dV(t, s)}{ds} x_0 = -V(t, s) B(s) x_0 - V(t, s) Ax_0 = -V(t, s) [A + B(s)] x_0$$

holds. This completes the proof of Theorem V.1.

We now consider construction of a solution to the non-homogeneous equation

$$\frac{dx}{dt} = [A + B(t)] x + f(t) \tag{29.23}$$

with the initial condition

$$x(t_0) = x_0 \in D(A) \ (0 \leqslant t_0 \leqslant t < \infty). \tag{29.24}$$

Here we have the following theorem.

Theorem V.2. *Let the operators A and $B(t)$ be as in Theorem V.1, and let the function $f(t) \in \mathfrak{X}$ be continuously differentiable.*

Then there exists a unique solution to the problem (29.23), (29.24). This solution is of the form

$$x(t) = V(t, t_0)\, x_0 + \int_{t_0}^{t} V(t, s)\, f(s)\, ds,$$

where $V(t, s)$ is the operator from Theorem V.1.

Proof. We construct the following type of sequence:

$$\begin{aligned} y_0(t) &= \int_{t_0}^{t} W_0(t, s)\, f(s)\, ds = \int_{t_0}^{t} T(t-s)\, f(s)\, ds, \\ y_n(t) &= \int_{t_0}^{t} W_n(t, s)\, f(s)\, ds \quad (n = 1, 2, \ldots), \end{aligned} \tag{29.25}$$

where $W_n(t, s)$ is the same operator as in Theorem V.1.

It is not difficult to verify that

$$y_n(t) = \int_{t_0}^{t} T(t-\sigma)\, B(\sigma)\, y_{n-1}(\sigma)\, d\sigma \quad (n = 1, 2, \ldots). \tag{29.26}$$

In fact

$$y_n(t) = \int_{t_0}^{t} \left[\int_{s}^{t} T(t-\sigma)\, B(\sigma)\, W_{n-1}(\sigma, s)\, d\sigma \right] f(s)\, ds =$$

$$= \int_{t_0}^{t} T(t-\sigma)\, B(\sigma) \left[\int_{t_0}^{\sigma} W_{n-1}(\sigma, s)\, f(s)\, ds \right] d\sigma =$$

$$= \int_{t_0}^{t} T(t-\sigma)\, B(\sigma)\, y_{n-1}(\sigma)\, d\sigma.$$

By Lemma V.1, the function $y_0(t)$ is continuously differentiable, and by induction this is true for any $y_n(t)$; i.e., we have

$$y_0'(t) = T(t-t_0)\, f(t_0) + \int_{t_0}^{t} T(t-s)\, f'(s)\, ds,$$

$$y_n'(t) = \int_{t_0}^{t} T(t-s)\, B'(s)\, y_{n-1}(s)\, ds + \int_{t_0}^{t} T(t-s)\, B(s)\, y_{n-1}'(s)\, ds$$

$$(n = 1, 2, \ldots). \tag{29.27}$$

From Eqs. (29.26) and (29.27) it is easy to obtain the estimate:

$$\| y_n(t) \| \leqslant M^n K \frac{(t-t_0)^{n+1}}{(n+1)!},$$
$$\| y_n'(t) \| \leqslant M^n K \frac{(t-t_0)^n + (t-t_0)^{n+1}}{n!}, \qquad (29.28)$$

where

$$K = \max_{0 \leqslant t_0 \leqslant t < \infty} [\| f(t) \|, \; \| f'(t) \|].$$

Setting

$$y(t) = \sum_{n=0}^{\infty} y_n(t), \qquad (29.29)$$

we can assert, by inequality (29.28), that the series (29.29) converges uniformly with respect to t and admits termwise differentiation. Hence, $y(t)$ is a continuously differentiable function.

By formulas (29.25) and (29.26), we have the following representations for the obtained function $y(t)$:

$$y(t) = \int_{t_0}^{t} T(t-s) f(s)\, ds + \int_{t_0}^{t} T(t-s) B(s) y(s)\, ds =$$
$$= \int_{t_0}^{t} V(t,s) f(s)\, ds, \qquad (29.30)$$

where $y(t_0) = 0$.

On the basis of Lemma V.1, from expression (29.30) it follows that

$$\frac{dy}{dt} = f(t) + A \int_{t_0}^{t} T(t-s) f(s)\, ds + B(t)\, y(t) +$$
$$+ A \int_{t_0}^{t} T(t-s) B(s) y(s)\, ds = f(t) + [A + B(t)]\, y(t),$$

i.e., the function $y(t) = \int_{t_0}^{t} V(t, s) f(s)\, ds$ is a particular solution of Eq. (29.23).

Thus, combining the results of Theorems V.1 and V.2, we arrive at the conclusion that the vector

$$x(t) = V(t, t_0) x_0 + \int_{t_0}^{t} V(t, s) f(s)\, ds$$

is the solution of the problem (29.23), (29.24), which was to be proved.

Note. In [70] the solvability of Eq. (29.20) is proved for weaker assumptions concerning the coefficients and the initial condition $x(0) = x_0$. In particular, the operator $B(t)$ can also be unbounded, although it must be subordinate to the operator A in a certain sense.

30. On the Solvability of Certain Operator Equations in Banach Space

In asymptotic decomposition of Eq. (28.1) we repeatedly encounter an equation of the form

$$AX - XA = F, \tag{30.1}$$

where A is the given operator satisfying the conditions (S_1); and F is a certain bounded operator.

The functional equation (30.1) is understood in the sense that the left and right sides of the equation coincide on vectors ψ in the domain $D(A)$:

$$(AX - XA)\psi = F\psi \quad (\psi \in D(A)).$$

Let α be some point in the complex plane λ which does not belong to the spectrum $\sigma(A)$. Then the operator $(A - \alpha I)^{-1} = H$ is a bounded operator, whose spectrum is obtained from the spectrum $\sigma(A)$ by means of the fractional-linear transformation

$$\mu = \frac{1}{\lambda - \alpha}. \tag{30.2}$$

(We assume that the choice of α ensures that the condition $\mu \,\overline{\in}\, \sigma(A)$ is satisfied.)

Thus, if by assumption the spectrum $\sigma(A)$ decomposes into $n+1$ spectral sets σ_k $(\sigma(A)=\overset{n}{\underset{0}{U}}\sigma_k)$, then the spectrum of the operator H consists of $n+1$ closed portions

$$\sigma(H)=\overset{n}{\underset{0}{U}}\sigma'_k,$$

where $\sigma'_k=1/\sigma_k-\alpha$ $(k=0,1,2,\ldots,n)$ are bounded sets and only σ'_0 contains the point $\mu=0$.

Furthermore, if Γ_k is an arc separating the spectral set σ_k from the remaining portion of the spectrum, $\sigma(A)-\sigma_k$, and $\tilde{\Gamma}_k$ encloses $\sigma(A)-\sigma_k$, then as a result of the transformation (30.2) we obtain the arc γ_k surrounding the set σ'_k, and the arc $\tilde{\gamma}_k$, enclosing $\sigma(H)-\sigma'_k$.

We construct for the operator H the projection operators J_k corresponding to the spectral set σ'_k:

$$J_k=-\frac{1}{2\pi i}\int\limits_{\gamma_k}R(\mu;\ H)\,d\mu \qquad (k=0,1,2,\ldots,n). \tag{30.3}$$

The projections J_k have the same properties as the operators P_k:

$$J_k^2=J_k;\qquad J_kJ_j=0\quad (k\neq j),\ J_kH=HJ_k.$$

In addition, it is not difficult to show that $J_k\equiv P_k$ $(k=0,1,\ldots,n)$.

To do this, we first express the resolvent of the operator H in terms of the resolvent of the given operator A. Here we use a well-known formula from generalized operator calculus [102]:

$$f(A)=f(\infty)I-\frac{1}{2\pi i}\int\limits_{\Gamma}f(\lambda)R(\lambda;\ A)\,d\lambda, \tag{30.4}$$

where $\Gamma=\overset{n}{\underset{0}{U}}\Gamma_k$ is the oriented envelope of the set $\Delta\supset\sigma(A)$; $f(\lambda)$ is some complex function, holomorphic on Δ.

Obviously, for our purposes (namely, construction of the resolvent of the operator H)

$$R(\mu;H)=[(A-\alpha I)^{-1}-\mu I]^{-1}, \tag{30.5}$$

as the function $f(\lambda)$ we should choose

$$f(\lambda) = [(\lambda - \alpha)^{-1} - \mu]^{-1}. \tag{30.6}$$

Then, by formula (30.4) we find

$$R(\mu;\ H) = -\frac{1}{\mu} I - \frac{1}{2\pi i} \int_{\Gamma} \frac{R(\lambda;\ A)\, d\lambda}{\dfrac{1}{\lambda - \alpha} - \mu}$$

and, consequently, the operator J_k is of the form

$$J_k = -\frac{1}{2\pi i} \int_{\gamma_k} R(\mu;\ H)\, d\mu = \frac{1}{2\pi i} \int_{\gamma_k} \frac{d\mu}{\mu} I +$$

$$+ \left(\frac{1}{2\pi i}\right)^2 \int_{\gamma_k} \int_{\Gamma} \frac{R(\lambda;\ A)}{\dfrac{1}{\lambda - \alpha} - \mu} d\lambda d\mu.$$

Applying the usual considerations from the theory of functions of a complex variable, we can write the following chain of equalities and prove the desired identity:

$$J_k = \delta I + \left(\frac{1}{2\pi i}\right)^2 \int_{\gamma_k} \int_{\Gamma_k} \frac{R(\lambda;\ A)}{\dfrac{1}{\lambda - \alpha} - \mu} d\lambda d\mu +$$

$$+ \left(\frac{1}{2\pi i}\right)^2 \int_{\gamma_k} \int_{\widetilde{\Gamma}_k} \frac{R(\lambda;\ A)}{\dfrac{1}{\lambda - \alpha} - \mu} d\lambda d\mu = \delta I + \left(\frac{1}{2\pi i}\right)^2 \int_{\Gamma_k} R(\lambda;\ A) \times$$

$$\times \left[\int_{\gamma_k} \frac{d\mu}{\dfrac{1}{\lambda - \alpha} - \mu} \right] d\lambda + \left(\frac{1}{2\pi i}\right)^2 \int_{\widetilde{\Gamma}_k} R(\lambda;\ A) \left[\int_{\gamma_k} \frac{d\mu}{\dfrac{1}{\lambda - \alpha} - \mu} \right] d\lambda =$$

$$= \delta I - \frac{1}{2\pi i} \int_{\Gamma_k} R(\lambda;\ A)\, d\lambda = P_k,$$

where

$$\delta = \begin{cases} 1, & \text{if } k = 0. \\ 0, & \text{if } k \neq 0. \end{cases}$$

Now we consider the operator equation

$$HX - XH = G, \tag{30.7}$$

where H is the constructed operator and G is some (unknown) bounded operator.

It is not hard to prove the following theorem.

Theorem V.3. *Let H and G be given bounded operators in the Banach space $\mathfrak{X}$.*

Given that the condition

$$GP_k = G, \ P_kG = 0 \tag{30.8}$$

holds, Eq. (30.7) has the solution

$$X = -\frac{1}{2\pi i}\int_{\gamma_k} R(\mu;\ H)\,GR(\mu;\ H)\,d\mu. \tag{30.9}$$

This solution is the only one with the properties

$$XP_k = X; \qquad P_kX = 0. \tag{30.10}$$

Proof. The proof consists of direct verification of solution (30.9).

Here we recall that we have already proved that $J_k = P_k$.

We substitute expression (30.9) on both sides of Eq. (30.7), as a result of which we obtain

$$\begin{aligned} HX &= -\frac{1}{2\pi i}\int_{\gamma_k} GR(\mu; H)\,d\mu - \frac{1}{2\pi i}\int_{\gamma_k} \mu R(\mu; H)GR(\mu; H)\,d\mu,\\ XH &= -\frac{1}{2\pi i}\int_{\gamma_k} R(\mu; H)\,Gd\mu - \frac{1}{2\pi i}\int_{\gamma_k} \mu R(\mu; H)\,GR(\mu; H)d\mu. \end{aligned} \tag{30.11}$$

Here we have used a well-known property of resolvents of bounded operators:

$$HR(\mu; H) = R(\mu; H)\,H = I + \mu R(\mu; H); \quad \mu \,\overline{\in}\, \sigma(H).$$

From Eq. (30.11) it follows that

$$HX - XH = GP_k - P_kG = G,$$

which was the assertion of the theorem.

It is not difficult to verify directly that the solution (30.9) satisfies condition (30.10). Let us now show that a solution with these properties is unique.

Let us suppose that in addition to the solution X we have another solution Y, satisfying condition (30.10), i.e.,

$$YP_k = Y, \; P_kY = 0.$$

But then, obviously, the element $Z = X - Y$ is a solution of the homogeneous equation

$$HZ - ZH = 0. \tag{30.12}$$

Since the right-hand side of Eq. (30.12) satisfies condition (28.8) [in this case $G \equiv 0$], then, by what was proved above, we can construct element Z by formula (30.9). As a result, we obtain $Z \equiv 0$, i.e., $X \equiv Y$, which was to be proved.

In conclusion, we note that the solution of Eq. (30.7), satisfying conditions (30.8), can also be written in the form

$$X = \frac{1}{2\pi i} \int\limits_{\tilde{\gamma}_k} R(\mu, \; H)\, GR(\mu; \; H)\, d\mu \tag{30.9$'$}$$

[compare with formula (30.9)].

Now we can return to consideration of the original equation (30.1) and show that, provided the condition

$$FP_k = F, \; P_kF = 0 \tag{30.13}$$

is fulfilled, then expression (30.9), in which

$$G = -HFH, \tag{30.14}$$

is a solution of Eq. (30.1), having the property (30.10).

We note that due to the equality $P_kH = HP_k$, which is true for bounded operators, fulfillment of condition (30.13) implies the fulfillment of similar conditions for the operator G from (30.14).

First of all, we will establish that the region $D(A)$ is invariant under the operator (30.9), i.e., $XD \subset D$.

In fact, from Eq. (30.7) we have

$$XH = HX - G = [A - \alpha I]^{-1} X + [A - \alpha I]^{-1} F [A - \alpha I]^{-1} =$$
$$= [A - \alpha I]^{-1} [X + F(A - \alpha I)^{-1}].$$

Let $f \in D(A)$ and $(A - \alpha I) f = g$, i.e., $f = Hg$. Then we may write

$$Xf \equiv XHg = [A - \alpha I]^{-1} [X + FH] g, \tag{30.15}$$

from which it follows that $Xf \in D$, since the bounded operator $H = (A - \alpha I)^{-1}$ maps the whole space $\mathfrak{X}$ into $D(A)$. We apply the operator $(A - \alpha I)$ to the left- and right-hand sides of Eq. (30.15)

$$(A - \alpha I) Xf = Xg + FHg = X (A - \alpha I) f + Ff$$

and, as a result, we obtain the desired equality

$$AXf - XAf = Ff, \ f \in D(A).$$

Thus, we have established the following theorem. (The solution of operator equations of a more general type is considered in [21].)

Theorem V.4. *Let the operator A be the same as in Theorem V.1, and let the bounded operator F be subject to the conditions (30.13).*

Then the operator equation (30.1) has the solution

$$X = \frac{1}{2\pi i} \int_{\gamma_k} R(\mu; H) HFHR(\mu; H)\, d\mu, \tag{30.16}$$

which is the unique solution satisfying the condition

$$XP_k = X, \ P_k X = 0.$$

Note. Suppose that the operator F depends on a parameter τ:

$$F \equiv F(\tau), \ \tau \in [0, L].$$

Then, from the form of formula (30.16) it follows that the solution $X(\tau)$ will have as many derivatives with respect to τ as does $F(\tau)$.

Henceforth, in this chapter, differentiability, continuity, and convergence will be understood in the sense of the operator norm.

31. Construction of a Formal Solution

Let now turn to consideration of the equation

$$\frac{dx}{dt} = [A + \varepsilon B(\tau, \varepsilon)]\, x \quad \left(0 \leqslant t \leqslant \frac{L}{\varepsilon}\right) \tag{31.1}$$

and demonstrate a method of constructing its formal solution, satisfying the condition

$$x(t_0) = x_0, \ x_0 \in D(A), \ 0 \leqslant t_0 \leqslant t \leqslant \frac{L}{\varepsilon}. \tag{31.2}$$

In addition to the assumptions which we have already formulated with respect to the properties of the operators A and $B(\tau, \varepsilon)$ (see Sec. 28), we will also assume that the operator $B(\tau, \varepsilon)$ admits representation in the form

$$B(\tau, \varepsilon) = \sum_{s=1}^{\infty} \varepsilon^{s-1} B_s(\tau), \ \| B(\tau, \varepsilon) \| \leqslant M_1, \tag{31.3}$$

where the $B_s(\tau)$ are sufficiently (infinitely) differentiable with respect to τ.

As follows from Theorem V.1, the problem (31.1) and (31.2) has an exact solution of the form

$$x(t, \varepsilon) = V(t, t_0, \varepsilon) x_0, \ x_0 \in D(A), \tag{31.4}$$

where $V(t, t_0, \varepsilon)$ is the operator studied in Sec. 29 and satisfies the conditions

$$V(t_0, t_0, \varepsilon) = I,$$
$$\| V(t, t_0, \varepsilon) \| \leqslant e^{\varepsilon M_1 (t - t_0)} \leqslant e^{M_1 L}.$$

In accordance with the structure of the spectrum of the operator A [see (28.3)], we will construct an operator $V(t, t_0, \varepsilon)$ for formal solution of Eq. (31.1) in the form

$$V(t, t_0, \varepsilon) = \sum_{k=0}^{n} V_k(\tau, \varepsilon) X_k(t, t_0, \varepsilon), \tag{31.5}$$

where the operators $X_k(t, t_0, \varepsilon)$ act on the subspaces $\mathfrak{X}_k = P_k[\mathfrak{X}]$:

$$X_k(t, t_0, \varepsilon) = P_k X_k(t, t_0, \varepsilon) = X_k(t, t_0, \varepsilon) P_k \tag{31.6}$$

and satisfy the equations

$$\frac{dX_k}{dt} = \Omega_k(\tau, \varepsilon) X_k(t, t_0, \varepsilon) \qquad (k = 0, 1, 2, \dots, n) \tag{31.7}$$

[in these subspaces Eq. (31.7) should be understood as an equality of the left- and right-hand sides on vectors from the domain $D(A)$].

We assume that for the coefficients of the expressions (31.5) and (31.7) we have the following representations:

$$V_k(\tau, \varepsilon) = \sum_{s=0}^{\infty} \varepsilon^s V_{ks}(\tau);$$

$$\Omega_k(\tau, \varepsilon) = \sum_{s=0}^{\infty} \varepsilon^s \Omega_{ks}(\tau). \tag{31.8}$$

Nothing can be said at present about the nature of the convergence of these expressions.

Before turning to the construction of the operators $V_k(\tau, \varepsilon)$ and $\Omega_k(\tau, \varepsilon)$, we will explain what supplementary conditions must be satisfied by the operator $\Omega_k(\tau, \varepsilon) \equiv \Omega_{k0} + \varepsilon \Omega_{\bar{k}}(\tau, \varepsilon)$, already subject to conditions (S_1) and (S_2), so that relationship (31.16) will hold. It is easy to verify that a sufficient condition for this is fulfillment of the equation

$$\Omega_k(\tau, \varepsilon) = P_k \Omega_k(\tau, \varepsilon) P_k. \tag{31.9}$$

In fact, when (31.9) holds, the operators $P_k X_k(t, t_0, \varepsilon)$ and $X_k(t, t_0, \varepsilon) P_k$, as well as the operator $X_k(t, t_0, \varepsilon)$, satisfy Eq. (31.7)

$$P_k \frac{d}{dt} X_k(t, t_0, \varepsilon) = P_k \Omega_k P_k (P_k X_k) = \Omega_k(\tau, \varepsilon) P_k X_k(t, t_0, \varepsilon),$$

$$\frac{d}{dt} X_k(t, t_0, \varepsilon) P_k = \Omega_k(t, \varepsilon) X_k(t, t_0, \varepsilon) P_k.$$

If we assume that all of these solutions coincide for $t = t_0$

$$X(t_0, t_0, \varepsilon) = P_k X_k(t_0, t_0, \varepsilon) = X_k(t_0, t_0, \varepsilon) P_k,$$

then relationship (31.6) will also be satisfied for any $t \in [0, L/\varepsilon]$, since, by Theorem V.1, Eq. (31.7) has a unique solution satisfying the given initial condition.

Thus, we have satisfied ourselves that Eq. (31.9) ensures fulfillment of condition (31.6) for the operators $X_k(t, t_0, \varepsilon)$; in other words, Eqs. (31.7) are equations in the subspace $\mathfrak{X}_k = P_k[\mathfrak{X}]$. Thus, by analogy with finite-dimensional cases, we can say that these equations, in a certain sense, are of lower order than Eq. (31.1).

Now we turn to construction of an operator $V(t, t_0, \varepsilon)$ which formally satisfies Eq. (31.1). To do this, we substitute expression (31.4) into (31.1), where $V(t, t_0, \varepsilon)$ has the form (31.5).

Using the representations (31.7) and (31.8), we obtain

$$\sum_{k=0}^{n}\left[\sum_{s=1}^{\infty}\varepsilon^{s}\frac{dV_{ks-1}}{d\tau}+\sum_{s=0}^{\infty}\varepsilon^{s}\sum_{j=0}^{s}V_{kj}(\tau)\,\Omega_{ks-j}(\tau)\right]X_k = \\ =\sum_{k=0}^{n}\left[\sum_{s=0}^{\infty}\varepsilon^{s}AV_{ks}(\tau)+\sum_{s=1}^{\infty}\varepsilon^{s}\sum_{j=0}^{s-1}B_{s-j}(\tau)\,V_{kj}(\tau)\right]X_k. \tag{31.10}$$

In Eq. (31.10) we isolate the coefficients of the various expressions of the type $\varepsilon^s X_k$, $k = 0, 1, 2, \ldots, n$; $s = 0, 1, 2, \ldots$. We find [taking account of the requirement (31.6)] a system of recurrent relationships for determination of the terms of the expansion (31.8):

$$\frac{dV_{ks-1}}{d\tau}P_k+\sum_{j=0}^{s}V_{kj}(\tau)\,\Omega_{ks-j}(\tau)\,P_k = AV_{ks}(\tau)\,P_k + \\ +\sum_{j=0}^{s-1}B_{s-j}(\tau)\,V_{kj}(\tau)\,P_k \tag{31.11}$$

$$(k=0, 1, \ldots, n;\quad s=0, 1, 2, \ldots;\quad V_{k-1}(\tau)\equiv 0).$$

From this we can determine all the quantities which are of interest to us. For $s = 0$ we have

$$V_{k0}(\tau)\,\Omega_{k0}(\tau)\,P_k = AV_{k0}(\tau)\,P_k. \tag{31.12}$$

This relationship is satisfied if we set

$$V_{k0}(\tau) = P_k;\quad \Omega_{k0} = AP_k. \tag{31.13}$$

Obviously, for such a choice of the operator $\Omega_{k0}(\tau)$, Eq. (31.9) is satisfied on the elements in the domain $D(A)$.

For $s = 1$ from system (31.11) we obtain

$$AV_{k1}(\tau)\,P_k - V_{k1}(\tau)\,AP_k = P_k\Omega_{k1}(\tau)\,P_k - B_1(\tau)\,P_k$$

or, on elements from $D(A)$:

$$AV_{k1}(\tau)\,P_k - V_{k1}(\tau)\,P_kA = P_k\Omega_{k1}(\tau)\,P_k - B_1(\tau)\,P_k. \tag{31.14}$$

To solve Eq. (31.14) we use the results of Sec. 30, from which it follows that Eq. (31.14) is solvable under the condition

$$P_k [P_k \Omega_{k1}(\tau) P_k - B_1(\tau) P_k] = 0, \tag{31.15}$$

which, together with (31.9), allows us to determine the operator

$$\Omega_{k1}(\tau) = P_k \Omega_{k1}(\tau) P_k = P_k B_1(\tau) P_k. \tag{31.16}$$

Thus, the desired solution $V_{k1}(\tau) P_k$ has the form:

$$V_{k1}(\tau) P_k = \frac{1}{2\pi i} \int_{\gamma_k} R(\mu;\ H) H [\Omega_{k1}(\tau) - B_1(\tau)] P_k H R(\mu;\ H)\, d\mu, \tag{31.17}$$

where

$$H = [A - \alpha I]^{-1}, \quad \alpha \bar{\in} \sigma(A).$$

Now we set

$$V_{k1}(\tau) = V_{k1}(\tau) P, \tag{31.18}$$

Here we note that, by Theorem V.4,

$$P_k V_{k1}(\tau) = 0. \tag{31.19}$$

If we consider Eq. (31.11) for arbitrary $s > 1$, then we obtain the equation

$$A V_{ks}(\tau) P_k - V_{ks}(\tau) P_k A = P_k \Omega_{ks}(\tau) P_k - T_{ks}(\tau) P_k, \tag{31.20}$$

where

$$T_{ks}(\tau) = \sum_{j=0}^{s-1} B_{s-j}(\tau) V_{kj}(\tau) - \sum_{j=1}^{s-1} V_{kj}(\tau) \Omega_{ks-j}(\tau) - \frac{dV_{ks-1}}{d\tau}.$$

If we suppose that all the quantities with index numbers less than s are already determined, then the operator T_{ks} is known, and Eq. (31.20) is solved as in the case $s = 1$.

From the condition for solvability

$$P_k [P_k \Omega_{ks}(\tau) P_k - T_{ks}(\tau) P_k] = 0$$

we find

$$\Omega_{ks}(\tau) = P_k\Omega_{ks}(\tau)P_k = P_kT_{ks}(\tau)P_k = \\ = \sum_{j=0}^{s-1} P_kB_{s-j}(\tau)V_{kj}(\tau) - P_k\frac{dV_{ks-1}}{d\tau} \tag{31.21}$$
$$(k = 0, 1, \ldots, n; \ s = 1, 2, \ldots).$$

Then

$$V_{ks}(\tau) = V_{ks}(\tau)P_k = \frac{1}{2\pi i}\int_{\gamma_k} R(\mu; \ H)H[\Omega_{ks}(\tau) - \\ - T_{ks}(\tau)]P_kHR(\mu; \ H)d\mu \tag{31.22}$$
$$(k = 0, 1, \ldots, n; \ s = 1, 2, \ldots).$$

In this way, we can determine the operators $\Omega_{ks}(\tau)$ and $V_{ks}(\tau)$ for sufficiently large s. We should note that the derivative $dV_{ks-1}/d\tau$ enters into the expression for $V_{ks}(\tau)$.

It is easy to verify, using the representations (31.21) and (31.22), that in the case of continuous differentiability with respect to τ of the operators $B_{p-j}(\tau)$ $[p \geqslant 1, \ j = 0, 1, 2, \ldots, p-1]$ (each $B_{p-j}(\tau)$ being differentiable $j + 2$ times, respectively) we can calculate the desired solutions $\Omega_{ks}(\tau)$ and $V_{ks}(\tau)$ for $0 \leqslant s \leqslant p$. Here, all of these functions will be continuously differentiable with respect to τ $(p - s + 2)$ times.

Thus, we have described an algorithm for constructing the terms of the expansions (31.8) for the operators $V_k(\tau, \varepsilon)$ and $\Omega_k(\tau, \varepsilon)$. If it were possible to determine an infinite number of terms of the above expansions, and then determine the resolving operators $X_k(t, t_0, \varepsilon)$ of Eqs. (31.7), then the constructed function

$$x(t, \varepsilon) = V(t, t_0, \varepsilon)x_0,$$

where $V(t, t_0, \varepsilon)$ has the structure (31.5), would be the formal solution of the problem (31.1), (31.2).

However, in reality, we always have to limit ourselves to only a finite number of steps in the above algorithm. Therefore, we consider the operator

$$V_k^{(p)}(t, t_0, \varepsilon) = \sum_{k=0}^{n} V_k^{(p)}(\tau, \varepsilon)X_k^{(p)}(t, t_0, \varepsilon), \tag{31.23}$$

where

$$V_k^{(p)}(\tau, \varepsilon) = \sum_{s=0}^{p} \varepsilon^s V_{ks}(\tau), \tag{31.24}$$

and $X_k^{(p)}(t, t_0, \varepsilon)$ are operators satisfying (in the sense previously indicated) the differential equations

$$\frac{dX_k^{(p)}(t, t_0, \varepsilon)}{dt} = \Omega_k^{(p)}(\tau, \varepsilon) X_k^{(p)}(t, t_0, \varepsilon) \qquad (k = 0, 1, 2, \ldots, n) \tag{31.25}$$

with the operator coefficients

$$\Omega_k^{(p)}(\tau, \varepsilon) = \sum_{s=0}^{p} \varepsilon^s \Omega_{ks}(\tau) = \Omega_{k0} + \varepsilon \overline{\Omega}_k^{(p)}(\tau, \varepsilon),$$
$$\overline{\Omega}_k^{(p)}(\tau, \varepsilon) = \sum_{s=1}^{p} \varepsilon^{s-1} \Omega_{ks}(\tau). \tag{31.26}$$

In accordance with our previous considerations, the operator $V^{(p)}(t, t_0, \varepsilon)$ has a continuous derivative with respect to t; consequently, we can differentiate it by using the relationship (31.11). As a result we obtain for $V^{(p)}(t, t_0, \varepsilon)$ the equation

$$\frac{dV^{(p)}(t, t_0, \varepsilon)}{dt} = [A + \varepsilon B^{(p)}(\tau, \varepsilon)] V^{(p)}(t, t_0, \varepsilon) + \varepsilon^{p+1} \Phi_p(t, t_0, \varepsilon), \tag{31.27}$$

where

$$B^{(p)} = \sum_{s=1}^{p} \varepsilon^{s-1} B_s(\tau),$$

$$\Phi_p(t, t_0, \varepsilon) = \sum_{k=0}^{n} \left[\frac{dV_{kp}(\tau)}{d\tau} + \sum_{s=p+1}^{2p} \varepsilon^{s-p-1} \sum_{j=s-p}^{p} (V_{ks-j}(\tau) \Omega_{kj}(\tau) - B_j(\tau) V_{ks-j}(\tau) \right] X_k^{(p)}(t, t_0, \varepsilon) \equiv \sum_{k=0}^{n} \Phi_k^{(p)}(\tau, \varepsilon) X_k^{(p)}(t, t_0, \varepsilon). \tag{31.28}$$

We will make a more detailed study of the operator $V^{(p)}(t, t_0, \varepsilon)$ in the next section.

32. Proof of Asymptotic Convergence

In order to elucidate the properties of the operator $V^{(p)}(t, t_0, \varepsilon)$, we consider the operators $X_k^{(p)}(t, t_0, \varepsilon)$ $(k = 0, 1, \ldots, n)$ determining the solution of the equations

$$\frac{dX_k^{(p)}(t, t_0, \varepsilon)}{dt} = [\Omega_{k0}(\tau) + \varepsilon\overline{\Omega}_k^{(p)}(\tau, \varepsilon)]\, X_k^{(p)}(t, t_0, \varepsilon) \qquad (k = 0, 1, 2, \ldots, n), \tag{32.1}$$

defined in the subspaces $P_k[\mathfrak{X}]$.

Due to our constructions, the coefficients $\Omega_k^{(p)}(\tau, \varepsilon) = \Omega_{k0} + \varepsilon\overline{\Omega}_k^{(p)}(\tau, \varepsilon)$ satisfy the conditions of Theorem V.1; therefore, we can assert that the operators $X_k^{(p)}(t, t_0, \varepsilon)$ solving Eqs. (32.1) are bounded

$$\| X_k^{(p)}(t, t_0, \varepsilon) \| \leqslant e^{\varepsilon N(t-t_0)} \leqslant e^{NL},$$
$$[N = \max_k \{N_k\}, \qquad N_k = \max_{0 \leqslant \tau \leqslant L, 0 < \varepsilon \leqslant \varepsilon_0} \| \overline{\Omega}_k^{(p)}(\tau, \varepsilon) \|, \qquad k = 0, 1, 2, \ldots, n], \tag{32.2}$$

and for the function $X_k^{(p)}(t, s, \varepsilon)\, y$ $(y \in D(A))$ of the parameter s $(0 \leqslant s \leqslant t \leqslant L/\varepsilon)$ we have the relationship

$$\frac{dX_k^{(p)}(t, s, \varepsilon)}{ds}\, y = -\, X_k^{(p)}(t, s, \varepsilon)\, [\Omega_{k0} + \varepsilon\overline{\Omega}_k^{(p)}(\sigma, \varepsilon)]\, y, \qquad \sigma = \varepsilon s. \tag{32.3}$$

Thus, on the basis of the properties of the operators $X_k^{(p)}(t, t_0, \varepsilon)$ and the properties of the operators $V_{kj}(\tau)$, $\Omega_{kj}(\tau)$ $(k = 0, 1, \ldots, n;$ $j = 1, 2, \ldots, p)$, constructed in the previous section, it follows that the operators

$$V^{(p)}(t, t_0, \varepsilon) = \sum_{k=0}^{n} V_k^{(p)}(\tau, \varepsilon)\, X_k^{(p)}(t, t_0, \varepsilon),$$
$$\Phi_p(t, t_0, \varepsilon) = \sum_{k=0}^{n} \Phi_k^{(p)}(\tau, \varepsilon)\, X_k^{(p)}(t, t_0, \varepsilon) \tag{32.4}$$

[see Eq. (31.27)] are bounded on the closed interval $0 \leqslant t_0 \leqslant t \leqslant L/\varepsilon$, and the operator functions $V^{(p)}(t, t_0, \varepsilon)\, y$, $\Phi^{(p)}(t, t_0, \varepsilon)\, y$, $y \in D(A)$, are continuously differentiable with respect to t and t_0.

It is not difficult to see that for the function $V^{(p)}(t, t_0, \varepsilon)\, y$, $y \in D(A)$, we also have the equation

$$\frac{dV^{(p)}(t, t_0, \varepsilon)}{dt}\, y = [A + \varepsilon B(\tau, \varepsilon)] V^{(p)}(t, t_0, \varepsilon)\, y + \varepsilon^{p+1} \Psi(t, t_0, \varepsilon)\, y, \tag{32.5}$$

where

$$\Psi(t, t_0, \varepsilon) = \Phi_p(t, t_0, \varepsilon) - \bar{B}^{(p)}(\tau, \varepsilon) V^{(p)}(t, t_0, \varepsilon),$$

$$\bar{B}^{(p)}(\tau, \varepsilon) = \sum_{s=1}^{\infty} \varepsilon^{s-1} B_{s+p}(\tau)$$

[compare with **(32.5)** and **(31.27)**].

In other words, $x^{(p)}(t, \varepsilon) = V^{(p)}(t, t_0, \varepsilon) y$, $y \in D(A)$ satisfies the original equation

$$\frac{dx}{dt} = [A + \varepsilon B(\tau, \varepsilon)] x(t, \varepsilon) \tag{32.6}$$

with accuracy up to expressions of the order of $O(\varepsilon^{p+1})$, since, according to the already-established properties of the operators $\Phi_p(t, t_0, \varepsilon)$, $V^{(p)}(t, t_0, \varepsilon)$ and conditions (S_2) placed on $B(\tau, \varepsilon)$, the operator $\Psi(t, t_0, \varepsilon)$ is bounded on the closed interval $0 \leqslant t_0 \leqslant t \leqslant L/\varepsilon$; the following estimate holds:

$$\| \Psi(t, t_0, \varepsilon) \| \leqslant C_1,$$

where C_1 is a constant which is independent of ε.

Now it is easy to show that the operator $V^{(p)}(t, t_0, \varepsilon)$ which we have constructed converges asymptotically to the operator $V(t, t_0, \varepsilon)$ which solves Eq. **(32.6)**. By what was proved above, $V(t, t_0, \varepsilon)$ has the following properties:

$$\begin{gathered} \frac{dV(t, t_0, \varepsilon)}{dt} y = [A + \varepsilon B(\tau, \varepsilon)] V(t, t_0, \varepsilon) y, \qquad y \in D(A), \\ V(t_0, t_0, \varepsilon) = I, \qquad \| V(t, t_0, \varepsilon) \| \leqslant e^{M_1 L}. \end{gathered} \tag{32.7}$$

We now consider the difference

$$Z(t, t_0 \varepsilon) = V^{(p)}(t, t_0, \varepsilon) - V(t, t_0, \varepsilon). \tag{32.8}$$

By **(32.5)** and **(32.7)**, the operator $Z(t, t_0, \varepsilon)$ satisfies the equation

$$\frac{dZ(t, t_0, \varepsilon)}{dt} y = [A + \varepsilon B(\tau, \varepsilon)] Z(t, t_0, \varepsilon) y + \varepsilon^{p+1} \Psi(t, t_0, \varepsilon) y,$$

where

$$Z(t_0, t_0, \varepsilon) = V^{(p)}(t_0, t_0, \varepsilon) - I.$$

Using the results of Theorem V.2, we can assert that for the operator $Z(t, t_0, \varepsilon)$ on the elements $y \in D(A)$ we have the representation

$$Z(t, t_0, \varepsilon) = V(t, t_0, \varepsilon) Z(t_0, t_0, \varepsilon) + \varepsilon^{p+1} \int_{t_0}^{t} V(t, s, \varepsilon) \Psi(s, t_0, \varepsilon)\, ds. \tag{32.9}$$

If, at the initial instant of time ($t = t_0$), the inequality

$$\| V^{(p)}(t_0, t_0, \varepsilon) - I \| \leqslant C_0 \varepsilon^p \tag{32.10}$$

is satisfied, then from Eq. (32.9), taking into account (32.8), it is easy to obtain the estimate

$$\| V^{(p)}(t, t_0, \varepsilon) - V(t, t_0, \varepsilon) \| \leqslant C\varepsilon^p. \tag{32.11}$$

(Here we use the boundedness of the operators $V(t, t_0, \varepsilon)$ and $\Psi(t, t_0, \varepsilon)$, which was established earlier.)

Thus, we have proved the following theorem.

Theorem V.5. *If the operators A and $B(\tau, \varepsilon)$ satisfy the conditions (S_1), (S_2), then from the estimate*

$$\| V^{(p)}(t_0, t_0, \varepsilon) - I \| \leqslant C_0 \varepsilon^p$$

for the operator $V^{(p)}(t, t_0, \varepsilon)$, we obtain the estimate

$$\| V^{(p)}(t, t_0, \varepsilon) - V(t, t_0, \varepsilon) \| \leqslant C\varepsilon^p \qquad \left(0 \leqslant t_0 \leqslant t \leqslant \frac{L}{\varepsilon}\right),$$

where C is some constant which is independent of ε.

33. Asymptotic Solutions of the Nonhomogeneous Equation

We now consider the nonhomogeneous equation

$$\frac{dx}{dt} = [A + \varepsilon B(\tau, \varepsilon)]\, x + f(\tau, \varepsilon)\, e^{\theta(t, \varepsilon)}, \tag{33.1}$$

where the operators A and $B(\tau, \varepsilon)$ are the same as in Sec. 31, and the vector-function $f(\tau, \varepsilon)$ is continuously differentiable with respect to $\tau \in [0, L]$ and admits the representation

$$f(\tau, \varepsilon) = \sum_{s=0}^{\infty} \varepsilon^s f_s(\tau), \qquad \| f(\tau, \varepsilon) \| \leqslant h. \tag{33.2}$$

In addition, suppose that the complex-valued function $\theta(t, \varepsilon)$ satisfies the conditions

$$\operatorname{Re} \theta(t, \varepsilon) \leqslant 0, \qquad \frac{d\theta}{dt} = \nu(\tau), \tag{33.3}$$

where $\nu(\tau)$ is a function which is continuous on $[0, L]$.

As follows from Theorem V.2, the solution of Eq. (33.1), satisfying the condition $x(0) = x_0$, is of the form

$$x(t, \varepsilon) = V(t, 0, \varepsilon) x_0 + \int_0^t V(t, s, \varepsilon) f(\sigma, \varepsilon) e^{\theta(s,\varepsilon)} ds, \qquad \sigma = \varepsilon s. \tag{33.4}$$

To construct approximations to this solution we introduce the operator

$$V^{(p)}(t, t_0, \varepsilon) = \sum_{j=0}^{n} V_j^{(p)}(\tau, \varepsilon) X_j^{(p)}(t, t_0, \varepsilon), \tag{33.5}$$

where $V_j^{(p)}(\tau, \varepsilon)$ and $X_j^{(p)}(t, t_0, \varepsilon)$ are the operators constructed in Sec. 31, where the initial conditions for $X_j^{(p)}(t, t_0, \varepsilon)$ are chosen such that

$$\| V^{(p)}(t_0, t_0, \varepsilon) - I \| \leqslant C_0 \varepsilon^p. \tag{33.6}$$

Now we set

$$x^{(p)}(t, \varepsilon) = V^{(p)}(t, 0, \varepsilon) x_0 + \int_0^t V^{(p)}(t, s, \varepsilon) f^{(p)}(\sigma, \varepsilon) e^{\theta(s,\varepsilon)} ds, \tag{33.7}$$

where

$$f^{(p)}(\tau, \varepsilon) = \sum_{s=0}^{p} \varepsilon^s f_s(\tau),$$

and estimate the difference

$$y(t, \varepsilon) = x(t, \varepsilon) - x^{(p)}(t, \varepsilon).$$

By (33.4) and (33.5), we have

$$x(t,\varepsilon)-x^{(p)}(t,\varepsilon)=[V(t,0,\varepsilon)-V^{(p)}(t,0,\varepsilon)]\,x_0+ \\ +\int_0^t [V(t,s,\varepsilon)-V^{(p)}(t,s,\varepsilon)]\,f^{(p)}(\sigma,\varepsilon)\,e^{\theta(s,\varepsilon)}ds+ \\ +\varepsilon^{p+1}\int_0^t V(t,s,\varepsilon)\,\bar{f}^{(p)}e^{\theta(s,\varepsilon)}ds, \tag{33.8}$$

where

$$\bar{f}^{(p)}(\tau,\varepsilon)=\sum_{s=1}^{\infty}\varepsilon^{s-1}f_{s+p}(\tau).$$

Using the results of the preceding section, it is easy to obtain an estimate for the element $y(t,\varepsilon)$. In fact,

$$\|y(t,\varepsilon)\|=\|x(t,\varepsilon)-x^{(p)}(t,\varepsilon)\|<C\,\|x_0\|\,\varepsilon^p+ \\ +Ch\,\varepsilon^p\frac{L}{\varepsilon}+\varepsilon^{p+1}e^{M_1L}h\,\frac{L}{\varepsilon}\leqslant C_2\varepsilon^{p-1},$$

where

$$C_2=ChL+C\,\|x_0\|\,\varepsilon_0+\varepsilon_0hLe^{M_1L}.$$

Thus, in the case of the nonhomogeneous equation (33.1) as well, the approximate solution (33.7) is of an asymptotic nature, i.e., for the solution $x^{(p)}(t,\varepsilon)$ the estimate

$$\|x(t,\varepsilon)-x^{(p)}(t,\varepsilon)\|\leqslant C_2\varepsilon^{p-1} \tag{33.9}$$

holds, provided at the initial instant of time ($t=0$) we had the inequality

$$\|x(0,\varepsilon)-x^{(p)}(0,\varepsilon)\|\leqslant C_0\varepsilon^p.$$

If we write out expression (33.7) in detail

$$x^{(p)}(t,\varepsilon)=\sum_{k=0}^{n}V_k^{(p)}(\tau,\varepsilon)\Bigg[X_k^{(p)}(t,0,\varepsilon)\,x_0+ \\ +\int_0^t X_k^{(p)}(t,s,\varepsilon)\,f^{(p)}(\sigma,\varepsilon)\,e^{\theta(s,\varepsilon)}ds\Bigg], \tag{33.10}$$

then it becomes clear that if the condition $P_k f(\sigma, \varepsilon)=0$, $P_k x_0=0$ is fulfilled for certain indices $k = 0, 1, \ldots, n$, then the terms with the corresponding indices k will not appear in expression (33.10).

Now we will show that in the nonresonance case the estimate (33.9) for the approximate solution of nonhomogeneous equation (33.1) can be improved. As before, this case is characterized by the fact that the values of the function $\nu(\tau)$ for $\tau \in [0, L]$ do not coincide with any of the points in the spectrum of the operator A.

Lemma V.2. *Suppose that the conditions formulated earlier with respect to the operators A, $B(\tau, \varepsilon)$, the vector-function $f(\tau, \varepsilon)$ and the scalar function $\theta(t, \varepsilon)$ are all satisfied. In addition, let the operators $X_k^{(p)}(t, t_0, \varepsilon)$ be chosen such that*

$$\| V^{(p)}(t, t, \varepsilon) - I \| \leqslant C_3 \varepsilon^{p+1}. \tag{33.11}$$

Then, in the nonresonance case, the approximate solution $x^{(p)}(t, \varepsilon)$ satisfies the equation

$$\frac{dx^{(p)}}{dt} = [A + \varepsilon B(\tau, \varepsilon)]\, x^{(p)} + f(\tau, \varepsilon)\, e^{\theta(t, \varepsilon)} + \varepsilon^{p+1} \varphi(t, \varepsilon),$$

where the vector-function $\varphi(t, \varepsilon)$ is bounded uniformly with respect to t and ε in the region $0 \leqslant t \leqslant L/\varepsilon$, $0 < \varepsilon \leqslant \varepsilon_0$.

Proof. We differentiate the approximate solution $x^{(p)}(t, \varepsilon)$, defined by formula (33.7) with respect to t. Then, because of the method of construction of expression (33.7), we obtain for $x^{(p)}(t, \varepsilon)$ the equation

$$\begin{aligned} \frac{dx^{(p)}}{dt} &= [A + \varepsilon B(\tau, \varepsilon)]\, x^{(p)} + f(\tau, \varepsilon)\, e^{\theta(t, \varepsilon)} + \\ &+ g(t, \varepsilon) + \varepsilon^{p+1} \int_0^t \Psi(t, s, \varepsilon)\, f^{(p)}(\sigma, \varepsilon)\, e^{\theta(s, \varepsilon)}\, ds, \end{aligned} \tag{33.12}$$

where

$$\begin{aligned} g(t, \varepsilon) &= \varepsilon^{p+1} [\Psi(t, t_0, \varepsilon)\, x_0 - \bar{f}^{(p)}(\tau, \varepsilon)\, e^{\theta(t, \varepsilon)}] + \\ &+ [V^{(p)}(t, t, \varepsilon) - I]\, f^{(p)}(\tau, \varepsilon)\, e^{\theta(t, \varepsilon)}. \end{aligned}$$

By the boundedness of the operator $\Psi(t, t_0, \varepsilon)$, proved in Sec. 32, and by the assumptions of this lemma, we can assert that the vector-function $g(t, \varepsilon)$ is of the order $O(\varepsilon^{p+1})$, i.e.,

$$\| g(t, \varepsilon) \| \leqslant C_4 \varepsilon^{p+1}, \qquad C_4 = \text{const.} \tag{33.13}$$

It is not difficult to verify that in the nonresonance case the last term on the right-hand side of Eq. (33.12) is also of the order $O(\varepsilon^{p+1})$, i.e., for the integral

$$I = \int_0^t \Psi(t, s, \varepsilon) f^{(p)}(\sigma, \varepsilon) e^{\theta(s,\varepsilon)} ds \tag{33.14}$$

we have the estimate

$$\| I \| < C_5 = \text{const.} \tag{33.15}$$

Here, we used the representation

$$\Psi(t, s, \varepsilon) = \Phi_p(t, s, \varepsilon) - \overline{B}^{(p)}(\tau, \varepsilon) V^{(p)}(t, s, \varepsilon)$$

and formulas (32.4). Then expression (33.14) can be rewritten as

$$I = \sum_{k=0}^{n} Q_k(\tau, \varepsilon) \int_0^t X_k^{(p)}(t, s, \varepsilon) f^{(p)}(\sigma, \varepsilon) e^{\theta(s,\varepsilon)} ds, \tag{33.16}$$

where

$$Q_k(\tau, \varepsilon) = \Phi_k^{(p)}(\tau, \varepsilon) - \overline{B}^{(p)}(\tau, \varepsilon) V_k^{(p)}(\tau, \varepsilon).$$

We note that, by previous considerations, the operators $Q_k(\tau, \varepsilon)$ are uniformly bounded.

Let us now investigate the integral in expression (33.16), for which we introduce the following notation:

$$\int_0^t X_k^{(p)}(t, s, \varepsilon) f^{(p)}(\sigma, \varepsilon) e^{\theta(s,\varepsilon)} ds = e^{\theta(t,\varepsilon)} \int_0^t Y_k(t, s, \varepsilon) f^{(p)}(\sigma, \varepsilon) ds, \tag{33.17}$$

where

$$Y_k(t, s, \varepsilon) = e^{-[\theta(t,\varepsilon) - \theta(s,\varepsilon)]} X_k^{(p)}(t, s, \varepsilon). \tag{33.18}$$

In accordance with the properties of the operators $X_k^{(p)}(t, s, \varepsilon)$ [see (32.3)], the equation

$$\frac{dY_k(t, s, \varepsilon)}{ds} = -Y_k(t, s, \varepsilon)[\Omega_{k0} - \nu(\sigma) I] - \varepsilon Y_k(t, s, \varepsilon) \overline{\Omega}_k^{(p)}(\sigma, \varepsilon). \tag{33.19}$$

holds. Since, by assumption, the function $\nu(\sigma)$, $\sigma = \varepsilon s$, does not coincide with the points of the spectrum of the operator A, and $\Omega_{k0} = AP_k$ (by construction), then for any $k = 0, 1, 3, \ldots, n$, there exists a bounded inverse operator $[\Omega_{k0} - \nu(\sigma) I]^{-1}$.

As a consequence of this, from Eq. (33.19) we have

$$Y_k(t, s, \varepsilon) = -\frac{dY_k}{ds}[\Omega_{k0} - \nu(\sigma) I]^{-1} - \\ - \varepsilon Y_k(t, s, \varepsilon)\overline{\Omega}_k^{(p)}(\sigma, \varepsilon)[\Omega_{k0} - \nu I]^{-1}. \tag{33.20}$$

Substituting the expression for $Y_k(t, s, \varepsilon)$ in relationship (33.17) and integrating by parts, we find

$$\int_0^t X_k^{(p)}(t, s, \varepsilon) f^{(p)}(\sigma, \varepsilon) e^{\theta(s,\varepsilon)} ds =$$

$$= -e^{\theta(t,\varepsilon)} X_k^{(p)}(t, t, \varepsilon)[\Omega_{k0} - \nu(\tau) I]^{-1} f^{(p)}(\tau, \varepsilon) +$$

$$+ e^{\theta(0,\varepsilon)} X^{(p)}(t, 0, \varepsilon)[\Omega_{k0} - \nu(0) I]^{-1} f^{(p)}(0, \varepsilon) + \varepsilon \int_0^t e^{\theta(s,\varepsilon)} X_k^{(p)}(t, s, \varepsilon) \times$$

$$\times \left\{ \frac{d}{d\sigma}[(\Omega_{k0} - \nu(\sigma) I)^{-1} f^{(p)}(\sigma, \varepsilon)] - \right.$$

$$\left. - \overline{\Omega}^{(p)}(\sigma, \varepsilon)[\Omega_{k0} - \nu(\sigma) I]^{-1} f^{(p)}(\sigma, \varepsilon) \right\} ds.$$

From the latter relationship it is easy to obtain the estimate

$$\left\| \int_0^t X_k^{(p)}(t, s, \varepsilon) f^{(p)}(\sigma, \varepsilon) e^{\theta(s,\varepsilon)} ds \right\| \leqslant \beta_k = \text{const}. \tag{33.21}$$

Since inequality (33.21) holds in this case for all k ($k = 0, 1, 2, \ldots, n$), the validity of inequality (33.15) is now obvious.

Collecting the obtained results, we can represent Eq. (33.12) in the form

$$\frac{dx^{(p)}}{dt} = [A + \varepsilon B(\tau, \varepsilon)] x^{(p)} + f(\tau, \varepsilon) e^{\theta(t,\varepsilon)} + \varepsilon^{p+1} \varphi(t, \varepsilon), \tag{33.22}$$

where $\varphi(t, \varepsilon)$ is a uniformly bounded function

$$\|\varphi(t, \varepsilon)\| \leqslant C_6 = \text{const}.$$

In other words, the approximate solution $x^{(p)}(t, \varepsilon)$ [given that the conditions of Lemma V.2 are satisfied], satisfies Eq. (33.1) with accuracy up to a quantity of the order $O(\varepsilon^{p+1})$. Lemma V.2 is proved.

Let

$$z(t, \varepsilon) = x^{(p)}(t, \varepsilon) - x(t, \varepsilon) \tag{33.23}$$

be the difference between the approximate and the exact solutions of Eq. (31.1). Then, by (33.1) and (33.22), we obtain for $z(t, \varepsilon)$ the equation

$$\frac{dz}{dt} = [A + \varepsilon B(\tau, \varepsilon)]\, z + \varepsilon^{p+1} \varphi(t, \varepsilon). \tag{33.24}$$

Here, by (33.7) and (33.4), the initial condition $z_0 = z(0, \varepsilon)$ is of the form

$$z_0 = x^{(p)}(0, \varepsilon) - x(0, \varepsilon) = [V^{(p)}(0, 0, \varepsilon) - I]\, x_0. \tag{33.25}$$

On the basis of Theorem V.2, we may write

$$z(t, \varepsilon) = V(t, 0, \varepsilon)\, z_0 + \varepsilon^{p+1} \int_0^t V(t, s, \varepsilon)\, \varphi(s, \varepsilon)\, ds,$$

from which (given that the conditions of Lemma V.2 are satisfied) there immediately follows the estimate

$$\| x^{(p)}(t, \varepsilon) - x(t, \varepsilon) \| = \| z(t, \varepsilon) \| \leqslant C_7 \varepsilon^p. \tag{33.26}$$

Thus, we can assert that for the approximate solution $x^{(p)}(t, \varepsilon)$ of the nonhomogeneous equation (33.1), constructed by formula (33.7), the following theorem is valid.

Theorem V.6. *Let the operators A and $B(\tau, \varepsilon)$ satisfy the conditions (S_1) and (S_2), and let the vector-function $f(\tau, \varepsilon)$ be continuously differentiable with respect to $\tau \in [0, L]$ and admit the representation (33.2). In addition, let the function $\theta(t, \varepsilon)$ satisfy the conditions (33.3). Then, in constructing the approximation $x^{(p)}(t, \varepsilon)$ to the exact solution of Eq. (33.1) under the given conditions (33.6), we obtain the following estimate:*

$$\| x^{(p)}(t, \varepsilon) - x(t, \varepsilon) \| \leqslant C_2 \varepsilon^{p-1};$$

and, in the nonresonance case with condition (33.11) holding, we obtain the improved estimate

$$\| x^{(p)}(t, \varepsilon) - x(t, \varepsilon) \| \leqslant C_7 \varepsilon^p.$$

34. Direct Construction of a Particular Solution to the Nonhomogeneous Equation

As was shown in Sec. 33 [see formulas (33.4), (33.7)], a particular solution of the equation

$$\frac{dx}{dt} = [A + \varepsilon B(\tau, \varepsilon)] x + f(\tau, \varepsilon) e^{\theta(t, \varepsilon)} \tag{34.1}$$

can always be expressed simply in terms of the general solution of the corresponding homogeneous equation. However, sometimes construction of the general solution presents significant difficulties, and at times it becomes impossible in the general case. In addition, it may be necessary to obtain a particular solution which has the same character as does the free term in Eq. (34.1). In that case, it will be useful to apply the method of direct construction of a particular asymptotic solution presented below.

In applying this method, we will distinguish two cases, as we have often done before:

1. resonance—the function $\nu(\tau) = d\theta/dt$ at certain values of $\tau \in [0, L]$ coincides with points of one or several, but not all of the spectral sets of the operator A;

2. nonresonance—the function $\nu(\tau)$, on the interval $[0, L]$, does not have any common values with the spectrum of the operator A.

Let us show how to construct a formal particular solution of Eq. (34.1) in the first case. We will assume that $\nu(\tau)$, for certain τ in $[0, L]$, coincides with points of the spectral set σ_k. (We recall that the spectrum $\sigma(A)$ of the operator A has the structure $\sigma(A) = \bigcup_0^n \sigma_j$; hence, $0 \leqslant k \leqslant n.$)

Given the above assumptions (and taking into account the conditions formulated in Sec. 33) we represent a particular solution of Eq. (34.1) in the form

$$x(t, \varepsilon) = [V_k(\tau, \varepsilon) \xi_k(t, \varepsilon) + h(\tau, \varepsilon)] e^{\theta(t, \varepsilon)}, \tag{34.2}$$

where $V_k(\tau, \varepsilon)$ is a certain operator; $h(\tau, \varepsilon)$ is a certain vector in the space $\mathfrak{X}$; $\xi_k(t, \varepsilon)$ is a solution of the equation

$$\frac{d\xi_k}{dt} = [\Omega_k(\tau, \varepsilon) - \nu(\tau) I]\,\xi_k + b_k(\tau, \varepsilon), \tag{34.3}$$

defined in the subspace $P_k[\mathfrak{X}]$, i.e.,

$$P_k \xi_k(t, \varepsilon) = \xi_k(t, \varepsilon). \tag{34.4}$$

Here, as usual, we will assume that the operators $V_k(\tau, \varepsilon)$, $\Omega_k(\tau, \varepsilon)$ and the vectors $h(\tau, \varepsilon)$, $b_k(\tau, \varepsilon)$ admit power series expansions in the parameter ε, of the type which we have encountered many times before.

Passing to the construction of the above expansions, we note that for condition (34.4) to be satisfied, it is sufficient that

$$P_k \Omega_k(\tau, \varepsilon) P_k = \Omega_k(\tau, \varepsilon), \qquad P_k b_k(\tau, \varepsilon) = b_k(\tau, \varepsilon). \tag{34.5}$$

[Equation (34.5) follows from the corresponding considerations in Sec. 31.]

Now we substitute (34.2) into Eq. (34.1), taking into account Eqs. (34.3) and (34.4). In the obtained identity, we separately equate the expressions preceding $e^{\theta(t,\varepsilon)}\xi_k(t, \varepsilon)$ and the coefficients of $e^{\theta(t,\varepsilon)}$ on both sides of the equation. We obtain two relationships for determining the unknown operators and vectors:

$$\varepsilon \frac{dV_k}{d\tau} P_k + V_k(\tau, \varepsilon)\,\Omega_k(\tau, \varepsilon) P_k = [A + \varepsilon B(\tau, \varepsilon)]\, V_k P_k, \tag{34.6}$$

$$\begin{aligned}[A - \nu(\tau) I]\, h(\tau, \varepsilon) = \varepsilon \frac{dh}{d\tau} + V_k(\tau, \varepsilon)\, b_k(\tau, \varepsilon) - \\ - f(\tau, \varepsilon) - \varepsilon B(\tau, \varepsilon)\, h(\tau, \varepsilon).\end{aligned} \tag{34.7}$$

Since relationship (34.6) coincides completely with the corresponding equality (31.10), we will not consider here the construction of the terms of the expansions of the operators $V_k(\tau, \varepsilon)$ and $\Omega_k(\tau, \varepsilon)$. They are constructed in the same way as in Sec. 31.

We will say a few words about finding the terms of the expansions of the vectors $h(\tau, \varepsilon)$ and $b_k(\tau, \varepsilon)$, taking into account that in Eq. (34.7) the operator $V_k(\tau, \varepsilon)$ can be considered to be already known. In expression (34.7), we isolate the coefficients of successive powers of the parameter ε; we obtain the following recurrent relationships for determining the unknowns $h_s(\tau)$ and $b_{ks}(\tau)$ $(s = 0, 1, 2, \ldots)$:

$$[A - \nu(\tau) I]\, h_s(\tau) = b_{ks}(\tau) + T_s(\tau) \equiv F_s(\tau), \qquad s = 0, 1, 2, \ldots, \tag{34.8}$$

where

$$T_s(\tau) = \frac{dh_{s-1}}{d\tau} + \sum_{m=0}^{s-1} V_{ks-m}(\tau)\, b_{km}(\tau) - f_s(\tau) - B_s(\tau). \qquad (34.9)$$

From Eq. (34.8) for $s = 0$, we obtain

$$[A - \nu(\tau) I]\, h_0(\tau) = b_{k0}(\tau) - f_0(\tau) \equiv F_0(\tau). \qquad (34.10)$$

In order to solve Eq. (34.10), we apply the same method as in Sec. 31, namely, we find $b_{k0}(\tau)$ from the solvability conditions of Eq. (34.10):

$$P_k F_0(\tau) = P_k [b_{k0}(\tau) - f_0(\tau)] = 0,$$

i.e., by (34.5)

$$b_{k0}(\tau) = P_k f_0(\tau). \qquad (34.11)$$

Now the unknown vector $h_0(\tau)$ is obtained, in accordance with the results of Sec. 30, by the formula

$$h_0(\tau) = \frac{1}{2\pi i} \int_{\gamma_k} \frac{R(\mu; H)\, H F_0(\tau)}{1 - \mu[\nu(\tau) - \alpha]}\, d\mu, \qquad (34.12)$$

where $H = (A - \alpha I)^{-1}$ is the bounded operator constructed in Sec. 30; γ_k is an arc surrounding the spectral set $\sigma'_k = 1/\sigma_k - \alpha$ of the operator H.

We use the other form of representation for the solution of Eq. (34.10), namely,

$$h_0(\tau) = -\frac{1}{2\pi i} \int_{\tilde{\gamma}_k} \frac{R(\mu; H)\, H F_0(\tau)}{1 - \mu[\nu(\tau) - \alpha]}\, d\mu,$$

where $\tilde{\gamma}_k$ contains the spectrum $\sigma(H) - \sigma'_k$; then we can represent this solution in the form

$$h_0(\tau) = \left[H - \frac{1}{\nu(\tau) - \alpha}\right]^{-1} [I - P_k] H f_0.^*$$

(We call attention to the fact that the inverse operator $[H - 1/\nu(\tau) - \alpha]^{-1}$, does not exist on the entire space, but does exist on the subspace $(I - P_k)\,[\mathfrak{X}]$.)

We solve Eq. (34.7) analogously for the subsequent values $s \geqslant 1$.

In particular, we obtain the vector $b_{ks}(\tau)$ from the condition

$$P_k F_s(\tau) \equiv P_k [b_{ks}(\tau) + T_s(\tau)] = 0,$$

i.e.,

$$b_{ks}(\tau) = P_k \left[f_s(\tau) + B_s(\tau) - \frac{dh_{s-1}}{d\tau} \right] \qquad (s = 1, 2, \ldots), \qquad \textbf{(34.13)}$$

and the vector $h_s(\tau)$ is determined by the formula

$$h_s(\tau) = \frac{1}{2\pi i} \int\limits_{\gamma_k} \frac{R(\mu; H)\, HF_s(\tau)}{1 - \mu\,[\nu(\tau) - \alpha]}\, d\mu \qquad (s = 1, 2, \ldots). \qquad \textbf{(34.14)}$$

Thus, we can find any term in the expansions of the unknown operators $V_k(\tau, \varepsilon)$, $\Omega_k(\tau, \varepsilon)$ and vectors $h(\tau, \varepsilon), b_k(\tau, \varepsilon)$; consequently, we can construct a formal particular solution to the non-homogeneous equation (34.1) in the resonance case.

We seek a particular solution of Eq. (34.1) in the non-resonance case in the form

$$x(t, \varepsilon) = h(\tau, \varepsilon)\, e^{\theta(t, \varepsilon)}.$$

For the homogeneous equation

$$\frac{dx}{dt} = [A + \varepsilon B(\tau, \varepsilon)]\, x$$

a particular solution, corresponding to the spectral set σ_k. is constructed by the formula

$$x(t, \varepsilon) = V_k(\tau, \varepsilon)\, \xi_k(t, \varepsilon),$$

where $\xi_k(t, \varepsilon)$ is a solution of the equation

$$\frac{d\xi_k}{dt} = \Omega_k(\tau, \varepsilon)\, \xi_k.$$

The asymptotic nature of the constructed formal solutions is easy to prove by the method used by us earlier (see, for example, Sec. 33). Here, we obtain the same estimates as shown in Theorem V.4.

In conclusion we note that the second-order equation

$$\frac{d^2y}{dt^2} + A(\tau, \varepsilon)\frac{dy}{dt} + B(\tau, \varepsilon)\, y = 0 \tag{34.15}$$

in the space $\mathfrak{X}$ can be reduced, by the usual method, to a first-order equation in the space $\mathfrak{X} \times \mathfrak{X}$.

In fact, setting

$$y = \psi_1, \qquad \frac{dy}{dt} = \psi_2,$$

we have, by (34.15),

$$\frac{d\psi_1}{dt} = \psi_2,$$

$$\frac{d\psi_2}{dt} = -B(\tau, \varepsilon)\,\psi_1 - A(\tau, \varepsilon)\,\psi_2,$$

or

$$\frac{d\psi}{dt} = H(\tau, \varepsilon)\,\psi,$$

where

$$\psi(t, \varepsilon) = \begin{bmatrix} \psi_1 \\ \psi_2 \end{bmatrix}, \qquad H(\tau, \varepsilon) = \begin{bmatrix} 0 & I \\ -B(\tau, \varepsilon) & -A(\tau, \varepsilon) \end{bmatrix}.$$

Thus, the method which we have developed in the preceding sections can be applied to the second-order equation (34.15) as well.

35. Applications

The results presented in Chap. 5 make it possible for us to answer questions about asymptotic solution (or decomposition) for a wide variety of problems.

When we are given specific operators, we can check whether the above-described method is applicable by verifying that conditions (S_1), (S_2) hold.

In particular, by using the results of Sec. 31, we can obtain very useful formulas for carrying out the asymptotic decomposition of a system of linear differential equations of order n (see Chapter 3) on digital computers.

We suppose that for the system of linear differential equations of order n:

$$\frac{dx}{dt} = A(\tau, \varepsilon)x$$

the conditions of Theorem III.1 hold.

In order to obtain formulas which are suitable for decomposition of the given system in the manner described above, we return to consideration of the system (13.7) of Chap. 3:

$$A_0(\tau)U_0(\tau) - U_0(\tau)\mathfrak{A}_0(\tau) = 0, \tag{35.1}$$

$$A_0(\tau)U_s(\tau) - U_s(\tau)\mathfrak{A}_0(\tau) = U_0(\tau)\mathfrak{A}_s(\tau) + B_s(\tau), \tag{35.2}$$

where $B_s(\tau)$ consists of unknown matrices with index numbers less than s.

As is known (see Sec. 13), Eq. (35.1) is satisfied for

$$U_0(\tau) = V(\tau), \qquad \mathfrak{A}_0(\tau) = W_0(\tau) = V^{-1}(\tau)A_0(\tau)V(\tau), \tag{35.3}$$

where $V(\tau)$ is the matrix which transforms $A_0(\tau)$ to block-diagonal form $W_0(\tau)$. We recall that $V(\tau)$, in accordance with the nature of the spectrum of the matrix $A_0(\tau)$, has the structure

$$V(\tau) = [V_1(\tau), V_2(\tau)], \tag{35.4}$$

where $V_k(\tau)$ is an $n \times r_k$ matrix $(k = 1, 2; r_1 + r_2 = n)$ whose columns are a basis of a subspace invariant under $A_0(\tau)$; in addition, these matrices are orthonormal, i.e., they are subject to the condition

$$V_k^*(\tau)V_k(\tau) = E_{r_k}. \tag{35.5}$$

The matrix equation (35.2), by (35.3), (35.4) and the block-diagonal structure of the matrix $W_0(\tau)$, decomposes into two equations, as follows:

$$A_0(\tau)U_{ks}(\tau) - U_{ks}(\tau)W_{k0}(\tau) = V_k(\tau)\mathfrak{A}_{ks}(\tau) + B_{ks}(\tau) \equiv F_{ks}(\tau)$$
$$(k = 1, 2;\ s = 1, 2, \ldots), \tag{35.6}$$

where

$$B_s(\tau) = \begin{bmatrix} B_{1s}(\tau) \\ B_{2s}(\tau) \end{bmatrix}.$$

In accordance with the results of Sec. 30, the solution of Eq. (35.6) can be represented in the form

$$U_{ks}(\tau) = \frac{1}{2\pi i} \int_{\widetilde{\Gamma}_k} [A_0(\tau) - \lambda E]^{-1} F_{ks}(\tau) [W_{k0}(\tau) - \lambda E]^{-1} d\lambda$$
$$(k = 1, 2; \; s = 1, 2, \ldots), \tag{35.7}$$

provided the operator $F_{ks}(\tau)$ satisfies the condition

$$P_k F_{ks}(\tau) = 0. \tag{35.8}$$

In formula (35.7), $\widetilde{\Gamma}_k$ is a smooth contour on the complex plane, enclosing all of the characteristic values of the matrix $A_0(\tau)$ which do not belong to the kth group.

Let us suppose that the solutions of all the equations of the form (35.6) with indices less than a certain fixed number s have already been obtained. Then, from Eq. (25.6) with the given index s, we can determine the unknown matrices $U_{ks}(\tau)$ and $\mathfrak{A}_{ks}(\tau)$.

In fact, we find $\mathfrak{A}_{ks}(\tau)$ by using condition (35.8):

$$P_k [V_k(\tau) \mathfrak{A}_{ks}(\tau) + B_{ks}(\tau)] = 0 \tag{35.9}$$

or

$$V_k(\tau) \mathfrak{A}_{ks}(\tau) = - P_k B_{ks}(\tau),$$

from which

$$\mathfrak{A}_{ks}(\tau) = - V_k^*(\tau) P_k B_{ks}(\tau). \tag{35.10}$$

We now show how we must carry out the calculation by formula (35.7) if $A_0(\tau)$ and $W_{k0}(\tau)$ are square matrices of orders n and $r_k (k = 1, 2)$, respectively. As a specific example, we will consider the case $k = 1$.

As is known [81], the inverse matrix to $W_{10}(\tau) - \lambda E$, i.e., $[W_{10}(\tau) - \lambda E]^{-1}$, can be constructed by the formula

$$[W_{10}(\tau) - \lambda E]^{-1} = \frac{B}{D_1(\lambda)}, \tag{35.11}$$

where B is the adjoint matrix to $W_{10}(\tau) - \lambda E$, and

$$D_1(\lambda) = \det [W_{10} - \lambda E] = \lambda^{r_1} + c_1 \lambda^{r_1 - 1} + \ldots + c_{r_1 - 1} \lambda + c_{r_1}. \tag{35.12}$$

We recall that the adjoint of a given matrix M (of order n) is a matrix of the form

$$\begin{bmatrix} M_{11} & M_{21} \dots & M_{n1} \\ M_{12} & M_{22} \dots & M_{n2} \\ \dots & \dots & \dots \\ M_{1n} & M_{2n} \dots & M_{nn} \end{bmatrix},$$

where M_{ij} are the cofactors of the elements m_{ij} in the determinant of the matrix M.

Since each cofactor in the determinant $\det[W_{10} - \lambda E]$ is a polynomial in λ of degree no greater that $r_1 - 1$, the matrix B in formula (35.11) can be represented in the form

$$B = B_0 \lambda^{r_1 - 1} + B_1 \lambda^{r_1 - 2} + \dots + B_{r_1 - 2}\lambda + B_{r_1 - 1}, \tag{35.13}$$

where the B_j ($j=0, 1, 2, \dots, r_1 - 1$) are matrices which are independent of λ.

On the basis of the equation

$$(\lambda^{r_1} + c_1 \lambda^{r_1 - 1} + \dots + c_{r_1 - 1}\lambda + c_{r_1}) E =$$
$$= (B_{r_1 - 1} + B_{r_1 - 2}\lambda + \dots + B_0 \lambda^{r_1 - 1})(W_{10} - \lambda E)$$

we obtain the following expressions for the matrices $B_j(\tau)$ ($j=0, 1, 2, \dots, r_1 - 1$):

$$\begin{aligned} &B_0 = -E, \\ &B_j = B_{j-1} W_{10} - c_j E, \qquad j = 1, 2, \dots, r_1 - 1 \\ &(B_{r_1 - 1} W_{10} = c_{r_1} E). \end{aligned} \tag{35.14}$$

Thus, for calculation of the unknown matrix $U_{1s}(\tau)$, we have, by (35.7) and (35.11), the formula

$$U_{1s}(\tau) = \frac{1}{2\pi i} \int\limits_{\widetilde{\Gamma}_1} [A_0(\tau) - \lambda E]^{-1} F_{1s}(\tau) \frac{B}{D_1(\lambda)} d\lambda, \tag{35.15}$$

where $\widetilde{\Gamma}_1$ is a contour surrounding the roots of the multinomial $D_2(\lambda)$ (see Chap. 3) and not containing the roots of the multinomial $D_1(\lambda)$.

Taking into account that for the matrix $[A_0(\tau) - \lambda E]^{-1}$ a representation analogous to (35.11) holds, and that (see Sec. 14)

$$\frac{1}{D(\lambda)} = \frac{d_1(\lambda)}{D_1(\lambda)} + \frac{d_2(\lambda)}{D_2(\lambda)},$$

we can rewrite (35.15) in the form

$$U_{1s}(\tau)=\frac{1}{2\pi i}\int\limits_{\widetilde{\Gamma}_1} d_2(\lambda)\,[A_0(\tau)-\lambda E]^{-1}\,F_{1s}(\tau)\,Bd\lambda. \qquad (35.16)$$

We note that, by the theory of operator calculus, we have, for the bounded operator T, the formula

$$f(T)\,P_k=-\frac{1}{2\pi i}\int\limits_{\Gamma_k} f(\lambda)\,(T-\lambda I)^{-1}\,d\lambda, \qquad (35.17)$$

where Γ_k is a smooth contour enclosing the spectral set σ_k of the operator T; $f(\lambda)$ is a rational function, having no poles within Γ_k.

Applying this formula to calculation of the integral in (35.16), we obtain, by (35.13), (35.14), and (35.18), the following expression for the matrix $U_{1s}(\tau)$:

$$\begin{aligned} U_{1s}(\tau)=d_2(A_0)\,[A_0^{r_1-1}F_{1s}(\tau)+A_0^{r_1-2}F_{1s}(\tau)\,G_1+\\ +A_0^{r_1-3}F_{s1}(\tau)\,G_2+\ldots+F_{s1}(\tau)\,G_{r_1-1}] \quad (s=1,2,\ldots), \end{aligned} \qquad (35.18)$$

where

$$\begin{aligned} &G_1=-B_1=W_{10}(\tau)+c_1E,\\ &G_j=G_{j-1}W_{10}(\tau)+c_jE, \qquad j=2,3,\ldots,r_1-1\\ &(G_{r_1-1}W_{10}(\tau)=-c_{r_1}E). \end{aligned} \qquad (35.19)$$

Due to the condition $P_1F_{1s}(\tau)=0$, the matrix $U_{1s}(\tau)$ has the same property, i.e.,

$$P_1U_{1s}(\tau)=0 \qquad (s=1,2,\ldots).$$

By using analogous arguments, we can obtain a formula for calculating the unknown matrix $U_{2s}(\tau)$, provided that the matrix $\mathfrak{A}_{2s}(\tau)$ is determined from the condition

$$P_2\,[V_2(\tau)\,\mathfrak{A}_{2s}(\tau)+B_{2s}(\tau)]=0.$$

The above formula is

$$U_{2s}(\tau)=d_1(A_0)\,[A_0^{r_2-1}F_{2s}(\tau)+A_0^{r_2-2}F_{2s}(\tau)\,H_1+\ldots+F_{s2}H_{r_2-1}], \qquad (35.18')$$

where

$$H_1 = W_{20}(\tau) + b_1 E,$$
$$H_i = H_{i-1}(\tau) W_{20}(\tau) + b_i E, \qquad i = 2, 3, \ldots, r_2 - 1,$$
$$(H_{r_2-1} W_{20} = -b_{r_2} E),$$
$$D_2(\lambda) = \lambda^{r_2} + b_1 \lambda^{r_2-1} + \ldots + b_{r_2-1}\lambda + b_{r_2}. \tag{35.19'}$$

In the case when the characteristic values of the matrix $A_0(\tau)$ can be decomposed into $k > 2$ isolated groups, the corresponding computational formulas can be found in [98].

We will demonstrate, on a very trivial example, how to carry out all the calculations connected with asymptotic decomposition of a system of linear differential equations.

Suppose we are given a third-order system

$$\frac{dx_1}{dt} = x_2,$$
$$\frac{dx_2}{dt} = x_3, \tag{35.20}$$
$$\frac{dx_3}{dt} = (1 + 0{,}01t)(2 + 0.01t)^2 x_1 - (2 + 0.01t)(4 + 0.03t) x_2 +$$
$$+ (5 + 0.03t) x_3.$$

We set $0.01\, t = \tau$ ($\varepsilon = 0.01$); then we may write the matrix $A(\tau)$, corresponding to system (35.20), in the form

$$A(\tau) = \begin{bmatrix} 0 & 1 & 0 \\ 0 & 0 & 1 \\ (1+\tau)(2+\tau)^2 & -(2+\tau)(4+3\tau) & 5+5\tau \end{bmatrix}.$$

It is easy to calculate that the characteristic polynomial of the matrix $A(\tau)$ is

$$D(\lambda) = [\lambda - (1+\tau)]\,[\lambda - (2+\tau)]^2 = 0, \tag{35.21}$$

and its roots form two isolated groups:

$$\lambda_1 = 1 + \tau; \qquad \lambda_2 = \lambda_3 = 2 + \tau.$$

By (35.21), we have the formula

$$\frac{1}{D(\lambda)}=\frac{d_1(\lambda)}{\lambda-(1+\tau)}+\frac{d_2(\lambda)}{[\lambda-(2+\tau)]^2},$$

where

$$d_1(\lambda)=1, \qquad d_2(\lambda)=-\lambda+\frac{(2+\tau)^2-1}{1+\tau}. \tag{35.22}$$

We determine the projection matrices $P_1(A)$ and $P_2(A)$:

$$P_1(A)=[A(\tau)-(2+\tau)E]^2=$$
$$=\begin{bmatrix}(2+\tau)^2 & -2(2+\tau) & 1\\ (2+\tau)^2(1+\tau) & -2(2+\tau)(1+\tau) & 1+\tau\\ (2+\tau)^2(1+\tau)^2 & -2(2+\tau)(1+\tau)^2 & (1+\tau)^2\end{bmatrix}, \tag{35.23}$$

$$P_2(A)=\left[-A(\tau)+\frac{(2+\tau)^2-1}{1+\tau}E\right][A(\tau)-(1+\tau)E]=$$
$$=\begin{bmatrix}1-(2+\tau)^2 & 2(2+\tau) & -1\\ -(1+\tau)(2+\tau)^2 & 2\tau^2+6\tau+5 & -(1+\tau)\\ -(1+\tau)^2(2+\tau)^2 & 2(2+\tau)(1+\tau)^2 & -\tau(2+\tau)\end{bmatrix}. \tag{35.24}$$

From the equations $P_1(A)y=0$ and $P_2(A)z=0$, we obtain the columns of the matrix $V(\tau)=[V_1(\tau), V_2(\tau)]$, $(V_2^*V_2=E_2)$:

$$V_1(\tau)=\begin{bmatrix}1\\ 1+\tau\\ (1+\tau)^2\end{bmatrix}, \quad V_2(\tau)=\begin{bmatrix}\frac{2}{\alpha} & -\frac{2+\tau}{\beta}\\ \frac{2+\tau}{\alpha} & \frac{2}{\beta}\\ 0 & \frac{(2+\tau)(\tau^2+4\tau+8)}{\beta}\end{bmatrix}, \tag{35.25}$$

where

$$\alpha=\sqrt{\tau^2+4\tau+8}, \quad \beta=\sqrt{(2+\tau)^2[1+\alpha^4]+4}.$$

We note that the columns of the marix $V_2(\tau)$ are orthonormal.

After carrying out the indicated preliminary calculations, we pass directly to decomposition of the system (35.20).

In accordance with the nature of the characteristic values of the matrix $A(\tau)$, system (35.20) can be represented asymptotically by using the transformation

$$x(t, \varepsilon) = U_1(\tau, \varepsilon)\xi_1(t, \varepsilon) + U_2(\tau, \varepsilon)\xi(t, \varepsilon), \tag{35.26}$$

where

$$U_2(\tau, \varepsilon) = \begin{bmatrix} u_{11}(\tau, \varepsilon) \\ u_{21}(\tau, \varepsilon) \\ u_{31}(\tau, \varepsilon) \end{bmatrix}, \quad U_2(\tau, \varepsilon) = \begin{bmatrix} u_{12}(\tau, \varepsilon) & u_{13}(\tau, \varepsilon) \\ u_{22}(\tau, \varepsilon) & u_{23}(\tau, \varepsilon) \\ u_{32}(\tau, \varepsilon) & u_{33}(\tau, \varepsilon) \end{bmatrix},$$

$\xi_1(t, \varepsilon)$ is a scalar function, and $\xi(t, \varepsilon)$ is a two-dimensional vector:

$$\xi(t, \varepsilon) = \begin{bmatrix} \xi_2(t, \varepsilon) \\ \xi_3(t, \varepsilon) \end{bmatrix}.$$

Thus, the system (35.20) can be represented asymptotically in the form of one independent equation

$$\frac{d\xi_1}{dt} = a(\tau, \varepsilon)\xi_1 \tag{35.27}$$

and a system of order two

$$\frac{d\xi_3}{dt} = w_{11}(\tau, \varepsilon)\xi_2 + w_{12}(\tau, \varepsilon)\xi_3, \qquad \frac{d\xi_3}{dt} = w_{21}(\tau, \varepsilon)\xi_2 + w_{22}(\tau, \varepsilon)\xi_3, \tag{35.28}$$

which corresponds to the matrix

$$W(\tau, \varepsilon) = \begin{bmatrix} w_{11}(\tau, \varepsilon) & w_{12}(\tau, \varepsilon) \\ w_{21}(\tau, \varepsilon) & w_{22}(\tau, \varepsilon) \end{bmatrix}.$$

The matrices $U_1(\tau, \varepsilon)$, $U_2(\tau, \varepsilon)$, $W(\tau, \varepsilon)$ and the function $a(\tau, \varepsilon)$, as is known, should satisfy the equations

$$A(\tau)U_1(\tau, \varepsilon) - a(\tau, \varepsilon)U_1(\tau, \varepsilon) = \varepsilon\frac{dU_1}{d\tau}, \tag{35.29}$$

$$AU_2(\tau, \varepsilon) - U_2(\tau, \varepsilon)W(\tau, \varepsilon) = \varepsilon\frac{dU_2}{d\tau}. \tag{35.30}$$

We will solve Eq. (35.29) by the method presented above, assuming that for $U_1(\tau, \varepsilon)$ and $a(\tau, \varepsilon)$ we have the representations

$$U_1(\tau, \varepsilon) = U_{10}(\tau) + \varepsilon U_{11}(\tau) + \varepsilon^2 U_{12}(\tau) + \dots,$$
$$a(\tau, \varepsilon) = a_0(\tau) + \varepsilon a_1(\tau) + \varepsilon^2 a_2(\tau) + \dots.$$

Due to the results of Sec. 13, we have

$$U_{10}(\tau) = V_1(\tau) = \begin{bmatrix} 1 \\ 1+\tau \\ (1+\tau)^2 \end{bmatrix},$$

and from the equation

$$A(\tau) U_{10}(\tau) - U_{10}(\tau) a_0(\tau) = 0$$

we find

$$a_0(\tau) = 1 + \tau.$$

In order to obtain the vector $U_{11}(\tau)$ and the function $a_1(\tau)$, we obtain from Eq. (35.29) the system

$$A(\tau) U_{11}(\tau) - a_0(\tau) U_{11}(\tau) = \frac{dU_{10}}{d\tau} + a_1(\tau) U_{10}(\tau) \equiv F_1(\tau).$$

Using the solvability condition $P_1 F_1(\tau) = 0$, we obtain $a_1(\tau)$:

$$a_1(\tau) = 2.$$

In accordance with the general formula (35.18), the unknown vector $U_{21}(\tau)$ is of the form

$$U_{11}(\tau) = d_2(A) F_1(\tau) =$$
$$= \left[-A(\tau) + \frac{(2+\tau)^2 - 1}{1+\tau} E \right] \begin{bmatrix} 2 \\ 3 + 2\tau \\ 2(2+\tau)(1+\tau) \end{bmatrix},$$

i.e.,

$$U_{11}(\tau) = \begin{bmatrix} 3 \\ 5 + 3\tau \\ (2+\tau)(4+3\tau) \end{bmatrix}.$$

Thus, limiting ourselves to the first approximation, we obtain the following values for the unknown quantities:

$$U_1^{(1)}(\tau, \varepsilon) = \begin{bmatrix} 1.03 \\ 1.05 + 1.03\tau \\ 1.08 + 2.1\tau + 1.03\tau^2 \end{bmatrix} =$$

$$= \begin{bmatrix} 1.03 \\ 1.05 + 0.0103\,t \\ 1.08 + 0.021t + 0.000103\,t^2 \end{bmatrix},$$

$$a^{(1)}(\tau, \varepsilon) = 1.02 + \tau = 1.02 + 0.01t.$$

Equation (35.30) is solved similarly. It is completely understandable that decomposition of a system of differential equations of high order can be carried out only by using high-speed digital computers. In that case, the entire calculation can be carried out at separate fixed points of the given interval $0 \leqslant t \leqslant L/\varepsilon$.

We will show, for example, how to construct the solution of Eq. (35.30) in this case.

In accordance with the usual method of asymptotic solution of the given equation, we represent $U_2(\tau, \varepsilon)$ and $W(\tau, \varepsilon)$ as power series in the parameter ε:

$$U_2(\tau, \varepsilon) = U_{20}(\tau) + \varepsilon U_{21}(\tau) + \varepsilon^2 U_{22}(\tau) + \dots,$$

$$W(\tau, \varepsilon) = W_0(\tau) + \varepsilon W_1(\tau) + \varepsilon^2 W_2(\tau) + \dots.$$

Then the matrices $U_{20}(\tau)$ and $W_0(\tau)$ are determined from the equation

$$A(\tau) U_{20}(\tau) - U_{20}(\tau) W_0(\tau) = 0, \qquad (35.31)$$

and the matrices $U_{21}(\tau)$ and $W_1(\tau)$ from the equation

$$A(\tau) U_{21}(\tau) - U_{21}(\tau) W_0(\tau) = \frac{dU_{20}}{d\tau} + U_{20}(\tau) W_1(\tau) \equiv F_2(\tau). \qquad (35.32)$$

We select m fixed points on the given interval of variation of the variable $\tau \in [0, L]$. We find the solution of system (35.31) at each of these points.

For example, if, at the point $\tau_0 = 0$, we carry out the entire calculation as described above, then we obtain

$$U_{20}(\tau_0) = V_2(\tau_0) = \begin{bmatrix} 0.707107 & -0.123091 \\ 0.707107 & 0.123091 \\ 0 & 0.984728 \end{bmatrix},$$

$$W_0(\tau) = U^*_{20} A(\tau) U_{20} = \begin{bmatrix} 0.5 & 0.783351 \\ 2.87228 & 3.5 \end{bmatrix}.$$

The values of $U_{20}(\tau_j)$ and $W_0(\tau_j)$, respectively, are then obtained for other fixed τ_j in the interval $[0,L]$.

The obtained values $U_{20}(\tau_j)$ $(j = 0, 1, 2, \ldots, m)$ make it possible for us to determine numerically the value $dU_{20}/d\tau \mid \tau = \tau_j$, and, consequently, to pass to the solution of system (35.32).

In this case, for $\tau_0 = 0$, we have

$$\left.\frac{dU_{20}}{d\tau}\right|_{\tau=\tau_0=0} = \begin{bmatrix} -0.176777 & -0.0587482 \\ 0.176777 & -0.120294 \\ 0 & 0.0223803 \end{bmatrix}.$$

By the solvability condition

$$P_2 F_2(\tau) = 0,$$

we find

$$W_1(\tau_0) = -U^*_{20}(\tau_0) P_2 \left.\frac{dU_{20}}{d\tau}\right|_{\tau=\tau_0=0},$$

i.e.,

$$W_1(\tau_0) = \begin{bmatrix} -2 & +0.506408 \\ -1.43614 & 0.25 \end{bmatrix}.$$

After this, the solution of Eq. (35.32) [the matrix $U_{21}(\tau)$] is determined, taking into account (35.18′) and (35.19′), by the formula

$$U_{21}(\tau) = d_1(A)[A(\tau) F_2(\tau) + F_2(\tau)(W_0(\tau) - 2(2+\tau)E)]. \quad (35.33)$$

At the point $\tau_0 = 0$, the matrix $U_{21}(\tau_0)$ is of the form

$$U_{21}(\tau_0) = [A(\tau_0) F_2(\tau_0) + F_2(\tau_0)(W_0(\tau_0) - 4E)] = $$

$$= \begin{bmatrix} 6.68537 & -1.45472 \\ 6.68537 & -1.45472 \\ 6.68537 & -1.45472 \end{bmatrix}.$$

The calculation is carried out analogously for the other fixed values $\tau_j \in [0, L]$. After numerical differentiation with respect to τ of the obtained matrix $U_{21}(\tau)$, we can pass to determination of the next term in the expansions of the matrices $U_2(\tau, \varepsilon)$ and $W(\tau, \varepsilon)$, i.e., to determination of $U_{22}(\tau)$ and $W_2(\tau)$.

Thus, after carrying out the calculation, we obtain (as a result of the first two steps), instead of the third-order system (35.20), one equation of first order

$$\frac{d\xi_1^{(1)}}{dt} = (1.02 + 0.01t)\,\xi_1^{(1)} \tag{35.34}$$

and a certain second-order system of differential equations. According to the calculations which we have carried out, this decomposed system, at the instant $t = 0$, has the form

$$\begin{aligned} \frac{d\xi_2^{(1)}}{dt} &= 0.048\xi_2^{(1)} + 0.788415\xi_3^{(1)}, \\ \frac{d\xi_3^{(1)}}{dt} &= 2.85792\xi_2^{(1)} + 3.5025\xi_3^{(1)}. \end{aligned} \tag{35.35}$$

An analogous representation is obtained for the other fixed values of t. In other words, in carrying out the calculation on computers, the coefficients of the decomposed systems will be obtained in tabular form.

The transformation which we used in realizing the asymptotic decomposition of system (35.20) into two systems (35.34) and (35.35) has, at the point $t = 0$, the form

$$\begin{aligned} x_1 &= 1.03\xi_1^{(1)} + 0.773961\xi_2^{(1)} - 0.136638\,\xi_3^{(1)}, \\ x_2 &= 1.05\xi_1^{(1)} + 0.773961\xi_2^{(1)} + 0.108544\xi_3^{(1)}, \\ x_3 &= 1.08\xi_1^{(1)} + 0.0668537\xi_2^{(1)} + 0.970181\xi_3^{(1)}. \end{aligned}$$

If we had carried out the calculation for the other values of t, we would have obtained (in tabular form) transformation (35.26) decomposing system (35.20) into two isolated subsystems (of first and second orders) on the entire given interval of variation of t.

Chapter 6

ASYMPTOTIC METHODS OF SOLVING LINEAR PARTIAL DIFFERENTIAL EQUATIONS

36. Formulation of the Problem

The results of Chap. 5 show that asymptotic methods can also be applied to many problems connected with partial differential equations. To do this, as we have already indicated in Sec. 35, it is necessary to investigate the properties of the operators which result when the problem is specifically formulated. In other words, we must investigate the given partial differential equations, along with the initial and boundary conditions. If the properties of these operators lie within the framework of conditions (S_1) and (S_2) of Chap. 5, then, by the method described there, we can carry out an asymptotic decomposition and at the same time (in the case of a simple spectrum) find the asymptotic solution of the given problem directly.

In this chapter we will demonstrate another approach to the solution of these problems by using a very simple particular example. This approach, although it is not completely substantiated theoretically, allows us to greatly simplify the obtained computational formulas and does, in many cases, give good practical results. This is indicated by comparison with other methods of calculation and also by experimental data.

Thus, let us consider the following mixed problem.

In the region

$$Q = [0 \leqslant x \leqslant l] \times \left[0 \leqslant t \leqslant \frac{L}{\varepsilon}\right]$$

we wish to find the solution of the equation

$$\frac{\partial^2 u}{\partial t^2} = \frac{\partial^2 u}{\partial x^2} + \varepsilon a(x, \tau) u(x, t) + p(x, \tau) e^{i\theta(t, \varepsilon)}, \qquad (36.1)$$

satisfying the boundary conditions

$$u(0, t) = u(l, t) = 0 \qquad (36.2)$$

and the initial conditions

$$u(x, 0) = \varphi_1(x), \quad u_t(x, 0) \equiv \frac{\partial u}{\partial t}(x, 0) = \varphi_2(x). \qquad (36.3)$$

(For simplicity we will assume that all the coefficients of Eq. (36.1) are real.)

As is known, questions of existence and uniqueness of solutions to the mixed problem for the general type of second-order hyperbolic equation have been well-studied [43]. According to the results of [43], the problem (36.1)-(36.3) has a classical solution if the coefficients and free term in Eq. (36.1) have, in the region Q, continuous derivatives with respect to t and x up to the third order, and the functions $\varphi_1(x)$ and $\varphi_2(x)$ are sufficiently differentiable ($\varphi_1(x)$ continuously differentiable five times; $\varphi_2(x)$—four times) and, in addition, the compatibility conditions are satisfied (for details about these conditions see [43]).

(Note: The term "classical solution" used above refers to a function which has continuous derivatives in Q up to second-order and satisfies all the formulated conditions in the general sense. In this chapter we will consider only such solutions.)

Henceforth, we will assume that the above solvability conditions are fulfilled.

It is not difficult to verify that the problem (36.1)-(36.3), given the present assumptions (or even weaker assumptions), can be expressed as an operator equation of the type (29.1) with the corresponding initial conditions. Here, the differential expression $Tu = \partial^2 u / \partial x^2$ and the boundary conditions (36.2) determine a closed linear operator A having properties (S_1); also, the expression $a(x, \tau)$, given our assumptions, generates a bounded multiplication operator $B(\tau)$, having the properties (S_2).

Thus, it is obvious that the results of Chap. 5 are applicable to asymptotic solution of the problem (36.1)-(36.3).

We will not dwell on this question in greater detail, passing instead to the above-mentioned method, which leads to a very simple algorithm for constructing the asymptotic solution to the problem (36.1)-(36.3).

Finally we note that, henceforth, in accordance with the requirements of the asymptotic method, the functions $a(x, \tau)$, $p(x, \tau)$ and $\nu(\tau) = d\theta/dt$ from Eq. (36.1) will not only satisfy the solvability conditions, but will also be assumed to be infinitely differentiable with respect to τ on the interval $[0, L]$.

(Note: As before, the requirement of infinite differentiability can, in practice, be changed to the condition that a finite (sufficient) number of partial derivatives with respect to τ exist.)

Then the following assertion will be true.

The integrals

$$I_k(\tau) = \int_0^l \left(\frac{\partial^k a(x, \tau)}{\partial \tau^k}\right)^2 dx, \quad S_k(\tau) = \int_0^l \left(\frac{\partial^k p(x, \tau)}{\partial \tau^k}\right)^2 dx \tag{36.4}$$

for any whole number $k \geqslant 0$, are continuous with respect to τ on the interval $[0, L]$.

Thus, we will seek a solution to Eq. (34.1) in the form of a series

$$u(x, t) = \sum_{m=1}^{\infty} z_m(t)\, v_m(x), \tag{36.5}$$

where $v_m(x)$ is an orthonormal system of characteristic functions of the boundary-value problem

$$\frac{d^2v}{dx^2} + \omega^2 v = 0, \qquad v(0) = v(l) = 0. \tag{36.6}$$

As is known, the characteristic values ω_n^2 and the corresponding characteristic functions $v_n(x)$ of problem (36.6) have the form

$$\omega_n^2 = \left(n\frac{\pi}{l}\right)^2, \qquad v_n(x) = \sqrt{\frac{2}{l}} \sin \omega_n x. \tag{36.7}$$

We substitute expression (36.5) into Eq. (36.1), assuming the possibility of termwise differentiation of the series with respect to both variables. Multiplying the obtained equation by $v_n(x)$ and integrating both parts of it with respect to x between the limits 0 and l, we obtain an infinite system of differential equations which are satisfied by the unknown functions $z_n(t)$:

$$\frac{d^2 z_n}{dt^2} + \omega_n^2 z_n = \varepsilon \sum_{m=1}^{\infty} A_{nm}(\tau) z_m + p_n(\tau) e^{i\theta(t,\varepsilon)} \qquad (n = 1, 2, 3, \ldots), \tag{36.8}$$

where

$$A_{nm}(\tau) = \int_0^l a(\tau, x) v_m(x) v_n(x)\, dx, \qquad p_n(\tau) = \int_0^l p(\tau, x) v_n(x)\, dx \tag{36.9}$$

[obviously, $A_{nm}(\tau) \equiv A_{mn}(\tau)$].

We obtain the initial values for system (36.8), if we transform conditions (36.3) in a similar way, namely,

$$z_n(0) = \int_0^l \varphi_1(x) v_n(x)\, dx = \alpha_n, \qquad z'_n(0) = \int_0^l \varphi_2(x) v_n(x)\, dx = \beta_n \quad (n = 1, 2, \ldots). \tag{36.10}$$

As a result of our assumptions, the coefficients $A_{nm}(\tau)$ and $P_n(\tau)$ are infinitely differentiable on the interval $[0, L]$:

$$\frac{d^k A_{nm}(\tau)}{d\tau^k} = \int_0^l \frac{\partial^k a(\tau, x)}{\partial \tau^k} v_m(x) v_n(x)\, dx, \qquad \frac{d^k p_n(\tau)}{d\tau^k} = \int_0^l \frac{\partial^k p(\tau, x)}{\partial \tau^k} v_n(x)\, dx \quad (k = 0, 1, 2, \ldots). \tag{36.11}$$

Here, by Parseval's equation, we have

$$\sum_{n=1}^{\infty} \left(\frac{d^k A_{nm}(\tau)}{d\tau^k} \right)^2 = \int_0^l \left(\frac{\partial^k a(\tau, x)}{\partial \tau^k} \right)^2 v_m^2(x)\, dx \leqslant \frac{2}{l} \int_0^l \left(\frac{\partial^k a(\tau, x)}{\partial \tau^k} \right)^2 dx.$$

$$\sum_{n=1}^{\infty}\left[\frac{d^k p_n(\tau)}{d\tau^k}\right]^2 = \int_0^l \left(\frac{\partial^k p(\tau, x)}{\partial\tau^k}\right)^2 dx \quad (k = 0, 1, 2, \ldots). \tag{36.12}$$

The series (36.12) for each $k \geqslant 0$ converges uniformly with respect to $\tau \in [0, L]$. This assertion follows directly from the properties of the integrals (36.4) and Dini's theorem [101] on uniform convergence of functional series with positive terms.

In the next section, we will present a rather simple algorithm for construction of asymptotic solutions to system (36.8), whose coefficients satisfy the above conditions (i.e., they are infinitely differentiable with respect to τ and the series (36.12) converge uniformly).

37. Construction of Formal Solutions

In constructing particular solutions to the system of equations

$$\frac{d^2 z_n(t)}{dt^2} + \omega_n^2 z_n = \varepsilon \sum_{m=1}^{\infty} A_{nm}(\tau) z_m + p_n(\tau) e^{i\theta(t,\varepsilon)} \tag{37.1}$$
$$(n = 1, 2, \ldots),$$

we will distinguish between the two familiar cases:

1. resonance—when the function $\nu(\tau) = d\theta/dt$ for certain values $\tau \in [0, L]$ coincides with one number (or several) in the sequence

$$\omega_n = \frac{\pi}{l} n \quad (n = 1, 2, \ldots);$$

2. nonresonance—the function $\nu(\tau)$ does not take values equal to ω_n $(n = 1, 2, \ldots)$ for any points $\tau \in [0, L]$.

For the sake of convenience in the subsequent presentation, we write system (37.1) in vector-matrix form

$$\frac{d^2 Z}{dt^2} + [\Omega - \varepsilon A(\tau)] Z = P(\tau) e^{i\theta(t,\varepsilon)}. \tag{37.2}$$

Here $Z(t, \varepsilon)$ and $P(\tau)$ are infinite-dimensional vectors; Ω is an infinite diagonal matrix on whose principal diagonal lie the elements of the numerical sequence ω_n^2; $A(\tau)$ is an infinite matrix.

We note that on the basis of the assumptions formulated in Sec. 36, the elements of the matrix $A(\tau)$ and the vector $P(\tau)$ are infinitely differentiable with respect to τ on the interval $[0, L]$ and the series (36.12) converge uniformly.

Now we consider construction of a formal particular solution to system (37.2) in the resonance case, i.e., when for certain values $\tau \in [0, L]$ we have the equation

$$\nu(\tau) = \omega_\alpha. \tag{37.3}$$

The algorithm for constructing the solution is described by the following theorem.

Theorem VI.1. *If the elements of the matrices $A(\tau)$, Ω and the vector $P(\tau)$ satisfy the conditions formulated above, then a formal particular solution of system (35.2) in the resonance case can be represented in the form*

$$Z_\alpha(t, \varepsilon) = [\Pi_\alpha(\tau, \varepsilon)\,\xi_\alpha(t, \varepsilon) + f_\alpha(\tau, \varepsilon)]\, e^{i\theta(t,\varepsilon)}, \tag{37.4}$$

where the scalar function $\xi_\alpha(t, \varepsilon)$ satisfies the equation

$$\frac{d\xi_\alpha}{dt} = [\lambda_\alpha(\tau, \varepsilon) - i\nu(\tau)]\,\xi_\alpha + b_\alpha(\tau, \varepsilon), \tag{37.5}$$

and the infinite-dimensional vectors $\Pi_\alpha(\tau, \varepsilon)$, $f_\alpha(\tau, \varepsilon)$, and the functions $b_\alpha(\tau, \varepsilon)$, $\lambda_\alpha(\tau, \varepsilon)$ admit the folowing formal expansions:

$$\begin{aligned} \Pi_\alpha(\tau, \varepsilon) &= \sum_{s=0}^{\infty} \varepsilon^s \Pi_\alpha^{(s)}(\tau), \qquad & f_\alpha(\tau, \varepsilon) &= \sum_{s=0}^{\infty} \varepsilon^s f_\alpha^{(s)}(\tau), \\ \lambda_\alpha(\tau, \varepsilon) &= \sum_{s=0}^{\infty} \varepsilon^s \lambda_\alpha^{(s)}(\tau), \qquad & b_\alpha(\tau, \varepsilon) &= \sum_{s=0}^{\infty} \varepsilon^s b_\alpha^{(s)}(\tau). \end{aligned} \tag{37.6}$$

Proof. To determine the terms of the expansions (37.6), we substitute the expression for the vector $Z_\alpha(t, \varepsilon)$ from (37.4) into system (37.3), taking into account (37.5). Equating separately the coefficients of the functions $\xi_\alpha(t, \varepsilon)$ and the free terms on both sides of the obtained identity, we obtain two relationships for determining the unknown terms of the expansions (37.6):

$$\begin{aligned} &\varepsilon^2 \frac{d^2\Pi_\alpha}{d\tau^2} + 2\varepsilon\lambda_\alpha(\tau, \varepsilon)\frac{d\Pi_\alpha}{d\tau} + \varepsilon\frac{d\lambda_\alpha}{d\tau}\Pi_\alpha(\tau, \varepsilon) + \\ &+ [\Omega + \lambda_\alpha^2(\tau, \varepsilon) E]\,\Pi_\alpha(\tau, \varepsilon) = \varepsilon A(\tau)\,\Pi_\alpha(\tau, \varepsilon), \end{aligned} \tag{37.7}$$

$$\varepsilon^2 \frac{d^2 f_\alpha}{d\tau^2} + 2i\varepsilon \nu(\tau) \frac{df}{d\tau} + i\varepsilon \frac{d\nu}{d\tau} f_\alpha(\tau, \varepsilon) +$$
$$+ [\Omega - \nu^2(\tau) E] f_\alpha(\tau, \varepsilon) + 2\varepsilon \frac{d\Pi_\alpha}{d\tau} b_\alpha(\tau, \varepsilon) +$$
$$+ [\lambda_\alpha(\tau, \varepsilon) + i\nu(\tau)] \Pi_\alpha(\tau, \varepsilon) b_\alpha(\tau, \varepsilon) + \varepsilon \Pi_\alpha(\tau, \varepsilon) \frac{db_\alpha}{d\tau}(\tau, \varepsilon) =$$
$$= \varepsilon A(\tau) f_\alpha(\tau, \varepsilon) + P(\tau). \tag{37.8}$$

In identities (37.7) and (37.8), E denotes the infinite unit matrix.

1. We first consider relationship (37.7). We successively isolate the coefficients of ε^s $(s = 0, 1, 2, \ldots)$; thus we obtain recurrent formulas for determining the terms $\lambda_\alpha^{(s)}(\tau)$ and $\Pi_\alpha^{(s)}(\tau)$:

$$[\Omega + (\lambda_\alpha^{(0)})^2 E] \Pi_\alpha^{(0)}(\tau) = 0, \tag{37.9}$$

$$[\Omega + (\lambda_\alpha^{(0)}(\tau))^2 E] \Pi_\alpha^{(s)}(\tau) = A(\tau) \Pi_\alpha^{(s-1)}(\tau) - [2\lambda_\alpha^{(0)}(\tau) \lambda_\alpha^{(s)}(\tau) +$$
$$+ \sum_{j=1}^{s-1} \lambda_\alpha^{(j)}(\tau) \lambda_\alpha^{(s-j)}(\tau)] \Pi_\alpha^{(0)}(\tau) - \sum_{k=1}^{s-1} \left[\sum_{j=0}^{s-k} \lambda_\alpha^{(j)}(\tau) \lambda_\alpha^{(s-k-j)}(\tau) + \right.$$
$$\left. + \frac{d\lambda_\alpha^{(s-1-k)}(\tau)}{d\tau} \right] \Pi_\alpha^{(k)}(\tau) - 2 \sum_{k=1}^{s-1} \lambda_\alpha^{(s-1-k)}(\tau) \frac{d\Pi_\alpha^{(k)}(\tau)}{d\tau} - \frac{d^2 \Pi_\alpha^{(s-2)}(\tau)}{d\tau^2} -$$
$$- \left| \frac{d\lambda_\alpha^{(s-1)}}{d\tau} \Pi_\alpha^{(0)}(\tau) + 2\lambda_\alpha^{(s-1)}(\tau) \frac{d\Pi_\alpha^{(0)}(\tau)}{d\tau} \right| \qquad (s = 1, 2, \ldots). \tag{37.10}$$

In expresson (37.10) only those sums for which $1 \leqslant k \leqslant s - 1$ have meaning; in addition, in accordance with (37.6), we set $\Pi_\alpha^{(-1)} \equiv 0$.

Let us determine, by Eq. (37.9), the quantities $\lambda_\alpha^{(0)}(\tau)$ and $\Pi_\alpha^{(0)}(\tau)$. For this, we set

$$\Pi_\alpha^{(0)}(\tau) = e_\alpha, \tag{37.11}$$

where e_α is an infinite-dimensional unit vector: the αth component is equal to one, the other components are equal to zero.

Now relationship (37.9) can be expressed in coordinate form in the following way:

$$[\omega_n^2 + (\lambda_\alpha^{(0)})^2] \delta_{\alpha n} = 0 \qquad (n = 1, 2, \ldots),$$

where $\delta_{\alpha n}$ is the Kronecker delta.

From this we have

$$\omega_\alpha^2 + (\lambda_\alpha^{(0)})^2 = 0$$

or

$$\lambda_\alpha^{(0)} = \pm i\omega_\alpha.$$

Henceforth, we will set

$$\Pi_\alpha(\tau, \varepsilon) b_\alpha(\tau, \varepsilon) + \varepsilon I. \tag{37.12}$$

In accordance with (37.11) and (37.12), we rewrite expression (37.10) in the form

$$[\Omega - \omega_\alpha^2 E]\,\Pi_\alpha^{(s)}(\tau) = F_\alpha^{(s)}(\tau) - 2i\omega_\alpha\lambda_\alpha^{(s)}(\tau)\,e_\alpha, \tag{37.13}$$

where

$$F_\alpha^{(s)}(\tau) = A(\tau)\,\Pi_\alpha^{(s-1)}(\tau) - e_\alpha \sum_{j=1}^{s-1} \lambda_\alpha^{(j)}(\tau)\,\lambda_\alpha^{(s-j)}(\tau) -$$
$$- \sum_{k=1}^{s-1} \left[\sum_{j=0}^{s-k} \lambda_\alpha^{(j)}(\tau)\,\lambda_\alpha^{(s-k-j)}(\tau) + \frac{d}{d\tau}\lambda_\alpha^{(s-1-k)}(\tau) \right] \Pi_\alpha^{(k)}(\tau) -$$
$$- 2\sum_{k=1}^{s-1} \lambda_\alpha^{(s-1-k)}(\tau) \frac{d\Pi_\alpha^{(k)}(\tau)}{d\tau} - \frac{d\lambda_\alpha^{(s-1)}(\tau)}{d\tau} e_\alpha - \frac{d^2\Pi_\alpha^{(s-2)}(\tau)}{d\tau^2}$$
$$(s = 1, 2, \ldots). \tag{37.14}$$

Representing Eq. (37.13) in coordinate form

$$(\omega_n^2 - \omega_\alpha^2)\,\Pi_{n\alpha}^{(s)}(\tau) = F_{n\alpha}^{(s)}(\tau) - 2i\omega_\alpha\lambda_\alpha^{(s)}(\tau)\,\delta_{\alpha n}, \tag{37.15}$$

we can successively determine $\lambda_\alpha^{(s)}(\tau)$ and the components of the vector $\Pi_\alpha^{(s)}(\tau)$ for any number $s \geqslant 1$. In fact, from Eq. (37.15) for $n \neq \alpha$ we have

$$\Pi_{n\alpha}^{(s)}(\tau) = \frac{F_{n\alpha}^{(s)}(\tau)}{\omega_n^2 - \omega_\alpha^2}, \tag{37.16}$$

or

$$\Pi_{n\alpha}^{(s)}(\tau) = \frac{1}{\omega_n^2 - \omega_\alpha^2} \left[\sum_{j=1}^{\infty} A_{nj}(\tau)\,\Pi_{j\alpha}^{(s-1)}(\tau) - \right.$$

$$- \sum_{k=1}^{s-1} \left[\sum_{j=0}^{s-k} \lambda_\alpha^{(j)}(\tau) \lambda_\alpha^{(s-k-j)}(\tau) + \frac{d\lambda_\alpha^{(s-1-k)}(\tau)}{d\tau} \right] \Pi_{n\alpha}^{(k)}(\tau) -$$

$$\left. - 2 \sum_{k=1}^{s-1} \lambda_\alpha^{(s-1-k)}(\tau) \frac{d\Pi_{n\alpha}^{(k)}(\tau)}{d\tau} - \frac{d^2 \Pi_{n\alpha}^{(s-2)}(\tau)}{d\tau^2} \right] \tag{37.17}$$

$$(n = 1, 2, \ldots; \qquad n \neq \alpha; \qquad s = 1, 2, \ldots).$$

In the case $n = \alpha$ from Eq. (37.15) it follows that

$$F_{\alpha\alpha}^{(s)}(\tau) - 2i\omega_\alpha \lambda_\alpha^{(s)}(\tau) = 0 \qquad (s = 1, 2, \ldots), \tag{37.18}$$

but the function $\Pi_{\alpha\alpha}^{(s)}(\tau)$ can be arbitrary, so, for simplicity, we suppose

$$\Pi_{\alpha\alpha}^{(s)}(\tau) \equiv 0 \qquad (s = 1, 2, \ldots). \tag{37.19}$$

Now, by formula (37.14) and Eq. (37.18), we obtain

$$\lambda_\alpha^{(s)}(\tau) = \frac{1}{2i\omega_\alpha} \left[\sum_{j=1}^{\infty} A_{\alpha j}(\tau) \Pi_{j\alpha}^{(s-1)}(\tau) - \right.$$

$$\left. - \sum_{j=1}^{s-1} \lambda_\alpha^{(j)}(\tau) \lambda_\alpha^{(s-j)}(\tau) - \frac{d\lambda_\alpha^{(s-1)}(\tau)}{d\tau} \right] \qquad (s \geqslant 1). \tag{37.20}$$

However, the expressions (37.17) and (37.20) can be considered formulas determining the terms of the expansions of the unknown quantities $\lambda_\alpha(\tau, \varepsilon)$ and $\Pi_\alpha(\tau, \varepsilon)$ only when we have proved the uniform convergence of the series which figure in (37.17) and (37.20) and also have verified the differentiability of the corresponding elements.

Let us study the formulas (37.17) and (37.20) from this point of view.

We note that $\Pi_\alpha^{(0)} = e_\alpha$ and $\lambda_\alpha^{(0)} = i\omega_\alpha$ are infinitely differentiable.

In the case $s = 1$, we have, by (37.17) and (37.20),

$$\Pi_{n\alpha}^{(1)}(\tau) = \frac{A_{n\alpha}(\tau)}{\omega_n^2 - \omega_\alpha^2} \quad (n = 1, 2, \ldots, n \neq \alpha), \tag{37.21}$$

$$\Pi_{\alpha\alpha}^{(1)} \equiv 0,$$

$$\lambda_\alpha^{(1)}(\tau) = \frac{A_{\alpha\alpha}(\tau)}{2i\omega_\alpha}. \tag{37.22}$$

From this it follows that $\Pi_{n\alpha}^{(1)}(\tau)$ and $\lambda_{\alpha}^{(1)}(\tau)$ are completely determined by formulas (37.17) and (37.20) and have as many derivatives with respect to τ as do the elements of the matrix $A(\tau)$. In addition, it is not difficult to show that the series

$$\sum_{n=1}^{\infty}\left|\frac{d^k\Pi_{n\alpha}^{(1)}(\tau)}{d\tau^k}\right|^2<\infty \tag{37.23}$$

for any whole number $k \geqslant 0$ converges uniformly with respect to $\tau \in [0, L]$.

In fact, by (37.21), for $k \geqslant 0$ we have

$$\sum_{n=1}^{\infty}\left|\frac{d^k\Pi_{n\alpha}^{(1)}(\tau)}{d\tau^k}\right|^2=\sum_{n=1}^{\alpha-1}\frac{1}{(\omega_n^2-\omega_\alpha^2)^2}\left|\frac{d^kA_{n\alpha}}{d\tau^k}\right|^2+\sum_{n=\alpha+1}^{\infty}\frac{1}{(\omega_n^2-\omega_\alpha^2)^2}\left|\frac{d^kA_{n\alpha}}{d\tau^k}\right|^2, \tag{37.24}$$

where the series on the right-hand side of Eq. (37.24) converges uniformly becuase of our assumptions [compare with the corresponding series (36.12)] and Abel's criterion for uniform convergence [101].

Now we suppose that the formulas (37.17), (37.20) have meaning for all s less than a certain natural number m $(s \leqslant m-1)$, and the functions $\Pi_{n\alpha}^{(s)}(\tau)$, $\lambda_{\alpha}^{(s)}(\tau)$ are differentiable with respect to τ (obviously, $\lambda_{\alpha}^{(s)}(\tau)$ and $\Pi_{\alpha n}^{(s)}(\tau)$ will have $(s-1)$ less derivatives than the elements of the matrix $A(\tau)$, in the case when the latter is not infinitely differentiable).

In addition, we suppose that the series

$$\sum_{n=1}^{\infty}\left|\frac{d^k\Pi_{n\alpha}^{(s)}(\tau)}{d\tau^k}\right|^2<\infty \ (0\leqslant s\leqslant m-1,\ k\geqslant 0), \tag{37.25}$$

constructed for any of the existing derivatives of the function $\Pi_{n\alpha}^{(s)}(\tau)$, converges uniformly with respect to τ.

It is not difficult to verify that, for the given assumptions, the functions $\Pi_{n\alpha}^{(m)}(\tau)$ and $\lambda_{\alpha}^{(m)}(\tau)$ are completely determined by the formulas (37.17) and (37.20) and are differentiable with respect to τ; also, the series

$$\sum_{n=1}^{\infty}\left|\frac{d^k\Pi_{n\alpha}^{(m)}(\tau)}{d\tau^k}\right|^2 (k=0,1,2,\ldots) \tag{37.26}$$

converges uniformly on the interval $[0, L]$.

In fact, the infinite series in expressions (37.17) and (37.20) converge for $s = m$; the convergence is uniform since, by the Cauchy-Bunyakovskiy inequality, we have the following estimate:

$$\sum_{j=1}^{\infty} | A_{nj}(\tau) \Pi_{j\alpha}^{(m-1)}(\alpha) | \leqslant \sqrt{\sum_{j=1}^{\infty} | A_{nj}(\tau) |^2} \sqrt{\sum_{j=1}^{\infty} | \Pi_{j\alpha}^{(m-1)}(\tau) |^2} \quad (n = 1, 2, \ldots).$$

Similarly, we can verify the uniform convergence of the series

$$\sum_{j=1}^{\infty} \left| \frac{d}{d\tau} [A_{nj}(\tau) \Pi_{j\alpha}^{(m-1)}(\tau)] \right| \leqslant \sum_{j=1}^{\infty} \left| \frac{dA_{nj}}{d\tau} \Pi_{j\alpha}^{(m-1)}(\tau) \right| + \sum_{j=1}^{\infty} \left| A_{nj}(\tau) \frac{d\Pi_{j\alpha}^{(m-1)}(\tau)}{d\tau} \right|,$$

i.e., the functions $\Pi_{n\alpha}^{(m)}(\tau)$ and $\lambda_{\alpha}^{(m)}(\tau)$ are differentiable with respect to τ [see formulas (37.17) and (37.20)].

Furthermore, by our assumptions and the form of formulas (37.17) and (37.20), the functions $\lambda_{\alpha}^{(m)}(\tau)$ and $\Pi_{n\alpha}^{(m)}(\tau)$ have only one derivative less than $\lambda_{\alpha}^{(m-1)}(\tau)$ and $\Pi_{n\alpha}^{(m-1)}(\tau)$.

In order to verify the uniform convergence of the series (37.26), it is sufficient to substitute the value of $\Pi_{n\alpha}^{(m)}(\tau)$ from expression (37.17) into the series (37.26) and carry out the corresponding estimate for the obtained expression. Not writing out in detail (because of its unwieldiness) the general term in the series (37.26), we will carry out only the estimates of some typical expressions. For example, in studying the convergence of the series

$$\sum_{n=1}^{\infty} \frac{1}{(\omega_n^2 - \omega_\alpha^2)^2} \left| \frac{d^k}{d\tau^k} \sum_{j=1}^{\infty} A_{nj}(\tau) \Pi_{j\alpha}^{(m-1)}(\tau) \right|^2$$

[see formulas (37.17) and (37.26)] we encounter series of the form

$$\sum = \sum_{n=1}^{\infty} \frac{1}{(\omega_n^2 - \omega_\alpha^2)^2} \left| \sum_{j=1}^{\infty} \frac{d^{k-l} A_{nj}}{d\tau^{k-l}} \frac{d^l \Pi_{j\alpha}^{(m-1)}(\tau)}{d\tau^l} \right|^2, \qquad (37.27)$$

where $0 \leqslant l \leqslant k$.

Using the Cauchy-Bunyakovskiy inequality, we find

$$\sum \leqslant \sum_{n=1}^{\infty}\left[\frac{1}{(\omega_n^2-\omega_\alpha^2)^2}\sum_{i=1}^{\infty}\left|\frac{d^{k-l}A_{nj}}{d\tau^{k-l}}\right|\right]\sum_{j=1}^{\infty}\left|\frac{d^l\Pi_{j\alpha}^{(m-1)}(\tau)}{d\tau^l}\right|^2,$$

from which [by (36.12) and (37.25)] the uniform convergence of the series (37.27) is obvious.

Furthermore, the question of uniform convergence of the series

$$\sum_{n=1}^{\infty}\frac{1}{(\omega_n^2-\omega_\alpha^2)^2}\left|\frac{d^k}{d\tau^k}\sum_{i=1}^{m-1}\beta_i(\tau)\Pi_{n\alpha}^{(i)}(\tau)\right|^2,$$

which is a component part of expression (37.26), where

$$\beta_i(\tau) = -\sum_{j=0}^{m-i}[\lambda_\alpha^{(j)}(\tau)\lambda_\alpha^{(m-i-j)}(\tau)+\lambda_\alpha^{(m-1-i)}(\tau)],$$

reduces to investigation of the convergence of a series of the form

$$\sum_{n=1}^{\infty}\frac{1}{(\omega_n^2-\omega_\alpha^2)^2}\left|\frac{d^l\Pi_{n\alpha}^{(i)}(\tau)}{d\tau^l}\right|^2 \quad (0\leqslant l\leqslant k,\quad 1\leqslant i\leqslant m-1),$$

which, by our assumptions, converges uniformly with respect to $\tau\in[0, L]$.

Thus, we can verify that the series (37.26) actually does converge uniformly, provided assumption (37.25) holds.

Thus, the recurrent formulas (37.17) and (37.20) allow us to determine, for the functions $\lambda_\alpha(\varepsilon, \tau)$ and the vectors $\Pi_\alpha(\varepsilon, \tau)$, the terms of the expansions (37.6) for any number s; these functions will be differentiable with respect to τ $(s-1)$ times less than the elements of the matrix $A(\tau)$, in the case when the latter have only a finite number of derivatives.

2. Now we pass to determination of the terms of the expansions (37.6) of the function $b_\alpha(\tau, \varepsilon)$ and the vector $f_\alpha(\tau, \varepsilon)$. For this we use identity (37.8). Equating the coefficients of like powers of the parameter ε on both sides of the equation, we

obtain recurrent relationships for finding the terms of the expansions

$$[\Omega - \nu^2(\tau) E] f_\alpha^{(0)}(\tau) + [\lambda_\alpha^{(0)}(\tau) + i\nu(\tau)] \Pi_\alpha^{(0)}(\tau) b_\alpha^{(0)}(\tau) = P(\tau), \tag{37.28}$$

$$[\Omega - \nu^2(\tau) E] f_\alpha^{(s)}(\tau) + [\lambda_\alpha^{(0)} + i\nu(\tau)] \Pi_\alpha^{(0)}(\tau) b_\alpha^{(s)}(\tau) =$$

$$= \left[A(\tau) - i\frac{d\nu}{d\tau} E\right] f_\alpha^{(s-1)}(\tau) - \sum_{j=1}^{s} \left[i\nu(\tau)\,\Pi_\alpha^{(j)}(\tau) + \right.$$

$$\left. + \sum_{k=0}^{j} \lambda_\alpha^{(k)}(\tau)\,\Pi_\alpha^{(j-k)}(\tau) \right] b_\alpha^{(s-j)}(\tau) - \sum_{j=0}^{s-1} \Pi_\alpha^{(j)}(\tau) \frac{d b_\alpha^{(s-1-j)}(\tau)}{d\tau} - \tag{37.29}$$

$$- 2\sum_{j=0}^{s-1} \frac{d\Pi_\alpha^{(j)}(\tau)}{d\tau} b_\alpha^{(s-1-j)}(\tau) - \frac{d^2 f_\alpha^{(s-2)}(\tau)}{d\tau^2} - 2i\nu(\tau) \frac{d f_\alpha^{(s-1)}(\tau)}{d\tau}.$$

Using the results of paragraph 1 of this section, we represent Eq. (37.28) in coordinate form

$$[\omega_n^2 - \nu^2(\tau)] f_{n\alpha}^{(0)}(\tau) + i[\omega_\alpha + \nu(\tau)] b_\alpha^{(0)}(\tau)\,\delta_{n\alpha} = p_n(\tau), \tag{37.30}$$

from which it is easy to find $f_{n\alpha}^{(0)}(\tau)$ and $b_\alpha^{(0)}(\tau)$.

Let $n=\alpha$. Then

$$[\omega_\alpha^2 - \nu^2(\tau)] f_{\alpha\alpha}^{(0)}(\tau) + i[\omega_\alpha + \nu(\tau)] b_\alpha^{(0)}(\tau) = p_\alpha(\tau). \tag{37.31}$$

Since in the resonance case the values of $\nu(\tau)$ and ω_α coincide for certain values $\tau \in [0, L]$, then we can choose $b_\alpha^{(0)}(\tau)$ in Eq. (37.31) such that the equation

$$i[\omega_\alpha + \nu(\tau)]\, b_\alpha^{(0)}(\tau) = p_\alpha(\tau), \tag{37.32}$$

is satisfied on the whole interval $[0, L]$, i.e.,

$$b_\alpha^{(0)}(\tau) = \frac{p_\alpha(\tau)}{i[\omega_\alpha + \nu(\tau)]}. \tag{37.33}$$

Obviously, for such a choice of $b_\alpha^{(0)}(\tau)$ we must, according to (37.31) and (37.32), set

$$f_{\alpha\alpha}^{(0)}(\tau) \equiv 0. \tag{37.34}$$

For $n \neq \alpha$ from Eq. (37.30) we obtain

$$f_{n\alpha}^{(0)}(\tau) = \frac{p_n(\tau)}{\omega_n^2 - \nu^2(\tau)}, \qquad n = 1, 2, \ldots, \; n \neq \alpha. \tag{37.35}$$

Similarly, we can successively determine $f_{n\alpha}^{(s)}(\tau)$ and $b_{\alpha}^{(s)}(\tau)$ for any natural number $s \geqslant 1$ by using (37.29).

We rewrite (37.29) in coordinate form, taking into account the results of paragraph 1:

$$[\omega_n^2 - \nu^2(\tau)]\, f_{n\alpha}^{(s)}(\tau) + i\,[\omega_\alpha + \nu(\tau)]\, b_\alpha^{(s)}(\tau)\delta_{n\alpha} = T_{n\alpha}^{(s)}(\tau) \qquad (37.36)$$
$$(n = 1, 2, \ldots;\ s = 1, 2, \ldots),$$

where

$$T_{n\alpha}^{(s)}(\tau) = \sum_{j=1}^{\infty} A_{nj}(\tau)\, f_{j\alpha}^{(s-1)}(\tau) - i\frac{d\nu}{d\tau} f_{n\alpha}^{(s-1)}(\tau) - \sum_{j=1}^{s}\Bigg[i\nu(\tau)\Pi_{n\alpha}^{(j)}(\tau) + \sum_{k=0}^{j} \lambda_\alpha^{(k)}(\tau)\,\Pi_{n\alpha}^{(j-k)}(\tau)\Bigg] b_\alpha^{(s-j)}(\tau) - \sum_{j=0}^{s-1} \Pi_{n\alpha}^{(j)}(\tau)\frac{db_\alpha^{(s-1-j)}(\tau)}{d\tau} - 2\sum_{j=0}^{s-1}\frac{d\Pi_{n\alpha}^{(j)}(\tau)}{d\tau}\, b_\alpha^{(s-1-j)}(\tau) - \frac{d^2 f_{n\alpha}^{(s-2)}(\tau)}{d\tau^2} - 2i\nu(\tau)\frac{df_{n\alpha}^{(s-1)}(\tau)}{d\tau}. \qquad (37.37)$$

For $n = \alpha$, relationship (37.36) takes the form

$$[\omega_\alpha^2 - \nu^2(\tau)]\, f_{\alpha\alpha}^{(s)}(\tau) + i\,[\omega_\alpha + \nu(\tau)]\, b_\alpha^{(s)}(\tau) = T_{\alpha\alpha}^{(s)}(\tau), \qquad (37.38)$$

and

$$T_{\alpha\alpha}^{(s)}(\tau) = \sum_{j=1}^{\infty} A_{\alpha j}(\tau)\, f_{j\alpha}^{(s-1)}(\tau) - i\frac{d\nu}{d\tau} f_{\alpha\alpha}^{(s-1)}(\tau) - \sum_{j=1}^{s} \lambda_\alpha^{(j)}(\tau)\, b_\alpha^{(s-j)}(\tau) - \frac{db_\alpha^{(s-1)}(\tau)}{d\tau} - \frac{d^2 f_{\alpha\alpha}^{(s-2)}(\tau)}{d\tau^2} - 2i\nu(\tau)\frac{df_{\alpha\alpha}^{(s-1)}(\tau)}{d\tau}. \qquad (37.39)$$

Reasoning as in the case $s = 0$, we choose $b_\alpha^{(s)}(\tau)$ in Eq. (37.38) such that for any $\tau \in [0, L]$, the equation

$$i\,[\omega_\alpha + \nu(\tau)]\, b_\alpha^{(s)}(\tau) = T_{\alpha\alpha}^{(s)}(\tau),$$

is satisfied; in other words,

$$b_\alpha^{(s)}(\tau) = \frac{T_{\alpha\alpha}^{(s)}(\tau)}{i\,[\omega_\alpha + \nu(\tau)]} \quad (s = 1, 2, \ldots). \qquad (37.40)$$

For such a choice of $b_\alpha^{(s)}(\tau)$, we must set, inequality (37.38):

$$f_{\alpha\alpha}^{(s)}(\tau) \equiv 0 \qquad (s = 1, 2, \ldots). \tag{37.41}$$

Returning to formula (37.40), we can represent it [taking into account (37.39) and (37.41)] in expanded form

$$b_\alpha^{(s)}(\tau) = \frac{1}{i\,[\omega_\alpha + \nu(\tau)]}\left[\sum_{j=1}^{\infty} A_{\alpha j}(\tau)\, f_{j\alpha}^{(s-1)}(\tau) - \sum_{j=1}^{s} \lambda_\alpha^{(j)}(\tau)\, b_\alpha^{(s-j)}(\tau) - \frac{db_\alpha^{(s-1)}(\tau)}{d\tau}\right]$$
$$(s = 1, 2, \ldots). \tag{37.42}$$

Let $n \neq \alpha$. Then, by (37.36), we have

$$[\omega_n^2 - \nu^2(\tau)]\, f_{n\alpha}^{(s)}(\tau) = T_{n\alpha}^{(s)}(\tau),$$

from which it follows that

$$f_{n\alpha}^{(s)}(\tau) = \frac{T_{n\alpha}^{(s)}(\tau)}{\omega_n^2 - \nu^2(\tau)} \quad (n = 1, 2, \ldots; \quad n \neq \alpha, \quad s = 1, 2, \ldots). \tag{37.43}$$

As in the case of paragraph 1, we must verify that formulas (37.42) and (37.43) have meaning, i.e., that the infinite series in these formulas converge and admit termwise differentiation with respect to τ.

From formulas (37.33) and (37.35) it follows that the functions $b_\alpha^{(0)}(\tau)$ and $f_{n\alpha}^{(0)}(\tau)$ have as many derivatives as do the components of the vector $P(\tau)$ and the function $\nu(\tau)$. In addition, it is not difficult to show that the series

$$\sum_{n=1}^{\infty}\left|\frac{d^m}{d\tau^m} f_{n\alpha}^{(0)}(\tau)\right|^2 \qquad (m = 0, 1, 2, \ldots) \tag{37.44}$$

converges uniformly.

In fact, writing out in detail a general term of the series (37.44), we have, by (37.35)

$$\sum_{n=1}^{\infty}\left|\frac{d^m}{d\tau^m} f_{n\alpha}^{(0)}(\tau)\right|^2 = \sum_{n=1}^{\alpha-1}\left|\frac{d^m f_{n\alpha}^{(0)}(\tau)}{d\tau^m}\right|^2 + \sum_{n=\alpha+1}^{\infty}\left|\sum_{j=0}^{m} C_m^j \times\right.$$

$$\times \left[\frac{d^{m-j}}{d\tau^{m-j}} \cdot \frac{1}{\omega_n^2 - \nu^2(\tau)} \right] \frac{d^j p_n(\tau)}{d\tau^j} \Bigg|^2 \qquad \left(C_m^j = \frac{m!}{j!(m-j)!} \right). \tag{37.45}$$

Thus, the question of convergence of the series (37.44) reduces to investigation of convergence of the series

$$\sum_{n=\alpha+1}^{\infty} \left| \sum_{j=0}^{m} C_m^j \left[\frac{d^{m-j}}{d\tau^{m-j}} \cdot \frac{1}{\omega_n^2 - \nu^2(\tau)} \right] \frac{d^j p_n(\tau)}{d\tau^j} \right|^2. \tag{37.46}$$

We first consider the expression for the kth derivative of the function $1/\omega_n^2 - \nu^2(\tau)$. Obviously, we have the following relationship:

$$\frac{d^k}{d\tau^k} \left[\frac{1}{\omega_n^2 - \nu^2(\tau)} \right] = \sum_{j=1}^{k} \frac{f_j(\nu(\tau), \nu'(\tau), \ldots, \nu^{(k)}(\tau))}{[\omega_n^2 - \nu^2(\tau)]^{j+1}}, \tag{37.47}$$

where $f_j[\nu(\tau), \nu'(\tau), \ldots, \nu^{(k)}(\tau)]$ is a multinomial in the function $\nu(\tau)$ and its derivatives with respect to τ up to the kth-order derivative, inclusive.

The polynomial $f_j(\nu, \nu', \ldots, \nu^{(k)})$ is independent of ω_n, and, because of the infinite differentiability of the function $\nu(\tau)$, is bounded with respect to τ on the interval $[0, L]$:

$$|f_j(\nu, \nu', \ldots, \nu^{(k)})| < M_j = \text{const.} \tag{37.48}$$

By (37.47) and (37.48), we have the following estimate for the series (37.46):

$$\sum_{n=\alpha+1}^{\infty} \left| \sum_{j=0}^{m} C_m^j \left[\frac{d^{m-j}}{d\tau^{m-j}} \cdot \frac{1}{\omega_n^2 - \nu^2(\tau)} \right] \frac{d^j p_n}{d\tau^j} \right|^2 \leqslant$$

$$\leqslant \sum_{n=\alpha+1}^{\infty} \left\{ \sum_{j=0}^{m} (C_m^j)^2 (m-j) \sum_{k=1}^{m-j} \frac{M_k^2}{[\omega_n^2 - \nu^2(\tau)]^{2k+2}} \sum_{j=0}^{m} \left(\frac{d^j p_n(\tau)}{d\tau^j} \right)^2 \right\} \leqslant$$

$$\leqslant \left[\sum_{j=0}^{m} (C_m^j)^2 (m-j) \sum_{k=1}^{m-j} \frac{M_k^2}{[\omega_{\alpha+1}^2 - \nu^2(\tau)]^{2k+2}} \right] \sum_{j=0}^{m} \sum_{n=\alpha+1}^{\infty} \left(\frac{d^j p_n}{d\tau^j} \right)^2.$$

From which, on the basis of our assumptions, it is obvious that the series (37.46), and therefore the series (37.44), converge uniformly.

By using similar considerations we can show that formulas (37.42) and (37.43) have meaning for any natural $s \geqslant 1$, and the functions $b_\alpha^{(s)}(\tau)$ and $f_{n\alpha}^{(s)}(\tau)$ which they determine are differentiable with respect to τ only s times less than the functions $b_\alpha^{(0)}$ and $f_{n\alpha}^{(0)}(\tau)$, in the case where the latter are not infinitely differentiable.

In addition, the series

$$\sum_{n=1}^{\infty} \left| \frac{d^m}{d\tau^m} f_{n\alpha}^{(s)}(\tau) \right|^2 \qquad (m \geqslant 0)$$

converge uniformly with respect to τ for any $s \geqslant 1$.

(We will not consider the above question in detail because of its unwieldiness and because of its uniformity to the previous considerations.)

Thus, in paragraphs 1 and 2 of this section we have exhibited an algorithm with which we can construct a particular solution of the infinite system (37.1) in the resonance case. This completes the proof of Theorem VI.1.

Note 1. The construction of a particular solution of system (37.1) in the case of more complicated resonance—when the function $\nu(\tau)$ for certain values $\tau \in [0, L]$ coincides with several numbers ω_k (for example, $\omega_1, \omega_2, \ldots, \omega_r$) but does not coincide with the other terms of the sequence $\{\omega_n\}$ $(n=r+1, r+2, \ldots)$ for any values—can be carried out in the same way as described in paragraphs 1 and 2; namely, a particular solution $Z(t, \varepsilon)$ of the nonhomogeneous system (37.2) is sought in the form

$$Z(t, \varepsilon) = \left[\sum_{k=1}^{r} \Pi_k(\tau, \varepsilon)\, \xi_k(t, \varepsilon) + f(\tau, \varepsilon) \right] e^{i\theta(t,\varepsilon)},$$

where the scalar functions $\xi_k(t, \varepsilon)$ are solutions of the equations

$$\frac{d\xi_k}{dt} = [\lambda_k(\tau, \varepsilon) - i\nu(\tau)]\, \xi_k + b_k(\tau, \varepsilon) \qquad (k = 1, 2, \ldots, r).$$

The terms of the expansions of the vectors $\Pi_k(\tau, \varepsilon)$, $f(\tau, \varepsilon)$, and the functions $\lambda_k(\tau, \varepsilon)$, $b_k(\tau, \varepsilon)$, in this case, are determined by formulas analogous to those presented in paragraphs 1 and 2.

Note 2. In the nonresonance case, a particular solution of system (37.2) is sought, according to the rule, in the form

$$Z(t, \varepsilon) = f(\tau, \varepsilon) e^{i\theta(t,\varepsilon)},$$

where $f(\tau, \varepsilon)$ is an infinite-dimensional unknown vector.

Here, because of the absence of the functions $\xi_k(t, \varepsilon)$, finding approximate solutions of the original system reduces only to solution of the algebraic equations and differentiation.

Note 3. If, in the mixed problem being considered, we are given a homogeneous equation corresponding to (36.1), then the unknown functions $z_n(t, \varepsilon)$ $(n = 1, 2, \ldots)$ [see formula (36.5)] are determined from the homogeneous system

$$\frac{d^2 z_n}{dt^2} + \omega_n^2 z_n = \varepsilon \sum_{m=1}^{\infty} A_{nm}(\tau) z_m \qquad (n = 1, 2, \ldots).$$

For finding a particular solution to this system, we again apply the method just described. In this case, the particular solution corresponding to the characteristic value ω_k is sought in the form

$$Z_k(t, \varepsilon) = \Pi_k(\tau, \varepsilon) \xi_k(t, \varepsilon),$$

where $\Pi_k(\tau, \varepsilon)$ and $\xi_k(t, \varepsilon)$ are as above, and the function $\xi_k(t, \varepsilon)$ satisfies a homogeneous equation of the form

$$\frac{d\xi_k}{dt} = \lambda_k(\tau, \varepsilon) \xi_k \qquad (k = 1, 2, \ldots).$$

38. Proof of Asymptotic Convergence

The algorithm described in Sec. 37 makes possible the determination of any term in the expansions in formulas (37.6). In practice (because of the unwieldiness of the calculations), we usually limit ourselves to the construction of the first m terms in these expansions. Thus, we obtain the so-called mth approximations of the desired solutions of system (37.2). Let us determine, for the resonance case considered in Sec. 37, the mth approximation, by using the expression

$$Z_\alpha^{(m)}(t, \varepsilon) = \left[\sum_{s=0}^{m} \varepsilon^s \Pi_\alpha^{(s)}(\tau) \xi_\alpha^{(m)}(t, \varepsilon) + \sum_{s=0}^{m} \varepsilon^s f^{(s)}(\tau) \right] e^{i\theta(t,\varepsilon)}, \tag{38.1}$$

where the function $\xi_\alpha^{(m)}(t, \varepsilon)$ is a solution of the equation

$$\frac{d\xi_\alpha^{(m)}}{dt} = \left[\sum_{s=0}^{m} \varepsilon^s \lambda_\alpha^{(s)}(\tau) - i\nu(\tau) \right] \xi_\alpha^{(m)} + \sum_{s=0}^{m} \varepsilon^s b_\alpha^{(s)}(\tau). \tag{38.2}$$

Let $Z(t, \varepsilon)$ be an exact solution of system (37.2) which satisfies the same initial conditions at $t = 0$ as does $Z_\alpha^{(m)}(t, \varepsilon)$. Then, just as was done in the preceding chapters (Chap. 2 in particular), we can show that the approximate solution $Z_\alpha^{(m)}(t, \varepsilon)$ converges asymptotically to the exact solution $Z(t \ \varepsilon)$.

Rather than dwell on the details of the proof, we shall indicate the basic steps.

First of all, we prove the following lemma.

Lemma VI.1. *Suppose that the conditions of Theorem VI.1 are satisfied. Then the mth approximation $Z_\alpha^{(m)}(t, \varepsilon)$ satisfies the equation*

$$\frac{d^2 Z_\alpha^{(m)}(t, \varepsilon)}{dt^2} + [\Omega - \varepsilon A(\tau)]\, Z_\alpha^{(m)}(t, \varepsilon) = P(\tau)\, e^{i\theta(t,\varepsilon)} + \varepsilon^m\, R(\tau, \varepsilon), \tag{38.3}$$

where $R(\tau, \varepsilon)$ is a vector-function which is uniformly bounded on the interval $[0, L]$. (Note: By boundedness of a real vector-function $Y(t)$ we mean, as usual, boundedness of the function

$$\|Y(t)\| = \sqrt{\sum_{j=1}^{\infty} y_j^2(t)}.\Big)$$

Proof. The proof is carried out in the same way as for Lemma II.1, namely, by substituting [taking into account the method of construction of $Z_\alpha^{(m)}(t, \varepsilon)$] expression (38.1) into Eq. (37.2) and by successively estimating the obtained expressions.

We consider the difference

$$X(t, \varepsilon) = Z_\alpha^{(m)}(t, \varepsilon) - Z_\alpha(t, \varepsilon), \tag{38.4}$$

where $Z_\alpha^{(m)}(t, \varepsilon)$ and $Z_\alpha(t, \varepsilon)$ are the approximate and exact solutions of system (37.2), corresponding to the same initial conditions.

Obviously, the vector-function $X(t, \varepsilon)$ satisfies the equation

$$\frac{d^2X}{dt^2} + \Omega X = \varepsilon A(\tau)\, X + \varepsilon^m R(\tau,\varepsilon) \tag{38.5}$$

and the initial conditions

$$X(0, \varepsilon) = 0; \qquad \left.\frac{dX}{dt}\right|_{t=0} = 0. \tag{38.6}$$

Theorem VI.2. *Suppose that the conditions of Theorem VI.1 are satisfied. In addition, the exact solution* $Z_\alpha(t, \varepsilon)$ *and its mth approximation* $Z_\alpha^{(m)}(t, \varepsilon)$ *are taken for the same initial conditions. Then we can find positive constants C and* $\varepsilon_1 (\varepsilon_1 \leqslant \varepsilon_0)$ *such that for* $\varepsilon < \varepsilon_1$ *the inequality*

$$\| Z_\alpha^{(m)}(t, \varepsilon) - Z_\alpha(t, \varepsilon) \| \leqslant C\varepsilon^{m-1} \tag{38.7}$$

will be satisfied on the interval $0 \leqslant t \leqslant L/\varepsilon$.

Proof. We represent the problem (38.5), (38.6) in coordinate form

$$\frac{d^2x_n}{dt^2} + \omega_n^2 x_n = \varepsilon \sum_{j=1}^{\infty} A_{nj}(\tau) x_j + \varepsilon^m r_n(\tau, \varepsilon), \tag{38.8}$$

$$x_n(0, \varepsilon) = 0, \qquad \left.\frac{dx_n}{dt}\right|_{t=0} = 0. \tag{38.9}$$

It is easy to see that the system of differential equations (38.8) with the initial conditions (38.9) is equivalent to the following system of integral equations:

$$x_n(t) = \frac{\varepsilon}{\omega_n} \int_0^t \sin \omega_n (t-s) \left[\sum_{j=1}^{\infty} A_{nj}(\sigma) x_j(s, \varepsilon)\right] ds +$$

$$+ \frac{\varepsilon^m}{\omega_n} \int_0^t \sin \omega_n (t-s) r_n(\sigma, \varepsilon)\, ds \qquad (\sigma = \varepsilon s), \ \ n = 1, 2, \ldots. \tag{38.10}$$

Using the Cauchy-Bunyakovskiy inequality, and also its analog for definite integrals, we obtain, on the basis of (38.10), the estimate

$$x_n^2(t, \varepsilon) \leqslant 2 \left\{ \frac{\varepsilon L}{\omega_n^2} \int_0^t \left[\sum_{j=1}^{\infty} A_{nj}(\sigma) \sum_{j=1}^{\infty} x_j^2(s, \varepsilon) \right] ds + \frac{\varepsilon^{2m-1} L}{\omega_n^2} \int_0^t r_n^2(\sigma, \varepsilon) ds \right\}. \tag{38.11}$$

By the uniform boundedness on $[0, L]$ of the expression

$$\left|\sum_{j=1}^{\infty} A_{nj}^2(\tau)\right| \leqslant K = \text{const}$$

[see (36.12)] and the convergence of the series $\sum_{n=1}^{\infty} \frac{1}{\omega_n^2} = M$, the estimate (38.11) implies the inequality

$$\| X(t, \varepsilon) \|^2 \leqslant 2\varepsilon LMK \int_0^t \| X(s, \varepsilon)\|^2 ds + 2\varepsilon^{2m-1} LM \int_0^t \| R(\sigma, \varepsilon) \|^2 ds. \tag{38.12}$$

Now, using the results of Lemma I.1, we obtain

$$\| X(t, \varepsilon) \|^2 \leqslant 2\varepsilon^{2m-1} LM \int_0^t e^{2\varepsilon LMK(t-s)} \| R(\sigma, \varepsilon) \|^2 ds$$

or

$$\| X(t, \varepsilon) \| \leqslant C\varepsilon^{m-1}, \tag{38.13}$$

where

$$C = \sqrt{2e^{2L^2MK} L^2MR^*}, \qquad R^* = \max_{0 \leqslant \tau \leqslant L} [\|R(\tau,\varepsilon)\|^2].$$

By (38.4), inequality (38.13) is, in fact, the desired inequality (38.7). Thus, Theorem VI.2 is proved, and we have proved that asymptotic convergence of the approximate solution to the exact solution.

In the nonresonance case for a particular solution of the homogeneous system, and also in the case of a small perturbing force: $\varepsilon p(x, \tau)\, e^{i\theta(t,\varepsilon)}$ [see Eq. (36.1)] the estimate (38.7) can be improved, since the mth approximation in these cases satisfies the original system with accuracy up to quantities of the order $O(\varepsilon^{m+1})$ rather than $O(\varepsilon^m)$, as obtained in the case when the conditions of Lemma VI.1 are satisfied.

In conclusion, we note that, in practice, the solution of a specific problem is often carried out in the following way. We cut off the infinite system (37.1) at some number N, limiting ourselves to investigation of solutions of a finite system, consisting of N second-order differential equations. The asymptotic solution of this shortened system is constructed by the method described in this chapter. A comparison of the results obtained in this way with the results obtained by other methods shows good agreement.

REFERENCES

1. Bellman, R., Stability Theory of Differential Equations, McGraw-Hill, New York, 1953.
2. Bogolyubov, N. N., O nekotorykh statisticheskikh metodakh v matematicheskoy fixike (On some statistical methods in mathematical physics), Izdatel'stvo Academii Nauk Ukr.S. S.R., Kiev, 1945.
3. Bogolyubov, N. N. and Yu. A. Mitropol'skiy, Asimptoticheskiye metody v teorii nelineyikh kolebaniy, Fizmatgiz, Moscow, 1958. (English translation: "Asymptotic methods in the theory of nonlinear oscillations," Hindustan Publishing Corp., Delhi, 1961; also Gordon and Breach Science Publishers, New York.)
4. Bogolyubov, N. N. and D. N. Zubarev, Ukrainskiy Matematicheskiy Zhurnal, Vol. 7, 1, 1955.
5. Breus, K. A., Doklady Academii Nauk, U.S.S.R., Vol. 108, 6, 1956.
6. Breus, K. A., Ukrainskiy Matematicheskiy Zhurnal, Vol. 10, 2, 1958.
7. Breus, K. A., Doklady Academii Nauk, U.S.S.R., Vol. 123, 1, 1958.
8. Breus, K. A. Ukrainskiy Matematicheskiy Zhurnal, Vol. 12, 4, 1960.
9. Vasil'yeva, A. B., Matem. sb., 31 (73), 3, 1952.
10. Vasil'yeva, A. B., Doklady Academii Nauk, Vol. 135, 6, 1960.
11. Vasil'yeva, A. B., Matem. sb., 50 (92), 1, 1960.
12. Vishik, M. I. and L. A. Lyusternik, Uspekhi Matematicheskikh Nauk, Vol. 12, 5, 1957.
13. Volosov, V. M., Metod usredneniya i nekotorye zadachi teorii nelineynykh kolebaniy (The averaging method and some problems in the theory of nonlinear oscillations), Author's abstract of Ph.D. dissertation, Izdatel'stvo Academii Nauk Ukr. S.S.R., Kiev, 1961.
14. Volosov, V. M., Uspekhi Matematicheskikh Nauk, Vol. 17, 6, 1962.

15. Gantmakher, F. R., Teoriya matrits (Matrix theory), Gosudarstvennoye Izdatel'stvo Tekhnicheskoy i Teoreticheskoy Literatury, Moscow, 1953.
16. Gradshteyn, I. S., Matem. sb., 27 (69), 1, 1950.
17. Gradshteyn, I. S., Matem. sb., 32 (74), 3, 1956.
18. Daletskiy, Yu. L. and S. G. Kreyn, Ukrainskiy Matematicheskiy Zhurnal, Vol. 2, 4, 1950.
19. Daletskiy, Yu. L., Doklady Academii Nauk, Vol. 92, 5, 1953.
20. Daletskiy, Yu. L., Izvestiye Kievskiy Politekhnicheskiy Institut, Vol. 19, 1956.
21. Daletskiy, Yu. L., Uspekhi Matematicheskikh Nauk, Vol. 14, 1 (85), 1959.
22. Daletskiy, Yu. L., Doklady Academii Nauk, U.S.S.R., Vol. 143, 5, 1962.
23. Yerugin, N. P., In the book: Trudy matem. instituta im. V. A. Steklova (Proceedings of the Steklov Mathematical Institute), 1946.
24. Yerugin, N. P., Prikladnaya Matematika i Mekhanika, Vol. 12, 2, 1948.
25. Yerugin, N. P., Prikladnaya Matematika i Mekhanika, Vol. 23, 5, 1959.
26. Zadiraka, K. V., Prikladnaya Matematika i Mekhanika, Vol. 16, 6, 1952.
27. Zadiraka, K. V., Dopovidi Academii Nauk, Ukr. R.S.R., 4, 1954.
28. Zadiraka, K. V., Ukrainskiy Matematicheskiy Zhurnal, 2, 1958.
29. Ilyukhin, A. G., Ukrainskiy Matematicheskiy Zhurnal, Vol. 13, 3, 1961.
30. Ilyukhin, A. G., Dopovidi Academii Nauk, Ukr. R.S.R., 8, 1961.
31. Ilyukhin, A. G., Ukrainskiy Matematicheskiy Zhurnal, Vol. 14, 3, 1962.
32. Ishlinskiy, A. Yu., Doklady Academii Nauk, U.S.S.R., Vol. 95, 5, 1954.
33. Kantorovich, L. V. and G. P. Akilov, Funktsional'nyy analiz v normirovannykh prostranstvakh (Functional analysis in normed spaces), Fizmatgiz, Moscow, 1959.
34. Kovtun, I. I., Dopovidi Academii Nauk, Ukr. R.S.R., 2, 1962.
35. Kovtun, I. I., Dopovidi Akademii Nauk, Ukr. R.S.R., 5, 1962.
36. Kovtun, I. I., Ukrainskiy Matematicheskiy Zhurnal, Vol. 14, 2, 1962.
37. Kovtun, I. I., Dopovidi Academii Nauk, Ukr. R.S.R., 2, 1963.
38. Kovtun, I. I., In the book: Priblizhennye metody resheniya differentsial'nykh uravneniy (Approximate methods of

solution of differential equations), Izdatel'stvo Academii Nauk Ukr. S.S.R., Kiev, 1963.

39. Coddington, E. A. and N. Levinson, Theory of Ordinary Differential Equations, McGraw-Hill, New York, 1955.
40. Kononenko, V. O., In the book: "Trudy Mezhdun. simpoziuma po nelineynym kolebaniyam" (Proceedings of the International symposium on nonlinear oscillations), Vol. 3, Izdatel'stvo Academii Nauk Ukr. S.S.R., Kiev, 1963.
41. Krylov, N. M. and N. N. Bogolyubov, Vvedeniye v nelineynuyu mekhaniku (Introduction to nonlinear mechanics), Izdatel'stvo Academii Nauk Ukr. S.S.R., Kiev, 1937.
42. Kuzhiy, A. I. and V. M. Shevelo, Prikladna Mekhanika, 1, 1955.
43. Ladyzhenskaya, O. A., Smeshannaya zadacha dlya giperbolicheskogo uravneniya (The mixed problem for the hyperbolic equation), Gosudarstvennoye Izdatel'stvo Tekhnicheskoy i Teoreticheskoy Literatury, Moscow, 1953.
44. Lykova, O. B., Ukrainskiy Matematicheskiy Zhurnal, Vol. 9, 2, 1957.
45. Lykova, O. B. and Yu. O. Mitropol'skiy, Visnyk Kievskoho Derzhavnoho Universyteta, ser. matem. ta mekh., Vol. 3, 2, 1960.
46. Lykova, O. B., Ukrainskiy Matematicheskiy Zhurnal, Vol. 12, 3, 1960.
47. Lyashchenko, N. Ya., Ukrainskiy Matematicheskiy Zhurnal, Vol. 7, 1, 1955.
48. Lyashchenko, N. Ya., Ukrainskiy Matematicheskiy Zhurnal, Vol. 7, 2, 1955.
49. Mal'tsev, A. I., Osnovy Lineynoy algebry (Fundamentals of linear algebra), 2nd edition, Gostekhizdat, Moscow, 1956.
50. Markush, I. I., Dopovidi Academii Nauk, Ukr. R.S.R., 1, 1960.
51. Markush, I. I., Dopovidi Academii Nauk, Ukr. R.S.R., 3, 1960.
52. Mitropol'skiy, Yu. A., Nestatsionarnye protsessy b nelineynykh kolebatel'nykh sistemakh (Nonstationary processes in nonlinear oscillatory systems), Izdatel'stvo Academii Nauk Ukr. S.S.R., Kiev, 1955.
53. Mitropol'skiy, Yu. A. and B. I. Moseyenkov, Doslidzheniya kolivan' v sistemakh z rozpodil'nimi parametrami (asimptotichni metodi) (Oscillations in systems with distributed parameters: asymptotic methods) Vid-vo Kievskogo Universiteta, 1962.
54. Mitropol'skiy, Yu. A., Problemy asimptoticheskoy teorii nestatsionarnykh kolebaniy (Problems in the asymptotic

theory of nonstationary oscillations), "Nauka," Moscow, 1964.
55. Pisarenko, G. S., Rasseyaniye energii pri mekhanicheskikh kolebaniyakh (Energy dissipation in mechanical oscillations), Izdatel'stvo Academii Nauk Ukr. S.S.R., Kiev, 1962.
56. Pugachev, V. S., In the book: Trudy akademii im. Zhukovskogo, Issue 70, 1940.
57. Pugachev, V. S., In the book: Trudy akademii im. Zhukovskogo, Issue 74, 1940.
58. Pugachev, V. S., Izvestiye Academii Nauk, S.S.S.R., Matematika, Vol. 5, 1;6, 1941.
59. Pugachev, V. S., Matem. sb. 15 (57), 1, 1944.
60. Pugachev, V. S., Prikladnaya Matematiki i Mekhanika, Vol. 10, 1, 1946.
61. Rapoport, I. M., O nekotorykh asimptoticheskikh metodakh v teorii differentsial'nykh uraveniy (On some asymptotic methods in the theory of differential equation), Izdatel'stvo Academii Nauk Ukr. S.S.R., Kiev, 1954.
62. Savin, G. M., Dopovidi Academii Nauk, Ukr. R.S.R., 2, 1954.
63. Savin, G. M. and V. M. Shevelo, Dopovidi Academii Nauk, Ukr. R.S.R., 2, 1954.
64. Savin, G. M., V. M. Shevelo and A. I. Kuzhiy, Prikladna mekhanika, Vol. 1, 3, 1955.
65. Savin, G. M. and S. F. Feshchenko, Dopovidi Akademii Nauk, Ukr. R.S.R., 6, 1958.
66. Savin, G. M. and S. F. Feshchenko, Dopovidi Akademii Nauk, Ukr. R.S.R., 11, 1960.
67. Savin, G. M. and O. A. Goroshko, Dinamika niti peremennoy dliny (Dynamics of a thread of variable length), Izdatel'stvo Academii Nauk Ukr. S.S.R., Kiev, 1962.
68. Smirnov, V. I., Kurs vysshey matematiki (Course in higher mathematics), Vol. 3, Chap. 1, Gosundarstvennoye Izdatel'stvo Tekhnicheskoy i Teoreticheskoy Literatury, Moscow, 1949; Vol. 3, Chap. 2, Gosudarstvennoye Izdatel'stvo Tekhnicheskoy i Teoreticheskoy Literatury, Moscow, 1953.
69. Sokolov, Yu. D., Prikladna mekhanika, Vol. 1, 1, 1955.
70. Solomyak, M. Z., Izvestiya vysshikh uchebnyth zavedeniy, Matematika, 1, 1960.
71. Steklov, V. A., Zadacha ob okhlazhdenii neodnorodnogo tverdogo sterzhnya (The problem of cooling a nonhomogeneous solid rod), Soobshch. Khar'kov. matem. obshch., 5, 1896.
72. Stonits'kiy, A. A., Dopovidi Akademii Nauk, Ukr. R.S.R., 1, 1962.
73. Stonits'kiy, A. A., Dopovidi Akademii Nauk, Ukr. R.S.R., 5, 1962.

74. Stonits'kiy, A. A., Ukrainskiy Matematicheskiy Zhurnal, Vol. 14, 3, 1962.
75. Stonits'kiy, A. A., Dopovidi Akademii Nauk, Ukr. R.S.R., 3, 1963.
76. Tamarkin, Ya. D., O nekotorykh obshchikh zadachakh teorii obyknovennykh lineynykh differentsial'nykh uravneniy i o razlozhennii proizvol'nykh funktsiy v ryady (On some general problems in the theory of ordinary linear differential equations and on series expansion of an arbitrary function), Petrograd, 1917.
77. Turrittin, H. L., Collected translations, Matematika, 1, IL, 1957.
78. Tikhonov, A. N., Matem. sb., 22 (64), 2, 1948.
79. Tikhonov, A. N., Matem. sb., 27 (69), 1, 1950.
80. Tikhonov, A. N., Matem. sb., 31 (73), 5, 1952.
81. Faddeyev, D. K. and V. N. Faddeyeva, Vychislitel'nye metody lineynoy algebry (Computational methods in linear algebra), Fizmatgiz, Moscow, 1963.
82. Feshchenko, S. F., Dopovidi Akademii Nauk, Ukr. R.S.R., Vol. 2, 3, 1947.
83. Feshchenko, S. F., Dopovidi Akademii Nauk, Ukr. R. S.R., Vol. 2, 9, 1947.
84. Feshchenko, S. F., Naukovi zapiski Kievskogo pedagogichnogo institutu. Ser. fiz.-matem., Vol. 6, 3, 1948.
85. Feshchenko, S. F., Dopovidi Akademii Nauk, Ukr. R.S.R. 1, 1949.
86. Feshchenko, S. F., Naukovi zapiski Kievskogo pedogogichnogo institutu. Ser. fiz.-matem., Vol. 9, 4, 99, 1949.
87. Feshchenko, S. F., Naukovi zapiski Kievskogo pedagogichnogo institutu. Ser. fiz.-matem., Vol. 9, 4, 149, 1949.
88. Feshchenko, S. F., Author's abstract of Ph.D. dissertation, Izdatel'stvo Akademii Nauk Ukr. S.S.R., Kiev, 1950.
89. Feshchenko, S. F., Dopovidi Akademii Nauk, Ukr. R.S.R., 3, 1951.
90. Feshchenko, S. F., Dopovidi Akademii Nauk, Ukr. R.S.R., 2, 1954.
91. Feshchenko, S. F. and A. I. Kuzhiy, Dopovidi Akademii Nauk, Ukr. R.S.R., 2, 1955.
92. Feshchenko, S. F., Dopovidi Akademii Nauk, Ukr. R.S.R., 3, 1955.
93. Feshchenko, S. F., Ukrainskiy Matematicheskiy Zhurnal, Vol. 7, 2 and 4, 1955.
94. Feshchenko, S. F. and N. I. Shkil', Prikladna mekhanika, Vol. 4, 3, 1958.
95. Feshchenko, S. F. and N. I. Shkil', Dopovidi Akademii Nauk, Ukr. R.S.R., 5, 1958.

96. Feshchenko, S. F. and N. I. Shkil', Ukrainskiy Matematicheskiy Zhurnal, Vol. 12, 4, 1960.
97. Feshchenko, S. F., Visnyk Kievskoho Derzhavnoho Universyteta, Ser. matem. ta mekhaniki, Vol. 2, 3, 1960.
98. Feshchenko, S. F. and L. D. Nikolenko, Dopovidi Akademii Nauk, Ukr. R.S.R., 8, 1961.
99. Feshchenko, S. F. and L. D. Nikolenko, Ukrainskiy Matematicheskiy Zhurnal, Vol. 13, 3, 1961.
100. Feshchenko, S. F. and N. I. Shkil', Ukrainskiy Matematicheskiy Zhurnal, 1, 1964.
101. Fikhtengol'ts, G. M., Kurs differentsial'nogo i integral'nogo ischisleniya (Differential and integral calculus), Vol. II, Fizmatgiz, Moscow, 1959.
102. Hille, E. and R. Phillips, Funktsional'nyy analiz i polugruppy (Functional analysis and semigroups), Fizmatgiz, Moscow, 1963.
103. Shevelo, V. M. and A. I. Kuzhiy, Dopovidi Akademii Nauk, Ukr. R.S.R., 6, 1954.
104. Shkil', N. I., Dopovidi Akademii Nauk, Ukr. R.S.R., 2, 1958.
105. Shkil', N. I., Naukovi zapiski Kievskogo pedagogichnogo institutu., Vol. 30, 3, 1958.
106. Shkil', N. I., Dopovidi Akademii Nauk, Ukr. R.S.R., 2, 1961.
107. Shkil', N. I., Ukrainskiy Matematicheskiy Zhurnal, Vol. 14, 4, 1962.
108. Shkil', N. I., Dopovidi Akademii Nauk, Ukr. R.S.R., 9, 1962.
109. Shkil', N. I., Dopovidi Akademii Nauk, Ukr. R.S.R., 5, 1963.
110. Shkil', N. I., Izvestiya vysshikh uchebnykh zavedeniy, Matematika, 2 (39), 1964.
111. Shkil', N. I., Doklady Akademii Nauk, U.S.S.R., Vol. 150, 5, 1963.
112. Shkil', N. I., Matem. sb., 111 (15), 1965.
113. Shkil', N. I., Visnyk Kievskoho Derzhavnoho Universyteta, 1, 1965.
114. Shkil', N. I., Dopovidi Akademii Nauk, Ukr. R.S.R., 6, 1965.
115. Shkil', N. I., Dopovidi Akademii Nauk, Ukr. R.S.R., 3, 1965.
116. Shtokalo, I. Z., Matem. sb., 19 (61), 2, 1946.
117. Shtokalo, I. Z., In the book: Sb. trudov In-ta matematiki, 9, Izdatel'stvo Akademii Nauk Ukr. S.S.R., Kiev, 1947.
118. Shtokalo, I. Z., Lineynye differentsial'nye uravneniya a peremennymi koeffitsientami (Linear differential equations

with variable coefficients), Izdatel'stvo Akademii Nauk Ukr. S.S.R., Kiev, 1960.
119. Birkhoff, G. D., Trans. Amer. Math. Soc., Vol. 9, 219-231, 1908.
120. Birkhoff, G. D., Trans. Amer. Math. Soc., Vol. 9, 373-395, 1908.
121. Horn, J., Math. Ann., Vol. 49, 1897.
122. Horn, J., Cryst. J., 198, 1910.
123. Liouville, J., J.L., 2 (1), 16-35, 418-436, 1837.
124. Liouville, J., J.L., 3 (1), 561-614 (VIII), 1838.
125. Poincaré, H., Rend. Pal., Vol. 8, X-XI, 1894.
126. Sibuya, R., J. Faculty of Sci., Univ. Tokyo, Sec. 1, 7, 5, 1958.
127. Sparre Sur le mouvement des projectiles oblongs, Inp. Rational, 1893.
128. Steklov, V., Ann. Poc. Toul. 3 (2), 1901.
129. Steklov, V., Rend. r. acc. dei Lineei, Vol. 196, 5, 1910.
130. Turrittin, H. L., Amer. J. Math., Vol. 58, 364-376, 1936.
131. Tryizinski, W. J., Acta math., Vol. 67, 1-2, 1936.
132. Fowler, R. H. et al., Phil. Trans. Roy. Soc. Ld., Vol. 221, 295-387, 1920.
133. Fowler and Lock, Proc. Ld. Math. Soc., Vol. 20, 2, 127-147, 1921.
134. Phillips, R., Trans. Amer. Math. Soc., Vol. 74, 2, 1953.
135. Hukuhara, M., Jap. J. Math., Vol. 20, 1-4, 1950.
136. Schlesinger, L., Handbuch der Theorie der Linearen Differentialgleichung, Bd. 1., 1895.

INDEX

Abel's criterion, 248
Akilov, 108
Arzela's theorem, 109
Asymptotic convergence, proof of, 213, 256
  solution, method of, 236

Banach space, 108, 187, 205
  operator equation in, 202
Block matrices, multiplication of, 93
Boundary-value problem, 173
  characteristic values of, 57
  solution of, 2
Bounded operators, property of resolvents of, 205

Cauchy-Bunyakovskiy inequality, 249, 250, 258
Cauchy problem, solution of, 26
Cauchy's formula, 71
Cayley's identity, 67
Chaplygin's method, 60
Continuity, definition of, 207
Convergence, 207

Daletskiy, Yu. L., 187
Decomposed systems, 121, 169
  solution of, 122
  specified structure of, 122
Decomposition method, 121
Differentiability, definition of, 207
Digital computers, high-speed, 236
Dini's theorem, 243
Direct construction, method of, 223
Divisors, multiple elementary, 122
  simple elementary, 123
Dynamical stresses, damping of, 16

Electronic computers, high-speed, 79
Expansion, power series, 224

Finite-dimensional cases, 209
Fixed-point principle, 200
  theorem, 207
Formal solutions, construction of, 243
Fractional-linear transformations, 202
Functions of complex variable, theory of, 204

Hilbert space, 187
Homogeneous equations, vector solutions of, 88
Hukuhara, M., 115
Hyperbolic equation, second-order, 240

Ilyukhin, A.G., 85
Infinite-dimensional spaces, 187
  vectors, 243, 244

Jordan blocks, 86, 95, 125
Jordan form, 144
  canonical, 86, 87, 88, 98
  normal, 89

Kantorovich, L.V., 108
Kreyn, S.G., 187
Kronecker delta, 26, 65, 245

Linear differential equations, asymptotic reduction of, 121
  decomposition of, 79
    asymptotic, 232
  system of, 228
Lipschitz condition, 109

Mean-value theorem, 113
Metric spaces, product of, 111
Motion, law of, 43
Multinomials, second-degree, 94

Nonhomogeneous equations, approximate solution of, 219
  asymptotic solution of, 216

Operator calculus, 203
  theory of, 231
Operator calculus for unbounded closed operators, theory of, 189

Operator norm, 194

Parseval's equation, 242
Phillips, R., 190
Piecewise-constant functions, 101

Ricatti equation, 157, 162, 169

Savin, G.N., 54
Scalar differential equations, 121
Shauder's principle, 108, 115
Sokolov, Yu.D., 42
Step functions, 101
Sturm's method, 23
Successive approximations, method of, 124, 125, 170, 193

Visco-electric thread, tension in, 16, 42